"IN THE PRESENCE OF WASHINGTON."

HUGH WYNNE

HUGH WYNNE

FREE QUAKER

SOMETIME BREVET LIEUTENANT-COLONEL ON
THE STAFF OF HIS EXCELLENCY
GENERAL WASHINGTON

BY

S. WEIR MITCHELL, M. D.

LL. D. HARVARD AND EDINBURGH

TWO VOLUMES IN ONE
VOL. I

THE GREGG PRESS / RIDGEWOOD, N. J.

First published in 1896 by The Century Co.
Republished in 1967 by
The Gregg Press Incorporated
171 East Ridgewood Avenue
Ridgewood, New Jersey, U.S.A.
Copyright© 1967 by
The Gregg Press, Inc.

Library of Congress Catalog Card Number: 67-29274

Printed in United States of America

AMERICANS
IN
FICTION

INTRODUCTION BY PROFESSOR CLARENCE GOHDES
Editor of *American Literature* Magazine

In the domain of literature the play may once have been the chief abstract and chronicle of the times, but during the nineteenth and twentieth centuries the novel has usurped the chief place in holding the mirror up to the homely face of society. On this account, if for no other, the Gregg Press series of reprints of American fiction merits the attention of all students of Americana and of librarians interested in building up adequate collections dealing with the social and literary history of the United States. Most of the three score and ten novels or volumes of short stories included in the series enjoyed considerable fame in their day but have been so long out of print as to be virtually unobtainable in the original editions.

Included in the list are works by writers not presently fashionable in critical circles — but nevertheless well known to literary historians — among them Joel Chandler Harris, Harriet Beecher Stowe, Thomas Bailey Aldrich, and William Gilmore Simms. A substantial element in the list consists of authors who are known especially for their graphic portrayal of a particular American setting, such as Gertrude Atherton (California), Arlo Bates (Boston), Alice Brown (New England), Edward Eggleston (Indiana), Mary Wilkins Freeman (New England), Henry B. Fuller (Chicago), Richard M. Johnston (Georgia), James Lane Allen (Kentucky), l.. N. Murfree (Tennessee), and Thomas Nelson Page (Virginia). There is even a novel by Frederic Remington, one of the most popular painters of the Western cowboy and Indian — and another, an impressive minor classic on the early mining region of Colorado, from the pen of Mary Hallock Foote. The professional student of American literature will rejoice in the opportunity afforded by the collection to extend his reading of fiction belonging to what is called the "local-color movement" — a major current in the development of the national belles-lettres.

Among the titles in the series are also a number of famous historical novels. Silas Weir Mitchell's *Hugh Wynne* is one of the best fictional treatments of the American Revolution. John Esten Cooke is the foremost Southern writer of his day who dealt with the Civil War. The two books by Thomas Dixon are among the most famous novels on the Reconstruction Era, with sensational disclosures of the original Ku Klux Klan in action. They supplied the grist for the first great movie "spectacular" — *"The Birth of a Nation* (1915).

Paul Leicester Ford's *The Honorable Peter Stirling* is justly ranked among the top American novels which portray American politics in action — a subject illuminated by other novelists in the Gregg list — A. H. Lewis, Frances H. Burnett, and Alice Brown, for example. Economic problems are forcefully put before the reader in works by Aldrich, Mrs. Freeman, and John Hay, whose novels illustrate the ominous concern over the early battles between labor and capital. From the sweatshops of Eastern cities in which newly arrived immigrants toiled for pittances, to the Western mining camps where the laborers packed revolvers, the working class of the times enters into various other stories in the Gregg list. The capitalist class, also, comes in for attention, with an account of a struggle for the ownership of a railroad in Samuel Merwin's *The Short-Line War* and with the devastating documentation of the foibles of the newly rich and their wives in the narratives of David Graham Phillips. It was Phillips whose annoying talent for the exposure of abuses led Theodore Roosevelt to put the term "muck-raker" into currency.

While it is apparent that local-color stories, the historical novel, and the economic novel have all been borne in mind in choosing the titles for this important series of reprints, it is evident that careful consideration has also been given to treatments of various minority elements in the American population. The Negro, especially, but also the Indian, the half-breed, Creoles, Cajuns — and even the West Coast Japanese — appear as characters in various of these novels or volumes of short stories and sketches. Joel Chandler Harris's *Free Joe* will open the eyes of readers who know that author solely as the creator of humorous old Uncle Remus. And there is a revelatory volume of dialect tales, written by a Negro author, *The Conjure Woman* by Charles W. Chesnutt.

In literary conventions and the dominating attitudes toward life, the works in the Gregg series range from the adventurous romance illustrated so well by Mayne Reid or the polite urbanity of Owen Wister to the mordant irony of Kate Chopin and the grimmer realism of Joseph Kirkland's own experiences on bloody Civil War battlefields or the depressing display of New York farm life by Harold Frederic. In short, the series admirably illustrates the general qualities of the fiction produced in the United States during the era covered, just as it generously mirrors the geographical regions, the people, and the problems of the times.

HUGH WYNNE

INTRODUCTORY

T is now many years since I began these memoirs. I wrote fully a third of them, and then put them aside, having found increasing difficulties as I went on with my task. These arose out of the constant need to use the first person in a narrative of adventure and incidents which chiefly concern the writer, even though it involve also the fortunes of many in all ranks of life. Having no gift in the way of composition, I knew not how to supply or set forth what was outside of my own knowledge, nor how to pretend to that marvellous insight, as to motives and thoughts, which they affect who write books of fiction. This has always seemed to me absurd, and so artificial that, with my fashion of mind, I have never been able to enjoy such works nor agreeably to accept their claim to such privilege of

1

insight.   In a memoir meant for my descendants, it was fitting and desirable that I should at times speak of my own appearance, and, if possible, of how I seemed as child or man to others.   This, I found, I did not incline to do, even when I myself knew what had been thought of me by friend or foe.   And so, as I said, I set the task aside, with no desire to take it up again.

Some years later my friend, John Warder, died, leaving to my son, his namesake, an ample estate, and to me all his books, papers, plate, and wines. Locked in a desk, I found a diary, begun when a lad, and kept, with more or less care, during several years of the great war.   It contained also recollections of our youthful days, and was very full here and there of thoughts, comments, and descriptions concerning events of the time, and of people whom we both had known.   It told of me much that I could not otherwise have willingly set down, even if the matter had appeared to me as it did to him, which was not always the case; also my friend chanced to have been present at scenes which deeply concerned me, but which, without his careful setting forth, would never have come to my knowledge.

A kindly notice, writ nine years before, bade me use his journal as seemed best to me.   When I read this, and came to see how full and clear were his statements of much that I knew, and of some things which I did not, I felt ripely inclined to take up again the story I had left unfinished; and now I have done so, and have used my friend as the third person, whom I could permit to say what he thought of me from time to time, and to tell of incidents I did not see, or record impressions and emotions of his own. This latter privilege pleases me because I shall, besides my own story, be able to let those dear to me gather from the confessions of his journal, and from my own statements, what manner of person was the true gentleman and gallant soldier to whom I owed so much.

I trust this tale of an arduous struggle by a new land against a great empire will make those of my own blood the more desirous to serve their country with honour and earnestness, and with an abiding belief in the great Ruler of events.

In my title of this volume I have called myself a "Free Quaker." The term has no meaning for most of the younger generation, and yet it should tell a story of many sad spiritual struggles, of much heart-searching distress, of brave decisions, and of battle and of camp.

At Fifth and Arch streets, on an old gable, is this record:

BY GENERAL SUBSCRIPTION,
FOR THE FREE QUAKERS.
ERECTED A. D. 1783,
OF THE EMPIRE, 8.

In the burying-ground across the street, and in and about the sacred walls of Christ Church, not far away, lie Benjamin Franklin, Francis Hopkinson, Peyton Randolph, Benjamin Rush, and many a gallant soldier and sailor of the war for freedom.

Among them, at peace forever, rest the gentle-folks
who stood for the king—the gay men and women who
were neutral, or who cared little under which George
they danced or gambled or drank their old Madeira.
It is a neighbourhood which should be forever full of
interest to those who love the country of our birth.

I

CHILD'S early life is such as those who rule over him make it; but they can only modify what he is. Yet, as all know, after their influence has ceased, the man himself has to deal with the effects of blood and breed, and, too, with the consequences of the mistakes of his elders in the way of education. For these reasons I am pleased to say something of myself in the season of my green youth.

The story of the childhood of the great is often of value, no matter from whom they are "ascended," as my friend Warder used to say; but even in the lives of such lesser men as I, who have played the part of simple pawns in a mighty game, the change from childhood to manhood is not without interest.

I have often wished we could have the recorded truth of a child's life as it seemed to him day by day, but this can never be. The man it is who writes the life of the boy, and his recollection of it is perplexed by the siftings of memory, which let so much of thought and feeling escape, keeping little more than barren facts, or the remembrance of periods of trouble or of emotion, sometimes quite valueless, while more important moral events are altogether lost.

As these pages will show, I have found it agreeable, and at times useful, to try to understand, as far as in me lay, not only the men who were my captains or mates in war or in peace, but also myself. I have often been puzzled by that well-worn phrase as to the wisdom of knowing thyself, for with what manner of knowledge you know yourself is a grave question, and it is sometimes more valuable to know what is truly thought of you by your nearest friends than to be forever teasing yourself to determine whether what you have done in the course of your life was just what it should have been.

I may be wrong in the belief that my friend Warder saw others more clearly than he saw himself. He was of that opinion, and he says in one place that he is like a mirror, seeing all things sharply except that he saw not himself. Whether he judged me justly or not, I must leave to others to decide. I should be glad to think that, in the great account, I shall be as kindly dealt with as in the worn and faded pages which tell brokenly of the days of our youth. I am not ashamed to say that my eyes have filled many times as I have lingered over these records of my friend, surely as sweet and true a gentleman as I have ever known. Perhaps sometimes they have even overflowed at what they read. Why are we reluctant to confess a not ignoble weakness, such as is, after all, only the heart's confession of what is best in life? What becomes of the tears of age?

This is but a wearisome introduction, and yet

necessary, for I desire to use freely my friend's journal, and this without perpetual mention of his name,
save as one of the actors who played, as I did, a
modest part in the tumult of the war, in which my
own fortunes and his were so deeply concerned. To
tell of my own life without speaking freely of the
course of a mighty story would be quite impossible.
I look back, indeed, with honest comfort on a struggle which changed the history of three nations, but
I am sure that the war did more for me than I for
it. This I saw in others. Some who went into it
unformed lads came out strong men. In others its
temptations seemed to find and foster weaknesses of
character, and to cultivate the hidden germs of evil.
Of all the examples of this influence, none has seemed
to me so tragical as that of General Arnold, because,
being of reputable stock and sufficient means, generous, in every-day life kindly, and a free-handed
friend, he was also, as men are now loath to believe,
a most gallant and daring soldier, a tender father,
and an attached husband. The thought of the fall
of this man fetches back to me, as I write, the remembrance of my own lesser temptations, and with
a thankful heart I turn aside to the uneventful story
of my boyhood and its surroundings.

I was born in the great city Governor William
Penn founded, in Pennsylvania, on the banks of the
Delaware, and my earliest memories are of the broad
river, the ships, the creek before our door, and of
grave gentlemen in straight-collared coats and broad-
brimmed beaver hats.

I began life in a day of stern rule, and among a people who did not concern themselves greatly as to a child's having that inheritance of happiness with which we like to credit childhood. Who my people were had much to do with my own character, and what those people were and had been it is needful to say before I let my story run its natural and, I hope, not uninteresting course.

In my father's bedroom, over the fireplace, hung a pretty picture done in oils, by whom I know not. It is now in my library. It represents a pleasant park, and on a rise of land a gray Jacobean house, with, at either side, low wings curved forward, so as to embrace a courtyard shut in by railings and gilded gates. There is also a terrace with urns and flowers. I used to think it was the king's palace, until, one morning, when I was still a child, Friend Pemberton came to visit my father with William Logan and a very gay gentleman, Mr. John Penn, he who was sometime lieutenant-governor of the province, and of whom and of his brother Richard great hopes were conceived among Friends. I was encouraged by Mr. Penn to speak more than was thought fitting for children in those days, and because of his rank I escaped the reproof I should else have met with.

He said to my father, " The boy favours thy people." Then he added, patting my head, " When thou art a man, my lad, thou shouldst go and see where thy people came from in Wales. I have been at Wyncote. It is a great house, with wings in the Italian manner, and a fine fountain in the court, and gates which were gilded when Charles II. came to see the squire, and which are not to be set open again until another king comes thither."

Then I knew this was the picture upstairs, and much pleased I said eagerly:

"My father has it in his bedroom, and our arms below it, all painted most beautiful."

"Thou art a clever lad," said the young lieutenant-governor, "and I must have described it well. Let us have a look at it, Friend Wynne."

But my mother, seeing that William Logan and Friend Pemberton were silent and grave, and that my father looked ill pleased, made haste to make excuse, because it was springtime and the annual house-cleaning was going on.

Mr. Penn cried out merrily, "I see that the elders are shocked at thee, Friend Wynne, because of these vanities of arms and pictures; but there is good heraldry on the tankard out of which I drank James Pemberton's beer yesterday. Fie, fie, Friend James!" Then he bowed to my mother very courteously, and said to my father, "I hope I have not got thy boy into difficulties because I reminded him that he is come of gentles."

"No, no," said my mother.

"I know the arms, madam, and well too: quarterly, three eagles displayed in fesse, and—"

"Thou wilt pardon me, Friend Penn," said my father, curtly. "These are the follies of a world which concerns not those of our society. The lad's aunt has put enough of such nonsense into his head already."

"Let it pass, then," returned the young lieutenant-governor, with good humour; "but I hope, as I said, that I have made no trouble for this stout boy of thine."

My father replied deliberately, "There is no harm done." He was too proud to defend himself, but I heard long after that he was taken to task by Thomas Scattergood and another for these vanities of arms and pictures. He told them that he put the picture where none saw it but ourselves, and, when they persisted, reminded them sharply, as Mr. Penn had done, of the crests on their own silver, by which these Friends of Welsh descent set much store.

I remember that, when the gay young lieutenant-governor had taken his leave, my father said to my mother, "Was it thou who didst tell the boy this foolishness of these being our arms and the like, or was it my sister Gainor?"

Upon this my mother drew up her brows, and spread her palms out,—a French way she had,—and cried, "Are they not thy arms? Wherefore should we be ashamed to confess it?"

I suppose this puzzled him, for he merely added, "Too much may be made of such vanities."

All of this I but dimly recall. It is one of the earliest recollections of my childhood, and, being out of the common, was, I suppose, for that reason better remembered.

I do not know how old I was when, at this time, Mr. Penn, in a neat wig with side rolls, and dressed very gaudy, aroused my curiosity as to these folks in

Wales. It was long after, and only by degrees, that I learned the following facts, which were in time to have a great influence on my own life and its varied fortunes.

In or about the year 1671, and of course before Mr. Penn, the proprietary, came over, my grandfather had crossed the sea, and settled near Chester on lands belonging to the Swedes. The reason of his coming was this: about 1669 the Welsh of the English church and the magistrates were greatly stirred to wrath against the people called Quakers, because of their refusal to pay tithes. Among these offenders was no small number of the lesser gentry, especially they of Merionethshire.

My grandfather, Hugh Wynne, was the son and successor of Godfrey Wynne, of Wyncote. How he chanced to be born among these hot-blooded Wynnes I do not comprehend. He is said to have been gay in his early days, but in young manhood to have become averse to the wild ways of his breed, and to have taken a serious and contemplative turn. Falling in with preachers of the people called Quakers, he left the church of the establishment, gave up hunting, ate his game-cocks, and took to straight collars, plain clothes, and plain talk. When he refused to pay the tithes he was fined, and at last cast into prison in Shrewsbury Gate House, where he lay for a year, with no more mind to be taxed for a hireling ministry at the end of that time than at the beginning.

His next brother, William, a churchman as men

go, seems to have loved him, although he was himself a rollicking fox-hunter; and, seeing that Hugh would die if left in this duress, engaged him to go to America. Upon his agreeing to make over his estate to William, those in authority readily consented to his liberation, since William had no scruples as to the matter of tithes, and with him there would be no further trouble. Thus it came about that my grandfather Hugh left Wales. He had with him, I presume, enough of means to enable him to make a start in Pennsylvania. It could not have been much. He carried also, what no doubt he valued, a certificate of removal from the Quarterly Meeting held at Tyddyn y Garreg. I have this singular document. In it is said of him and of his wife, Ellin ("for whom it may concern"), that "they are faithfull and beloved Friends, well known to be serviceable unto Friends and brethren, since they have become convinced; of a blameless and savory conversation. Also are P'sons Dearly beloved of all Souls. His testimony sweet and tender, reaching to the quicking seed of life; we cannot alsoe but bemoan the want of his company, for that in difficult occasion he was sted-fast—nor was one to be turned aside. He is now seasonable in intention for the Plantations, in order into finding his way clear, and freedom in the truth according to the measure manifested unto him," etc.

And so the strong-minded man is commended to. Friends across the seas. In the records of the meetings for sufferings in England are certain of his letters from the jail. How his character descended to my sterner parent, and, through another generation, to me, and how the coming in of my mother's gentler blood helped in after-days, and amid stir of war, to modify in me, this present writer, the ruder qualities of my race, I may hope to set forth.

William died suddenly in 1679 without children, and was succeeded by the third brother, Owen. This gentleman lived the life of his time, and, dying in 1700 of much beer and many strong waters, left one son, Owen, a minor. What with executors and other evils, the estate now went from ill to worse. Owen Wynne 2d was in no haste, and thus married as late as somewhere about 1740, and had issue, William, and later, in 1744, a second son, Arthur, and perhaps others; but of all this I heard naught until many years after, as I have already said.

It may seem a weak and careless thing for a man thus to cast away his father's lands as my ancestor did; but what he gave up was a poor estate, embarrassed with mortgages and lessened by fines, until the income was, I suspect, but small. Certain it is that the freedom to worship God as he pleased was more to him than wealth, and assuredly not to be set against a so meagre estate, where he must have lived among enmities, or must have diced, drunk, and hunted with the rest of his kinsmen and neighbours.

I have a faint memory of my aunt, Gainor Wynne, as being fond of discussing the matter, and of how angry this used to make my father. She had a notion that my father knew more than he was willing to say, and that there had been something further agreed between the brothers, although what this was she knew not, nor ever did for many a day. She was given, however, to filling my young fancy with tales about the greatness of these Wynnes, and of how the old homestead, rebuilded in James I.'s reign, had been the nest of Wynnes past the memory of man. Be all this as it may, we had lost Wyncote for the love of a freer air, although all this did not much concern me in the days of which I now write.

Under the mild and just rule of the proprietary, my grandfather Hugh prospered, and in turn his son John, my father, to a far greater extent. Their old home in Wales became to them, as time went on, less and less important. Their acres here in Merion and Bucks were more numerous and more fertile. I may add that the possession of many slaves in Maryland, and a few in Pennsylvania, gave them the feeling of authority and position, which the colonial was apt to lose in the presence of his English rulers, who, being in those days principally gentlemen of the army, were given to assuming airs of superiority.

In a word, my grandfather, a man of excellent wits and of much importance, was of the council of William Penn, and, as one of his chosen advisers, much engaged in his difficulties with the Lord Baltimore as to the boundaries of the lands held of the crown. Finally, when, as Penn says, "I could not prevail with my wife to stay, and still less with Tishe," which was short for Lætitia, his daughter, an obstinate wench, it was to men like Markham, Logan, and my grandfather that he gave his full confidence

and delegated his authority; so that Hugh Wynne
had become, long before his death, a person of so
much greater condition than the small squires to
whom he had given up his estate, that he was
like Joseph in this new land. What with the indifference come of large means, and disgust for a
country where he had been ill treated, he probably
ceased to think of his forefathers' life in Wales as
of a thing either desirable or in any way suited to
his own creed.

Soon the letters, which at first were frequent, that
is, coming twice a year, when the London packet
arrived or departed, became rare; and if, on the
death of my great-uncle William, they ceased, or if
any passed later between us and the next holder
of Wyncote, I never knew. The Welsh squires had
our homestead, and we our better portion of wealth
and freedom in this new land. And so ended my
knowledge of this matter for many a year.

You will readily understand that the rude life
of a fox-hunting squire or the position of a strict
Quaker on a but moderate estate in Merionethshire
would have had little to tempt my father. Yet one
thing remained with him awhile as an unchanged
inheritance, to which, so far as I remember, he only
once alluded. Indeed, I should never have guessed
that he gave the matter a thought but for that visit
of Mr. John Penn, and the way it recurred to me in
later days in connection with an incident concerning
the picture and the blazoned arms.

I think he cared less and less as years went by. In

earlier days he may still have liked to remember
that he might have been Wynne of Wyncote; but
this is a mere guess on my part. Pride spiritual is
a master passion, and certain it is that the creed and
ways of Fox and Penn became to him, as years created habits, of an importance far beyond the pride
which values ancient blood or a stainless shield.

The old house, which was built much in the same
fashion as the great mansion of my Lord Dysart on
the Thames near to Richmond, but smaller, was, after
all, his family home. The picture and the arms were
hid away in deference to opinions by which in general he more and more sternly abided. Once, when
I was older, I went into his bedroom, and was surprised to find him standing before the hearth, his
hands crossed behind his back, looking earnestly at
the brightly coloured shield beneath the picture of
Wyncote. I knew too well to disturb him in these
silent moods, but hearing my steps, he suddenly
called me to him. I obeyed with the dread his sternness always caused me. To my astonishment, his
face was flushed and his eyes were moist. He laid
his hand on my shoulder, and clutched it hard as he
spoke. He did not turn, but, still looking up at the
arms, said, in a voice which paused between the words
and sounded strange:

"I have been insulted to-day, Hugh, by the man
Thomas Bradford. I thank God that the Spirit pre-
vailed with me to answer him in Christian meekness.
He came near to worse things than harsh words.
Be warned, my son. It is a terrible set-back from

right living to come of a hot-blooded breed like these Wynnes."

I looked up at him as he spoke. He was smiling. "But not all bad, Hugh, not all bad. Remember that it is something, in this nest of disloyal traders, to have come of gentle blood."

Then he left gazing on the arms and the old home of our people, and said severely, "Hast thou gotten thy tasks to-day?"

"Yes."

"It has not been so of late. I hope thou hast considered before speaking. If I hear no better of thee soon thou wilt repent it. It is time thou shouldst take thy life more seriously. What I have said is for no ear but thine."

I went away with a vague feeling that I had suffered for Mr. Bradford, and on account of my father's refusal to join in resistance to the Stamp Act; for this was in November, 1765, and I was then fully twelve years of age.

My father's confession, and all he had said following it, made upon me one of those lasting impressions which are rare in youth, but which may have a great influence on the life of a man. Now all the boys were against the Stamp Act, and I had at the moment a sudden fear at being opposed to my father. I had, too, a feeling of personal shame because this strong man, whom I dreaded on account of his severity, should have been so overwhelmed by an insult. There was at this period, and later, much going on in my outer life to lessen the relentless influence of

2

the creed of conduct which prevailed in our home for
me, and for all of our house. I had even then begun
to suspect at school that non-resistance did not add
permanently to the comfort of life. I was sorry that
my father had not resorted to stronger measures
with Mr. Bradford, a gentleman whom, in after-
years, I learned greatly to respect.

More than anything else, this exceptional experience as to my father left me with a great desire to
know more of these Wynnes, and with a certain share
of that pride of race, which, to my surprise, as I think
it over now, was at that time in my father's esteem
a possession of value. I am bound to add that I also
felt some self-importance at being intrusted with
this secret, for such indeed it was.

Before my grandfather left Wales he had married
a distant cousin, Ellin Owen, and on her death, child-
less, he took to wife, many years later, her younger sister, Gainor;[1] for these Owens, our kinsmen, had also
become Friends, and had followed my grandfather's
example in leaving their home in Merionethshire. To
this second marriage, which occurred in 1713, were
born my aunt, Gainor Wynne, and, two years later,
my father, John Wynne. I have no remembrance
of either grandparent. Both lie in the ground at
Merion Meeting-house, under nameless, unmarked
graves, after the manner of Friends. I like it not.

My father, being a stern and silent man, must
needs be caught by his very opposite, and, accord-

---

[1] Thus early we shed the English prejudice against marriage with a deceased wife's sister.

ing to this law of our nature, fell in love with Marie
Beauvais, the orphan of a French gentleman who
had become a Quaker, and was of that part of France
called the Midi. Of this marriage I was the only
surviving offspring, my sister Ellin dying when I
was an infant. I was born in the city of Penn, on
January 9, 1753, at 9 P. M.

II

HAVE but to close my eyes to see the house in which I lived in my youth. It stood in the city of Penn, back from the low bluff of Dock Creek, near to Walnut street. The garden stretched down to the water, and before the door were still left on either side two great hemlock-spruces, which must have been part of the noble woods under which the first settlers found shelter. Behind the house was a separate building, long and low, in which all the cooking was done, and upstairs were the rooms where the slaves dwelt apart.

The great garden stretched westward as far as Third street, and was full of fine fruit-trees, and in the autumn of melons, first brought hither in one of my father's ships. Herbs and simples were not wanting, nor berries, for all good housewives in those days were expected to be able to treat colds and the lesser maladies with simples, as they were called, and to provide abundantly jams and conserves of divers kinds.

There were many flowers too, and my mother loved to make a home here for the wildings she found in the governor's woods. I have heard her regret that the most delicious of all the growths of spring, the

20

ground-sweet, which I think they now call arbutus, would not prosper out of its forest shelter.

The house was of black and red brick, and double; that is, with two windows on each side of a white Doric doorway, having something portly about it. I use the word as Dr. Johnson defines it: a house of port, with a look of sufficiency, and, too, of ready hospitality, which was due, I think, to the upper half of the door being open a good part of the year. I recall also the bull's-eye of thick glass in the upper half-door, and below it a great brass knocker. In the white shutters were cut crescentic openings, which looked at night like half-shut eyes when there were lights within the rooms. In the hall were hung on pegs leathern buckets. They were painted green, and bore, in yellow letters, "Fire" and "J. W."

The day I went to school for the first time is very clear in my memory. I can see myself, a stout little fellow about eight years old, clad in gray homespun, with breeches, low shoes, and a low, flat beaver hat. I can hear my mother say, "Here are two big apples for thy master," it being the custom so to propitiate pedagogues. Often afterward I took eggs in a little basket, or flowers, and others did the like.

"Now run! run!" she cried, "and be a good boy; run, or thou wilt be late." And she clapped her hands as I sped away, now and then looking back over my shoulder.

I remember as well my return home to this solid house, this first day of my going to school. One is apt to associate events with persons, and my mother stood leaning on the half-door as I came running back. She was some little reassured to see me smiling, for, to tell the truth, I had been mightily scared at my new venture.

This sweet and most tender-hearted lady wore, as you may like to know, a gray gown, and a blue chintz apron fastened over the shoulders with wide bands. On her head was a very broad-brimmed white beaver hat, low in the crown, and tied by silk cords under her chin. She had a great quantity of brown hair, among which was one wide strand of gray. This she had from youth, I have been told. It was all very silken, and so curly that it was ever in rebellion against the custom of Friends, which would have had it flat on the temples. Indeed, I never saw it so, for, whether at the back or at the front, it was wont to escape in large curls. Nor do I think she disliked this worldly wilfulness, for which nature had provided an unanswerable excuse. She had serious blue eyes, very large and wide open, so that the clear white was seen all around the blue, and with a constant look as if of gentle surprise. In middle life she was still pliant and well rounded, with a certain compliment of fresh prettiness in whatever gesture she addressed to friend or guest. Some said it was a French way, and indeed she made more use of her hands in speech than was common among people of British race.

Her goodness seems to me to have been instinctive, and to have needed neither thought nor effort. Her faults, as I think of her, were mostly such as arise from excess of loving and of noble moods. She would be lavish where she had better have been merely generous, or rash where some would have lacked even the commoner qualities of courage. Indeed, as to this, she feared no one—neither my grave father nor the grimmest of inquisitive committees of Friends.

As I came she set those large, childlike eyes on me, and opening the lower half-door, cried out:

"I could scarce wait for thee! I wish I could have gone with thee, Hugh; and was it dreadful? Come, let us see thy little book. And did they praise thy reading? Didst thou tell them I taught thee? There are girls, I hear," and so on—a way she had of asking many questions without waiting for a reply.

As we chatted we passed through the hall, where tall mahogany chairs stood dark against the white-washed walls, such as were in all the rooms. Joyous at escape from school, and its confinement of three long, weary hours, from eight to eleven, I dropped my mother's hand, and, running a little, slid down the long entry over the thinly sanded floor, and then slipping, came down with a rueful countenance, as nature, foreseeing results, meant that a boy should descend when his legs fail him. My mother sat down on a settle, and spread out both palms toward me, laughing, and crying out:

"So near are joy and grief, my friends, in this world of sorrow."

This was said so exactly with the voice and manner of a famous preacher of our Meeting that even

I, a lad then of only eight years, recognised the imitation. Indeed, she was wonderful at this trick of mimicry, a thing most odious among Friends. As I smiled, hearing her, I was aware of my father in the open doorway of the sitting-room, tall, strong, with much iron-gray hair. Within I saw several Friends, large rosy men in drab, with horn buttons and straight collars, their stout legs clad in dark silk hose, without the paste or silver buckles then in use. All wore broad-brimmed, low beavers, and their gold-headed canes rested between their knees.

My father said to me, in his sharp way, "Take thy noise out into the orchard. The child disturbs us, wife. Thou shouldst know better. A committee of overseers is with me." He disliked the name Marie, and was never heard to use it, nor even its English equivalent.

Upon this the dear lady murmured, "Let us fly, Hugh," and she ran on tiptoe along the hall with me, while my father closed the door. "Come," she added, "and see the floor. I am proud of it. We have friends to eat dinner with us at two."

The great room where we took our meals is still clear in my mind. The floor was two inches deep in white sand, in which were carefully traced zigzag lines, with odd patterns in the corners. A bare table of well-rubbed mahogany stood in the middle, with a thin board or two laid on the sand, that the table might be set without disturbing the patterns. In the corners were glass-covered buffets, full of silver and Delft ware; and a punch-bowl of Chelsea was on the broad window-ledge, with a silver-mounted cocoanut ladle.

"The floor is pretty," she said, regarding it with pride, "and I would make flowers too, but that thy father thinks it vain, and Friend Pemberton would set his bridge spectacles on his nose, and look at me, until I said naughty words, oh, very! Come out; I will find thee some ripe damsons, and save thee cake for thy supper, if Friend Warder does not eat it all. He is a little man, and eats much. A solicitous man," and she became of a sudden the person she had in mind, looking somehow feeble and cautious and uneasy, with arms at length, and the palms turned forward, so that I knew it for Joseph Warder, a frequent caller, of whom more hereafter.

"What is so—solicitous?" I said.

"Oh, too fearful concerning what may be thought of him. Vanity, vanity! Come, let us run down the garden. Canst thou catch me, Hugh?" And with this she fled away, under the back stoop and through the trees, light and active, her curls tumbling out, while I hurried after her, mindful of damsons, and wondering how much cake Friend Warder would leave for my comfort at evening.

Dear, ever dear lady, seen through the mist of years! None was like you, and none as dear, save one who had as brave a soul, but far other ways and charms.

And thus began my life at school, to which I went twice a day, my father not approving of the plan of three sessions a day, which was common, nor, for

some reason, I know not what, of schools kept by
Friends. So it was that I set out before eight, and
went again from two to four. My master, David
Dove, kept his school in Vidall's Alley, nigh to
Chestnut, above Second. There were many boys and
girls, and of the former John Warder, and Graydon,
who wrote certain memoirs long after. His mother,
a widow, kept boarders in the great Slate-roof House
near by; for in those days this was a common resource of decayed gentlewomen, and by no means
affected their social position. Here came many
officers to stay, and their red coats used to please my
eyes as I went by the porch, where at evening I saw
them smoking long pipes, and saying not very nice
things of the local gentry, or of the women as they
passed by, and calling "*Mohair!*" after the gentlemen, a manner of army word of contempt for citizens.
I liked well enough the freedom I now enjoyed, and
found it to my fancy to wander a little on my way to
school, although usually I followed the creek, and,
where Second street crossed it, lingered on the bridge
to watch the barges or galleys come up at full of tide
to the back of the warehouses on the northeast bank.

I have observed that teachers are often eccentric,
and surely David Dove was no exception, nor do I
now know why so odd a person was chosen by many
for the care of youth. I fancy my mother had to do
with the choice in my case, and was influenced by
the fact that Dove rarely used the birch, but had a
queer fancy for setting culprits on a stool, with the
birch switch stuck in the back of the jacket, so as to

stand up behind the head. I hated this, and would
rather have been birched *secundum artem* than to
have seen the girls giggling at me. I changed my
opinion later.

Thus my uneventful life ran on, while I learned to
write, and acquired, with other simple knowledge,
enough of Latin and Greek to fit me for entrance at
the academy, which Dr. Franklin had founded in 1750,
in the hall on Fourth street, built for Whitefield's
preaching.

At this time I fell much into the company of John
Warder, a lad of my own age, and a son of that
Joseph who liked cake, and was, as my mother said,
solicitous. Most of the games of boys were not
esteemed fitting by Friends, and hence we were
somewhat limited in our resources; but to fish in the
creek we were free; also to haunt the ships and hear
sea yarns, and to skate in winter, were not forbidden.
Jack Warder I took to because he was full of stories,
and would imagine what things might chance to my
father's ships in the West Indies; but why, in those
early days, he liked me, I do not know.

Our school life with Dove ended after four years
in an odd fashion. I was then about twelve, and
had become a vigorous, daring boy, with, as it now
seems to me, something of the fortunate gaiety of
my mother. Other lads thought it singular that in
peril I became strangely vivacious; but underneath
I had a share of the relentless firmness of my father,
and of his vast dislike of failure, and of his love of
truth. I have often thought that the father in me

saved me from the consequences of so much of my
mother's gentler nature as might have done me harm
in the rude conflicts of life.

David Dove, among other odd ways, devised a plan
for punishing the unpunctual which had considerable success. One day, when I had far overstayed
the hour of eight, by reason of having climbed into
Friend Pemberton's gardens, where I was tempted by
many green apples, I was met by four older boys. One
had a lantern, which, with much laughter, he tied
about my neck, and one, marching before, rang a bell.
I had seen this queer punishment fall on others, and
certainly the amusement shown by people in the
streets would not have hurt me compared with the
advantage of pockets full of apples, had I not of a
sudden seen my father, who usually breakfasted at
six, and was at his warehouse by seven. He looked
at me composedly, but went past us saying nothing.

On my return about eleven, he unluckily met me
in the garden, for I had gone the back way in order
to hide my apples. I had an unpleasant half-hour,
despite my mother's tears, and was sent at once to
confess to Friend James Pemberton. The good
man said I was a naughty boy, but must come later
when the apples were red ripe, and I should take all
I wanted, and I might fetch with me another boy,
or even two. I never forgot this, and did him some
good turns in after-years, and right gladly too.

In my own mind I associated David Dove with
this painful interview with my father. I disliked
him the more because, when the procession entered

the school, a little girl for whom Warder and I had
a boy friendship, in place of laughing, as did the rest,
for some reason began to cry. This angered the
master, who had the lack of self-control often seen in
eccentric people. He asked why she cried, and on
her sobbing out that it was because she was sorry
for me, he bade her take off her stays. These being
stiff, and worn outside the gown, would have made
the punishment of the birch on the shoulders of tri-
fling moment.

As it was usual to whip girls at school, the little
maid said nothing, but did as she was bid, taking a
sharp birching without a cry. Meanwhile I sat with
my head in my hands, and my fingers in my ears lest
I should hear her weeping. After school that evening, when all but Warder and I had wandered home,
I wrote on the outside wall of the school-house with
chalk, "David Dove Is A Cruel Beast," and went
away somewhat better contented.

Now, with all his seeming dislike to use the rod,
David had turns of severity, and then he was far
more brutal than any man I have ever known.
Therefore it did not surprise us next morning that
the earlier scholars were looking with wonder and
alarm at the sentence on the wall, when Dove, appearing behind us, ordered us to enter at once.

Going to his desk, he put on his spectacles, which
then were worn astride of the nose. In a minute he
set on below them a second pair, and this we knew to
be a signal of coming violence. Then he stood up,
and asked who had written the opprobrious epithet

on the wall. As no one replied, he asked several in
turn, but luckily chose the girls, thinking, perhaps,
that they would weakly betray the sinner. Soon he
lost patience, and cried out he would give a king's
pound to know.

When he had said this over and over, I began to
reflect that, if he had any real idea of doing as he
promised, a pound was a great sum, and to consider
what might be done with it in the way of marbles of
Amsterdam, tops, and of certain much-desired books,
for now this latter temptation was upon me, as it
has been ever since. As I sat, and Dove thundered,
I remembered how, when one Stacy, with an oath,
assured my father that his word was as good as his
bond, my parent said dryly that this equality left him
free to choose, and he would prefer his bond. I saw
no way to what was for me the mysterious security
of a bond, but I did conceive of some need to stiffen
the promise Dove had made before I faced the
penalty.

Upon this I held up a hand, and the master cried,
"What is it?"

I said, "Master, if a boy should tell thee wouldst
thou surely give a pound?"

At this a lad called "Shame!" thinking I was a
telltale.

When Dove called silence and renewed his pledge,
I, overbold, said, "Master, I did it, and now wilt
thou please to give me a pound—a king's pound?"

"I will give thee a pounding!" he roared; and
upon this came down from his raised form, and gave

me a beating so terrible and cruel that at last the
girls cried aloud, and he let me drop on the floor,
sore and angry. I lay still awhile, and then went to
my seat. As I bent over my desk, it was rather the
sense that I had been wronged, than the pain of the
blows, which troubled me.

After school, refusing speech to any, I walked
home, and ministered to my poor little bruised body
as I best could. Now this being a Saturday, and
therefore a half-holiday, I ate at two with my father
and mother.

Presently my father, detecting my uneasy movements, said, "Hast thou been birched to-day, and for
what badness?"

Upon this my mother said softly, "What is it, my
son? Have no fear." And this gentleness being too
much for me, I fell to tears, and blurted out all my
little tragedy.

As I ended, my father rose, very angry, and cried
out, "Come this way!" But my mother caught me,
saying, "No! no! Look, John! see his poor neck
and his wrist! What a brute! I tell thee, thou
shalt not! it were a sin. Leave him to me," and she
thrust me behind her as if for safety.

To my surprise, he said, "As thou wilt," and my
mother hurried me away. We had a grave, sweet
talk, and there it ended for a time. I learned that,
after all, the woman's was the stronger will. I was
put to bed and declared to have a fever, and given
sulphur and treacle, and kept out of the paternal
paths for a mournful day of enforced rest.

On the Monday following I went to school as usual, but not without fear of Dove. When we were all busy, about ten o'clock, I was amazed to hear my father's voice. He stood before the desk, and addressed Master Dove in a loud voice, meaning, I suppose, to be heard by all of us.

"David Dove," he said, "my son hath been guilty of disrespect to thee, and to thy office. I do not say he has lied, for it is my belief that thou art truly an unjust and cruel beast. As for his sin, he has suffered enough [I felt glad of this final opinion]; but a bargain was made. He, on his part, for a consideration of one pound sterling, was to tell thee who wrote certain words. He has paid thee and thou hast taken interest out of his skin. Indeed, Friend Shylock, I think he weighs less by a pound. Thou wilt give him his pound, Master David."

Upon this a little maid near by smiled at me, and Warder punched me in the ribs. Master Dove was silent a moment, and then answered that there was no law to make him pay, and that he had spoken lightly, as one might say, "I would give this or that to know." But my father replied at once:

"The boy trusted thee, and was as good as his word. I advise thee to pay. As thou art Master to punish boys, so will I, David, use thy birch on thee at need, and trust to the great Master to reckon with me if I am wrong."

All this he said so fiercely that I trembled with joy, and hoped that Dove would deny him; but, in place of this, he muttered something about Meeting and Friends, and meanwhile searched his pockets and brought out a guinea. This my father dropped into his breeches pocket, saying, "The shilling will be for interest" (a guinea being a shilling over a king's pound). After this, turning to me, he said, "Come with me, Hugh," and went out of the school-house, I following after, very well pleased, and thinking of my guinea. I dared not ask for it, and I think he forgot it. He went along homeward, with his head bent and his hands behind his back. In common, he walked with his head up and his chin set forward, as though he did a little look down on the world of other men; and this in truth he did, being at least six feet three inches in his stocking-feet, and with no lack of proportion in waist or chest.

Next day I asked my mother of my guinea, but she laughed gaily, and threw up her hands, and cried, "A bad debt! a bad debt, Hugh! Dost thou want more interest? My father used to say they had a proverb in the Midi, 'If the devil owe thee money it were best to lose it.' *Le diable!* Oh, what am I saying? *Mon fils,* forget thy debt. What did thy father say?" And I told it again to her amusement; but she said at last, very seriously:

"It has disturbed thy father as never before did anything since he would not join with Friend Bradford against the Stamp Act. I would I had seen him then, or this time. I like sometimes to see a strong man in just anger. Oh, *mon Dieu!* what did I say! I am but half a Quaker, I fear." My mother never would turn away from the creed of her peo-

3

ple, but she did not altogether fancy the ways of
Friends.

"Eh, *mon fils*, sometimes I say naughty words.
Give me a sweet little pat on the cheek for my badness, and always come to me with all thy troubles."
Then I kissed her, and we went out to play hide-and-
find in the orchard.

My father's grim, sarcastic humour left him as
years went on, and he became as entirely serious
as I ever knew a man to be. I think on this occasion his after-annoyance, which endured for days,
was more because of having threatened Dove than
for any other cause. He no doubt regarded me as
the maker of the mischief which had tempted him
for a moment to forget himself, and for many a day
his unjust severity proved that he did not readily
forgive. But so it was always. My mother never
failed to understand me, which my father seemed
rarely able to do. If I did ill he used the strap with
little mercy, but neither in these early years, nor in
those which followed, did he ever give me a word of
praise. Many years afterward I found a guinea in a
folded paper, laid away in my father's desk. On the
outer cover he had written, "This belongs to Hugh.
He were better without it."

My mother scarce ever let slip her little French ex-
pletives or phrases in my father's hearing. He hated
all French things, and declared the language did not
ring true—that it was a slippery tongue, in which it
was easy to lie. A proud, strong man he was in
those days, of fixed beliefs, and of unchanging loy-

alty to the king. In his own house he was feared by
his son, his clerks, and his servants; but not by my
mother, who charmed him, as she did all other men,
and had in most things her desire.

Outside of his own walls few men cared to oppose
him. He was rich, and coldly despotic; a man exact
and just in business, but well able, and as willing, to
help with a free hand whatever cause was of interest
to Friends. My Aunt Gainor, a little his senior, was
one of the few over whom he had no manner of control. She went her own way, and it was by no means
his way, as I shall make more clear by and by.

Two days later I was taken to the academy, or the
college, as some called it, which is now the university.
My father wrote my name, as you may see it in the
catalogue, and his own signature, with the date of 6th
mnth 4th, 1763. Beneath it is the entry of John Warder and his father, Joseph; for Jack had also been
removed from Dove's dominion because of what my
father said to Joseph, a man always pliable, and advised to do what larger men thought good. Thus it
came about that my friend Jack and I were by good
fortune kept in constant relation. Our schoolmate,
the small maid so slight of limb, so dark and tearful,
was soon sent away to live with an aunt in Bristol,
on the Delaware, having become an orphan by the
death of her mother. Thus it came about that Darthea Peniston passed out of my life for many years,
having been, through the accident of her tenderness,
the means for me of a complete and fortunate change.

III

HE academy was, and still is, a plain brick building, set back from Fourth street, and having a large gravelled space in front and also at the back. The main school-room occupied its whole westward length, and upstairs was a vast room, with bare joists above, in which, by virtue of the deed of gift, any Christian sect was free to worship if temporarily deprived of a home. Here the great Whitefield preached, and here generations of boys were taught. Behind the western playground was the graveyard of Christ Church. He was thought a brave lad who, after school at dusk in winter, dared to climb over and search around the tombs of the silent dead for a lost ball or what not.

I was mightily afraid of the academy. The birch was used often and with severity, and, as I soon found, there was war between the boys and the town fellows who lived to north and east. I was also to discover other annoyances quite as little to the taste of Friends, such as stone fights or snowball skirmishes. Did time permit, I should like well to linger long over this school life. The college, as it

was officially called, had a great reputation, and its
early catalogues are rich with names of those who
made an empire. This task I leave to other pens,
and hasten to tell my own personal story.

In my friend Jack Warder's journal there is a kind
page or two as to what manner of lad I was in his
remembrance of me in after-years. I like to think
it was a true picture.

"When Hugh Wynne and I went to school at
the academy on Fourth street, south of Arch, I used
to envy him his strength. At twelve he was as tall
as are most lads at sixteen, but possessed of such
activity and muscular power as are rarely seen, bidding fair to attain, as he did later, the height and
massive build of his father. He was a great lover
of risk, and not, as I have always been, fearful.
When we took apples, after the fashion of all Adam's
young descendants, he was as like as not to give
them away. I think he went with us on these, and
some wilder errands, chiefly because of his fondness
for danger, a thing I could never comprehend. He
still has his mother's great eyes of blue, and a fair,
clear skin. God bless him! Had I never known
him I might perhaps have been, as to one thing, a
happier man, but I had been less deserving of such
good fortune as has come to me in life. For this is
one of the uses of friends: that we consider how such
and such a thing we are moved to do might appear
to them. And this for one of my kind, who have
had—nay, who have—many weaknesses, has been
why Hugh Wynne counts for so much to me.

"We, with two other smaller boys, were, at that time, the only sons of Friends at the academy, and were, thanks to the brute Dove, better grounded in the humanities than were some, although we were late in entering."

I leave this and other extracts as they were writ. A more upright gentleman than John Warder I know not, nor did ever know. What he meant by his weaknesses I cannot tell, and as to the meaning of one phrase, which he does not here explain, these pages shall perhaps discover.

Not long after our entrance at the academy, my father charged me one morning with a note to. my aunt, Gainor Wynne, which I was to deliver when the morning session was over. As this would make me late, in case her absence delayed a reply, I was to remain and eat my midday meal. My father was loath always to call upon his sister. She had early returned to the creed of her ancestors, and sat on Sundays in a great square pew at Christ Church, to listen to the Rev. Robert Jennings. Hither, in September of 1763, my aunt took me, to my father's indignation, to hear the great Mr. Whitefield preach.

Neither Aunt Gainor's creed, dress, house, nor society pleased her brother. She had early made clear, in her decisive way, that I was to be her heir, and she was, I may add, a woman of large estate. I was allowed to visit her as I pleased. Indeed, I did so often. I liked no one better, always excepting my mother. Why, with my father's knowledge of her views, I was thus left free I cannot say. He was

the last of men to sacrifice his beliefs to motives
of gain.

When I knocked at the door of her house on Arch
street, opposite the Friends' Meeting-house, a black
boy, dressed as a page, let me in. He was clad in
gray armozine, a sort of corded stuff, with red buttons, and he wore a red turban. As my aunt was
gone to drive, on a visit to that Madam Penn who
was once Miss Allen, I was in no hurry, and was
glad to look about me. The parlour, a great room
with three windows on the street, afforded a strange
contrast to my sober home. There were Smyrna
rugs on a polished floor, a thing almost unheard of.
Indeed, people came to see them. The furniture was
all of red walnut, and carved in shells and flower re-
liefs. There were so many tables, little and larger,
with claw-feet or spindle-legs, that one had to be
careful not to overturn their loads of Chinese dragons, ivory carvings, grotesque Delft beasts, and fans,
French or Spanish or of the Orient. There was also
a spinet, and a corner closet of books, of which
every packet brought her a variety. Upstairs was a
fair room full of volumes, big and little, as I found
to my joy rather later, and these were of all kinds:
some good, and some of them queer, or naughty.
Over the wide, white fireplace was a portrait of herself by the elder Peale, but I prefer the one now in
my library. This latter hung, at the time I speak of,
between the windows. It was significant of my aunt's
idea of her own importance that she should have
wished to possess two portraits of herself. The lat-

ter was painted by Sir Joshua Reynolds when she
was in England in 1750, and represents her as a fine,
large woman with features which were too big for
loveliness in youth, but in after-years went well with
her abundant gray hair and unusual stature; for, like
the rest of us, she was tall, of vigorous and wholesome build and colour, with large, well-shaped hands,
and the strength of a man—I might add, too, with
the independence of a man. She went her own
way, conducted the business of her estate, which
was ample, with skill and ability, and asked advice
from no one. Like my father, she had a liking to
control those about her, was restlessly busy, and
was never so pleased as when engaged in arranging
other people's lives, or meddling with the making
of matches.

To this ample and luxurious house came the better class of British officers, and ombre and quadrille
were often, I fear, played late into the long nights of
winter. Single women, after a certain or uncertain
age, were given a brevet title of "Mistress." Mistress Gainor Wynne lost or won with the coolness of
an old gambler, and this habit, perhaps more than
aught beside, troubled my father. Sincere and consistent in his views, I can hardly think that my
father was, after all, unable to resist the worldly advantages which my aunt declared should be mine.
It was, in fact, difficult to keep me out of the obvious risks this house and company provided for a
young person like myself. He must have trusted to
the influence of my home to keep me in the ways of

Friends. It is also to be remembered, as regards my father's motives, that my Aunt Gainor was my only relative, since of the Owens none were left. My mother was a prime favourite with this masterful lady. She loved nothing better than to give her fine silk petticoats or a pearl-coloured satin gown ; and if this should nowadays amaze Friends, let them but look in the " Observer," and see what manner of finery was advertised in 1778 as stole from our friend, Sarah Fisher, sometime Sarah Logan, a much respected member of Meeting. In this, as in all else, my mother had her way, and, like some of the upper class of Quakers, wore at times such raiment as fifty years later would have surely brought about a visit from a committee of overseers.

Waiting for Aunt Gainor, I fell upon an open parcel of books just come by the late spring packet. Among these turned up a new and fine edition of " Captain Gulliver's Travels," by Mr. Dean Swift. I lit first, among these famous adventures, on an extraordinary passage, so wonderful, indeed, and so amusing, that I heard not the entrance of my father, who at the door had met my aunt, and with her some fine ladies of the governor's set. There were Mrs. Ferguson, too well known in the politics of later years, but now only a beautiful and gay woman, Madam Allen, and Madam Chew, the wife of the Attorney-General.

They were eagerly discussing, and laughingly inquiring of my father, what colour of masks for the street was to be preferred. He was in no wise embarrassed by these fine dames, and never, to my thinking, was seen to better advantage than among what he called "world's people." He seemed to me more really at home than among Friends, and as he towered, tall, and gravely courteous in manner, I thought him a grand gentleman.

As I looked up, the young Miss Chew, who afterward married Colonel Eager Howard, was saying saucily, "Does not Madam Wynne wear a mask for her skin? It is worth keeping, Mr. Wynne."

"Let me recommend to you a vizard with silver buttons to hold in the mouth, or, better, a riding-mask," cried Aunt Gainor, pleased at this gentle badgering, "like this, John. See, a flat silver plate to hold between the teeth. It is the last thing."

"White silk would suit her best," cried Mrs. Ferguson, "or green, with a chin-curtain—a loo-mask. Which would you have, sir?"

"Indeed," he said quietly, "her skin is good enough. I know no way to better it."

Then they all laughed, pelting the big man with many questions, until he could not help but laugh, as he declared he was overwhelmed, and would come on his business another day. But on this the women would not stay, and took themselves and their high bonnets and many petticoats out of the room, each dropping a curtsey at the door, and he bowing low, like Mr. John Penn, as never before I had seen him do.

No sooner were they gone than he desired me to give him the note he had written to his sister, since

now it was not needed, and then he inquired what
book I was reading. Aunt Gainor glanced at it, and
replied for me, "A book of travels, John, very im-
proving too. Take it home, Hugh, and read it. If
you find in it no improprieties, it may be recommended to your father." She loved nothing better
than to tease him.

"I see not what harm there could be in travels,"
he returned. "Thou hast my leave. Gainor, what
is this I hear? Thou wouldst have had me sell thee
for a venture threescore hogsheads of tobacco from
Annapolis. I like not to trade with my sister, nor
that she should trade at all; and now, when I have
let them go to another, I hear that it is thou who
art the real buyer. I came hither to warn thee that
other cargoes are to arrive. Thou wilt lose."

Aunt Gainor said nothing for a moment, but let
loose the linen safeguard petticoat she wore against
mud or dust when riding, and appeared in a rich brocade of gray silken stuff, and a striped under-gown.
When she had put off her loose camlet over-jacket,
she said, "Will you have a glass of Madeira, or shall
it be Hollands, John? Ring the bell, Hugh."

"Hollands," said my father.

"What will you give me for your tobacco to-day,
John?"

"Why dost thou trifle?" he returned.

"I sold it again, John. I am the better by an hundred pounds. Two tobacco-ships are wrecked on
Hinlopen. An express is come. Have you not
heard?"

"Farewell," he said, rising. He made r.j comment
on her news. I had an idea that he would not have
been unhappy had she lost on her venture.

Joseph Warder was her agent then and afterward.
She rarely lost on her purchases. Although generous, and even lavish, she dearly loved a good bargain, and, I believe, liked the game far more than she
cared for success in the playing of it.

"Come, Hugh," she said, "let us eat and drink.
Take the book home, and put it away for your own
reading. Here is sixpence out of my gains. I hope
you will never need to trade, and, indeed, why should
you, whether I live or die? How would the king's
service suit you, and a pair of colours?"

I said I should like it.

"There is a pretty tale, Hugh, of the French gentlemen, who, being poor, have to make money in commerce. They leave their swords with a magistrate,
and when they are become rich enough take them
back again. There is some pleasing ceremony, but
I forget. The Wynnes have been long enough in
drab and trade. It is time we took back our swords,
and quitted bow-thouing and bow-theeing."

I said I did not understand.

"Oh, you will," said Aunt Gainor, giving me a
great apple-dumpling. "Take some molasses. Oh,
as much as you please. I shall look away, as I do
when the gentlemen take their rum."

You may be sure I obeyed her. As to much that
she said, I was shocked; but I never could resist a
laugh, and so we made merry like children, as was

usual, for, as she used to say, "To learn when to laugh and when not to laugh is an education."

When my meal was over, and my stomach and my pockets all full, Aunt Gainor bade me sit on her knees, and began to tell me about what fine gentlemen were the Wynnes, and how foolish my grandfather had been to turn Quaker and give up fox-hunting and the old place. I was told, too, how much she had lost to Mr. Penn last night, and more that was neither well for me to hear nor wise for her to tell; but as to this she cared little, and she sent me away then, as far too many times afterward, full of my own importance, and of desire to escape some day from the threatened life of the ledger and the day-book.

At last she said, "You are getting too heavy, Hugh. Handsome Mrs. Ferguson says you are too big to be kissed, and not old enough to kiss," and so she bade me go forth to the afternoon session of the academy.

After two weeks at the academy I got my first lesson in the futility of non-resistance, so that all the lessons of my life in favour of this doctrine were, of a sudden, rendered vain. We were going home in the afternoon, gay and happy, Jack Warder to take supper with me, and to use a boat my aunt had given me.

Near to High street was a vacant lot full of bushes and briers. Here the elder lads paused, and one said, "Wynne, you are to fight."

I replied, "Why should I fight? I will not."

"But it is to get your standing in the school, and Tom Alloway is to fight you."

"This was a famous occasion in our lives," writes my friend Jack; "for, consider: I, who was a girl for timidity, was sure to have my turn next, and here were we two little fellows, who had heard every First-day, and ever and ever at home, that all things were to be suffered of all men (and of boys too, I presume). I was troubled for Hugh, but I noticed that while he said he would not fight he was buttoning up his jacket and turning back the cuff of one sleeve. Also he smiled as he said, 'No, I cannot;' and many times since I have seen him merry in danger.

"For, of a truth, never later did he or I feel the sense of a great peril as we did that day, with the bigger boys hustling us, and Alloway crying, 'Coward!' I looked about for some man who would help us, but there was no one; only a cow hobbled near by. She looked up, and then went on chewing her cud. I, standing behind Hugh, said, 'Run! run!'

"The counsel seemed good to me who gave it. As I think on it now, I was in great perplexity of soul, and had a horrible fear as to bodily hurt. I turned, followed by Hugh, and ran fleetly across the open ground and through the bushes. About mid-way I looked back. Two lads were near upon us, when I saw Hugh drop upon his hands and knees. Both fellows rolled over him, and he called out, as they fell to beating him, 'Run, Jack!'

"But I was no longer so minded. I kicked one boy, and struck another, and even now recall how a strange joy captured me when I struck the first blow."

There was a fine scrimmage, for no quarter was

asked or given, and I saw my poor Jack's girl face bloody. This was the last I remember clearly, for the lust of battle was on me, and I can recall no more of what chanced for a little, than I could in later years of the wild melley on the main street of Germantown, or of the struggle in the redoubt at Yorktown.

Presently we were cast to right and left by a strong hand, and, looking up, as I stood fierce and panting, I saw Friend Rupert Forest, and was overwhelmed with fear; for often on First-day I had heard him preach solemnly, and always it was as to turning the other cheek, and on the wickedness of profane language. Just now he seemed pleased rather than angered, and said, smiling:

"This is a big war, boys. What is it about?"

I said, "I must fight for my standing, and I will not."

"I think thou wert scarcely of that mind just now. There will be bad blood until it is over."

To this I replied, "It is Alloway I am to fight."

To my surprise, he went on to say, "Then take off thy jacket and stand up, and no kicking."

I asked nothing better, and began to laugh. At this my foe, who was bigger and older than I, cried out that I would laugh on the other side of my mouth—a queer boy phrase of which I could never discover the meaning.

"And now, fair play," said Friend Forest. "Keep cool, Hugh, and watch his eyes."

I felt glad that he was on my side, and we fell to with no more words. I was no match for the prac-

tised fists of my antagonist; but I was the stronger,
and I kept my wits better than might have been expected. At last I got his head under my arm with a
grip on his gullet, and so mauled him with my right
fist that Friend Forest pulled me away, and my man
staggered back, bloody, and white too, while I was
held like a dog in leash.

"He hath enough, I think. Ask him."

I cried out, "No! Damn him!" It was my first
oath.

"Hush!" cried Forest. "No profane language."

"I will not speak to him," said I, "and—and—he
is a beast of the pit." Now this fine statement I
had come upon in a book of Mr. William Penn's my
father owned, wherein the governor had denounced
one Mr. Muggleton.

Friend Forest laughed merrily. "Thou hast thy
standing, lad." For Alloway walked sullenly away,
not man enough to take more or to confess defeat.
Jack, who was still white, said:

"It is my turn now, and which shall it be?"

"Shade of Fox!" cried Friend Forest. "The war
is over. Come, boys, I must see you well out of this."
And so reassuring us, he went down Fourth street,
and to my home.

My father was in the sitting-room, taking his long-
stemmed reed pipe at his ease. He rose as we followed Friend Forest into the room.

"Well," he said, "what coil is this?" For we were
bloody, and hot with fight and wrath, and, as to our
garments, in very sad disorder.

Friend Forest very quietly related our story, and made much of his own share in the renewal of our battle. To my surprise, my father smiled.

"It seems plain," he said, "that the lads were not to blame. But how wilt thou answer to the Meeting, Rupert Forest?"

"To it, to thee, to any man," said the Quaker.

"It is but a month ago that thy case was before Friends because of thy having beaten Friend Waln's man. It will go ill with thee—ill, I fear."

"And who is to spread it abroad?"

"Not I," said my father.

"I knew that," returned the Friend, simply. "I am but a jack-in-the-box Quaker, John. I am in and out in a moment, and then I go back and repent."

"Let us hope so. Go to thy mother, Hugh; and as to thee, John Warder, wait until I send with thee a note to thy father. There are liquors on the table, Friend Forest."

My mother set us in order, and cried a little, and said:

"I am glad he was well beaten. Thou shouldst never fight, my son; but if thou must, let it be so that thy adversary repent of it. *Mon Dieu! mon Dieu! j'en ai peur;* the wild Welsh blood of these Wynnes! And thy poor little nose—how 't is swelled!"

Not understanding her exclamations, Jack said as much, but she answered:

"Oh, it is a fashion of speech we French have. I shall never be cured of it, I fear. This wild blood—

4

what will come of it?" And she seemed—as Jack
writes long after, being more observing than I—as
if she were looking away into the distance of time,
thinking of what might come to pass. She had,
indeed, strange insight, and even then, as I knew
later, had her fears and unspoken anxieties. And
so, with a plentiful supper, ended a matter which
was, I may say, a critical point in my life.

IV

FTER this my days went by more peacefully. The help and example of Jack
assisted me greatly in my lessons, which
I did little relish. I was more fond of
reading, and devoured many books as I
sat under our orchard trees in the spring, or nestled
up to the fire on the long winter evenings, coiled on
the settle, that its high back might keep off drafts.
My aunt lent me an abundance of books after that
famous "Travels" of Mr. Gulliver. Now and then
my father looked at what she gave me, but he soon
tired of this, and fell asleep in the great oak chair
which Governor Penn gave my grandfather.

Many volumes, and some queer ones, I fell upon in
my aunt's house, but, save once, as to the naughtiness of Mrs. Aphra Behn, she never interfered. We
liked greatly a book called "Peter Wilkins," by one
Paltock, full of a queer folk, who had winged "graun-
dees," a sort of crimson robe made of folds of their
own skin. None read it now. My dear Jack fancied
it much more than I.

I was nigh to fifteen before we read "Robinson
Crusoe," but even earlier I devoured at my aunt's

"Captain Jack" and "The History of the Devil."
The former book filled us with delight. Jack and
I used to row over to Windmill Island, on the great
Delaware, and there at the south end we built a hut,
and slew bullfrogs, and found steps on the sand, I
being thereafter Friday, and Jack my master. We
made, too, a sail and mast for my boat, and, thus
aided, sailed of Saturdays up and down the noble
river, which I have always loved.

A still greater joy was to go in our chaise with my
mother to the governor's woods, which extended from
Broad street to the Schuylkill, and from Callowhill
to South street. There we tied the horse, and under
the great trees we found in spring arbutus, even beneath the snow, and later fetched thence turkey-foot
ferns, and wild honeysuckle, and quaker-ladies, with
jack-in-the-pulpits and fearful gray corpse-lights hid
away in the darker woods. In the forest my mother
seemed even younger than at home, and played with
us, and told us quaint tales of her French people, or
fairy stories of Giant Jack and others, which were
by no means such as Friends approved.

In our house one same stern, unbending rule prevailed. I have been told by my aunt, Gainor Wynne,
that when he was young my father was not always so
steadfast in conduct as to satisfy Friends. When I
was old enough to observe and think, he had surely
become strict enough; but this severity of opinion
and action increased with years, and showed in ways
which made life difficult for those near to him. In
fact, before I attained manhood the tinted arms and

the picture of Wyncote were put away in the attic
room. My mother's innocent love of ornament also
became to him a serious annoyance, and these peculiarities seemed at last to deepen whenever the political horizon darkened. At such times he became
silent, and yet more keen than usual to detect and
denounce anything in our home life which was not
to his liking.

The affairs of a young fellow between the ages of
childhood and younger manhood can have but meagre
interest. Our school life went on, and while we
worked or played, our elders saw the ever-increas-
ing differences between king and colonies becoming
year by year more difficult of adjustment. Except
when some noisy crisis arose, they had for us lads
but little interest.

Most people used the city landings, or lightered
their goods from ships in the stream. We, however,
had a great dock built out near to the mouth of Dock
Creek, and a warehouse. Hither came sloops from
my father's plantation of tobacco, near Annapolis,
and others from the "permitted islands," the Cape
de Verde and the Madeiras. Staves for barrels,
tobacco, and salt fish were the exports, and in return
came Eastern goods brought to these islands, and
huge tuns of Madeira wine. Rum, too, arrived from
New England, and salted mackerel. What else my
father imported, of French goods or tea, reached us
from England, for we were not allowed to trade with
the continent of Europe nor directly with India.

Once my father took me with him to Lewes, near

Cape Hinlopen, on one of his ships, and to my joy we
were met there by Tom, our black slave, with horses, and
rode back during two days by Newcastle and Chester.
As I rode ill, of course, and was sore for a week, my
father thought it well that I should learn to ride, and
this exercise I took to easily. Just before I was sixteen my aunt gave me a horse, and after we had sep-
arated abruptly a few times, and no harm to any, I
became the master, and soon an expert rider, as was
needful in a land where most long journeys were
made on horseback.

It seems to me now, as I look back, that the events
of life were preparing me and my friend Jack for
what was to follow. Our boating made every part
of the two rivers familiar. Now that I had a horse,
Jack's father, who would always do for him readily
what my Aunt Gainor did for me, yielded to his
desire to ride; and so it was that we began, as leisure served, to extend our rides to Germantown, or
even to Chestnut Hill. Thus all the outlying country became well known to both of us, and there was
not a road, a brook, or a hill which we did not know.

Until this happy time I had been well pleased to
follow my aunt on a pillion behind her servant,
Cæsar, but now I often went with her, perched on
my big horse, and got from my aunt, an excellent
horsewoman, some sharp lessons as to leaping, and
certain refinements in riding that she had seen or
known of in London.

A Captain Montresor—he who afterward, when a
colonel, was Howe's engineer—used to ride with her

in the spring of '69. He was a tall, stout man of
middle age, and much spoken of as likely to marry
my Aunt Gainor, although she was older than he,
for, as fat Oliver de Lancey said years after, "There
is no age to a woman's money, and guineas are always young." My aunt, Gainor Wynne, was still a
fine gentlewoman, and did not look her years. As
concerned this question of age, she was like a man,
and so in fact she was in some other ways. She
would tell any one how old she was. She once informed Mr. de Lancey that she was so much more of
a man than any British officer she knew that she did
not see how she could decently marry any of them.

I think it was about this time that I saw a little
scene which much impressed me, and which often re-
curs to my memory. We—that is, Mr. Montresor, and
my Aunt Gainor and I—of a Saturday afternoon rode
over by the lower ferry and up Gray's Lane, and so
to Mr. Hamilton's country-seat. "The Woodlands,"
as it was called, stood on a hill amid many beautiful
trees and foreign shrubs and flowers. Below it ran
the quiet Schuylkill, and beyond, above the governor's woods, could be seen far away Dr. Kearsley's
fine spire of Christ Church. No better did Master
Wren himself ever contrive, or more proportioned to
the edifice beneath it.

On the porch were Mr. Hamilton and Mrs. Penn,
with saucy gray eyes, and Mrs. Ferguson. A slim
young girl, Rebecca Franks, was teasing a cat. She
teased some one all her days, and did it merrily, and
not unkindly. She was little and very pretty, with a

dark skin. Did she dream she should marry a British soldier—a baronet and general—and end her days in London well on in the century yet to come?

Andrew Allen, whose father, the chief justice, took his wife, Margaret, from this house, sat on the steps near Miss Franks, and beside her little Peggy Shippen, who already gave promise of the beauty which won for her so pitiful a life. Nothing in this garden of gay women and flowers foretold the tragedy of West Point. I think of it now with sad wonder.

In one or another way these people became known in our annals. Most of them were of the more exclusive party known as the governor's set, and belonged to the Church of England. With the Galloways, Cadwaladers, Willings, Shippens, Rawles, and others, they formed a more or less distinct society, affecting London ways, dining at the extreme hour of four, loving cards, the dance, fox-hunting, and to see a main of game-cocks. Among them—not of them— came and went certain of what were called "genteel" Quakers—Morrises, Pembertons, Whartons, and Logans. They had races too,—that is, the governor's set,—and one of my delights was, on the way to the academy, to stop in Third street, above Chestnut, and see the race-horses in the Widow Nichols's stables at the sign of the Indian Queen.

But I have left the laughter of the last century echoing among the columns of Andrew Hamilton's home. The guests were made welcome, and had a dish of tea or a glass of punch; and those desiring no more bohea set a spoon across the cup, and fell into groups. My aunt opened the velvet bag which hung at her waist, to pay Mrs. Ferguson a small gambling debt of the night before.

"Ah, here!" she cried gaily, "Mr. Montresor, this is for you. One of Mr. Grenville's stamps; I kept two. I was lucky enough to get them from Master Hughes, the stamp officer—a great curiosity. You shall have one."

Mr. Montresor bowed. "I will keep it," he said, "until it comes into use again."

"That will be never," said Andrew Allen, turning.

"Never!" repeated Miss Wynne. "Let us hope, sir, it may be a lesson to all future ministers."

"A man was wanted in New York in place of Mr. Gage," cried Mrs. Ferguson. "As to those New England Puritans, they were in rebellion before they came over, and have been ever since."

"And what of New York, and this town, and Virginia?" said my Aunt Gainor, with her great nose well up.

"I would have put an end to their disloyal ways, one and all," cried Mrs. Ferguson.

"It is curious," said Mr. Galloway, "that the crown should be so thwarted. What people have more reason to be contented?"

"Contented!" said Miss Wynne. "Already they talk of taxes in which we are to have no voice. Contented! and not a ship dare trade with France. It amazes me that there is a man in the plantations to sit quiet under it."

"I am of your opinion, madam," said Mr. Macpherson, "and I might go still further."

"They consider us as mere colonials, and we may not so much as have a bishop of our own. I would I had my way, sir."

"And what would you do, Mistress Wynne?" asked Mr. Chew.

"I would say, 'Mr. Attorney-General, give us the same liberty all the English have, to go and come on the free seas!'"

"And if not?" said Montresor, smiling.

"And if not," she returned, "then—" and she touched the sword at his side. I wondered to see how resolute she looked.

The captain smiled. "I hope you will not command a regiment, madam."

"Would to God I could!"

"I should run," he cried, laughing. And thus pleasantly ended a talk which was becoming bitter to many of this gay company.

Destiny was already sharpening the sword we were soon to draw, and of those who met and laughed that day there were sons who were to be set against fathers, and brothers whom war was to find in hostile ranks. A young fellow of my age, the son of Mr. Macpherson, sat below us on the steps with the girls. He was to leave his young life on the bastion at Quebec, and, for myself, how little did I dream of what I should get out of the devil-pot of war which was beginning to simmer!

Very soon I was sent with Rebecca Franks and

Miss Chew to gather flowers. Miss Franks evidently
despised my youth, and between the two little maids
I, being unused to girls, had not a pleasant time, and
was glad to get back to the porch, where we stood
silent until bidden to be seated, upon which the girls
curtseyed and I bowed, and then sat down to eat
cakes and drink syllabub.

At last my aunt put on her safeguard petticoat,
the horses came, and we rode away. For a while she
was silent, answering the captain in monosyllables;
but just beyond the ferry his horse cast a shoe, and
went so lame that the officer must needs return to
Woodlands leading him, there to ask a new mount.

For yet a while my aunt rode on without a word,
but at last she began to rally me as to Miss Chew.
I had to confess I cared not for her or the other, or,
indeed, for maids at all.

"It will come," said she. "Oh, it will come soon
enough. Peggy Chew has the better manners. And,
by the way, sir, when you bow, keep your back
straight. Mr. Montresor has a pretty way of it.
Observe him, Hugh. But he is a fool, and so are
the rest; and as for Betty Ferguson, I should like to
lay a whip over her back like that," and she hit my
horse sharply, poor thing, so that I lost a stirrup
and came near to falling.

When the beast got quiet I asked why these nice
people, who had such pleasant ways, were all fools.

"I will tell you," she said. "There are many and
constant causes of trouble between us and the king.
When one ends, like this Stamp Act, another is

hatched. It was the best of us who left England, and we are trained to rely on ourselves, and have no need of England. You will live to see dark days, Hugh—just what, God alone can tell; but you will live to see them, and your life will have to answer some questions. This may seem strange to you, my lad, but it will come."

What would come I knew not. She said no more, but rode homeward at speed, as she liked best to do.

Thus time went by, until I was full sixteen, having been at the college a year later than was usual. I had few battles to fight, and contrived to keep these to myself, or to get patched up at my Aunt Wynne's, who delighted to hear of these conflicts, and always gave me a shilling to heal my wounds. My dear, fair-haired Jack, Aunt Gainor thought a girl-boy, and fit only to sell goods, or, at best, to become a preacher. His father she used and disliked.

Meanwhile we had been through Horace and Cicero,—and Ovid for our moral improvement, I suppose,—with Virgil and Sallust, and at last Cæsar, whom alone of them all I liked. Indeed, Jack and I built over a brook in my Aunt Gainor's garden at Chestnut Hill a fair model of Cæsar's great bridge over the Rhine. This admired product of our ingenuity was much praised by Captain Montresor, who was well aware of my aunt's weakness for a certain young person.

My father's decisions came always without warning. In the fall of 1769 I was just gone back to the academy, and put to work at mathematics and some

Greek under James Wilson, at that period one of the
tutors, and some time later an associate judge of
the Supreme Court. This great statesman and lawyer of after-days was a most delightful teacher. He
took a fancy to my Jack, and, as we were insepa-
rable, put up with my flippancy and deficient scholar-
ship. Jack's diary says otherwise, and that he saw in
me that which, well used, might make of me a man
of distinction. At all events, he liked well to walk
with us on a Saturday, or to go in my boat, which
was for us a great honour. My father approved of
James Wilson, and liked him on the holiday to share
our two-o'clock dinner. Then, and then only, did I
understand the rigour and obstinacy of my father's
opinions, for they ofttimes fell into debate as to the
right of the crown to tax us without representation.
Mr. Wilson said many towns in England had no
voice in Parliament, and that, if once the crown
yielded the principle we stood on, it would change
the whole political condition in the mother-land;
and this the king would never agree to see. Mr.
Wilson thought we had been foolish to say, as
many did, that, while we would have no internal
taxes, we would submit to a tax on imports. This he
considered even worse. My father was for obedience
and non-resistance, and could not see that we were
fighting a battle for the liberty of all Englishmen.
He simply repeated his opinions, and was but a child
in the hands of this clear-headed thinker. My father
might well have feared for the effect of Mr. Wilson's
views on a lad of my age, in whose mind he opened

vistas of thought far in advance of those which, without him, I should ever have seen.

John Wynne was, however, too habitually accustomed to implicit obedience to dream of danger, and thus were early sown in my mind the seeds of future action, with some doubt as to my father's ability to cope with a man like our tutor, who considerately weighed my father's sentiments (they were hardly opinions), and so easily and courteously disposed of them that these logical defeats were clear even to us boys.

Our school relations with this gentleman were abruptly broken.   One day, in late October of 1769, we went on a long walk through the proprietary's woods, gathering for my mother boughs of the many-tinted leaves of autumn.   These branches she liked to set in jars of water in the room where we sat, so that it might be gay with the lovely colours she so much enjoyed.   As we entered the forest about Eighth street Mr. Wilson joined us, and went along, chatting agreeably with my mother.   Presently he said to me: "I have just left your father with Mr. Pemberton, talking about some depredations in Mr. Penn's woods.   He tells me you boys are to leave school, but for what I do not know.   I am sorry."

Jack and I had of late expected this, and I, for one, was not grieved, but my friend was less well pleased.

We strolled across to the Schuylkill, and there, sitting down, amused ourselves with making a little crown of twisted twigs and leaves of the red and yel-

low maples. This we set merrily on my mother's gray
beaver, while Mr. Wilson declared it most becoming.
Just then Friend Pemberton and my father came
upon us, and, as usual when the latter appeared, our
laughter ceased.

"I shall want thee this afternoon, Hugh," he said.
"And what foolishness is this on thy head, wife?
Art thou going home in this guise?"

"It seems an innocent prettiness," said Pemberton,
while my mother, in no wise dismayed, looked up
with her big blue eyes.

"Thou wilt always be a child," said my father.

"*Je l'espére*," said the mother; "must I be put in
a corner? The *bon Dieu* hath just changed the
forest fashions. I wonder is He a Quaker, Friend
Pemberton?"

"Thou hast ever a neat answer," said the gentle
old man. "Come, John, we are not yet done."

My father said no more, and we boys were still as
mice. We went homeward with our mirth quite at
an end, Jack and Wilson leaving us at Fourth street.

In the afternoon about six—for an hour had been
named—I saw my aunt's chaise at the door. I knew
at once that something unusual was in store, for
Mistress Wynne rarely came hither except to see my
mother, and then always in the forenoon. Moreover,
I noticed my father at the window, and never had I
known him to return so early. When I went in he
said at once:

"I have been telling thy aunt of my intention in
regard to thee."

"And I utterly disapprove of it," said my aunt.

"Wait," he said. "I desire that thou shalt enter as one of my clerks; but first it is my will that, as the great and good proprietary decreed, thou shouldst acquire some mechanic trade; I care not what."

I was silent; I did not like it. Even far later, certain of the stricter Friends adhered to a rule which was once useful, but was now no longer held to be of imperative force.

"I would suggest shoemaking," said my Aunt Gainor, scornfully, "or tailoring."

"I beg of thee, Gainor," said my mother, "not to discontent the lad."

"As to this matter," returned my father, "I will not be thwarted. I asked thee to come hither, not to ridicule a sensible decision, but to consult upon it."

"You have had all my wisdom," said the lady. "I had thought to ask my friend, Charles Townsend, for a pair of colours; but now that troops are sent to Boston to override all reason, I doubt it. Do as you will with the boy. I wash my hands of him."

This was by no means my father's intention. I saw his face set in an expression I well knew; but my mother laid a hand on his arm, and, with what must have been a great effort, he controlled his anger, and said coldly: "I have talked this over with thy friend, Joseph Warder, and he desired that his son should share in my decision as to Hugh. Talk to him, Gainor."

"I do not take counsel with my agent, John. He does as I bid him. I could shift his opinions at a word. He is a Tory to-day, and a Whig to-morrow, and anything to anybody. Why do you talk such nonsense to me? Let me tell you that he has already been to ask me what I think of it. He feels some doubt, poor man. Indeed, he is disposed to consider. Bother! what does it matter what he considers?"

"If he has changed his mind I have not. Joseph hath ever a coat of many colours."

"I shall tell him," she cried, laughing. The Quaker rule of repression and non-resistance by no means forbade the use of the brutal bludgeon of sarcasm, as many a debate in Meeting could testify. She rose as she spoke, and my mother said gently:

"Thou wilt not tell him, Gainor."

Meanwhile I stood amazed at a talk which so deeply concerned me.

"Shall it be a smithy?" said my father.

"Oh, what you like. The Wynnes are well down in the world—trade, horseshoeing. Good evening."

"Gainor! Gainor!" cried my mother; but she was gone in wrath, and out of the house.

"Thou wilt leave the academy. I have already arranged with Lowry, in South street, to take thee. Three months should answer."

To this I said, "Yes, yes," and went away but little pleased, my mother saying, "It is only for a time, my son."

AYS my friend Jack in his journal:
"The boys were in these times keen
politicians whenever any unusual event
occurred, and the great pot was like soon
to boil furiously, and scald the cooks.
Charles Townsend's ministry was long over. The
Stamp Act had come and gone. The Non-importation Agreement had been signed even by men like
Andrew Allen and Mr. Penn. Lord North, a gentle
and obstinate person, was minister. The Lord Hills-
borough, a man after the king's heart, had the colonial office. The troops had landed in Boston, and
the letters of Dickinson and Vindex had fanned
the embers of discontent into flame.

"Through it all we boys contrived to know everything that was happening. I had a sense of fear about
it, but to Hugh I think it was delightful. A fire, a mob,
confusion, and disorder appeal to most boys' minds
as desirable. My father was terrified at the disturb-
ance of commerce, and the angry words which began
to be heard. Mr. John Wynne very coolly ad-
justed his affairs, as I have heard, and settled down
with the Friends, such as Waln and Shoemaker and

66

Pemberton and the rest, to accept whatever the king
might decree."

Jack and I talked it all over in wild boy fashion,
and went every day at six in the morning to Lowry's
on South street. At first we both hated the work,
but this did not last; and, once we were used to
it, the business had for fellows like ourselves a
certain charm. The horses we learned to know and
understand. Their owners were of a class with which
in those days it was not thought seemly for persons
of our degree to be familiar; here it was unavoidable, and I soon learned how deep in the hearts of
the people was the determination to resist the authority of the crown.

The lads we knew of the gay set used to come and
laugh at us, as we plied the hammer or blew the
bellows; and one day Miss Franks and Miss Peggy
Chew, and I think Miss Shippen, stood awhile without the forge, making very merry. Jack got red in
the face, but I was angry, worked on doggedly, and
said nothing. At last I thrashed soundly one Master
Galloway, who called me a horse-cobbler, and after
that no more trouble.

I became strong and muscular as the work went on,
and got to like our master, who was all for liberty,
and sang as he struck, and taught me much that was
useful as to the management of horses, so that I
was not long unhappy. My father, pleased at my
diligence, once said to me that I seemed to be attentive to the business in hand; and, as far as I
remember, this was the only time in my life that

he ever gave me a word of even the mildest com-
mendation.

It was what Jack most needed. His slight,
graceful figure filled out and became very straight,
losing a stoop it had, so that he grew to be a well-
built, active young fellow, rosy, and quite too pretty,
with his blond locks. After our third month began,
Lowry married a widow, and moved away to her farm
up the country and beyond the Blue Bell tavern,
where he carried on his business, and where he was to
appear again to me at a time when I sorely needed
him. It was to be another instance of how a greater
Master overrules our lives for good.

Just after we had heard the news of the widow,
my father came into the forge one day with Joseph
Warder. He stood and watched me shoe a horse, and
asked Lowry if I had learned the business. When
he replied that we both might become more expert,
but that we could make nails, and shoe fairly well,
my father said:

"Take off these aprons, and go home. There will
be other work for both of you."

We were glad enough to obey, and, dropping our
leathern aprons, thus ended our apprenticeship.
Next week Tom Lowry, our master, appeared with
a fine beaver for me, saying, as I knew, that it was
the custom to give an apprentice a beaver when his
time was up, and that he had never been better
served by any.

My Aunt Gainor kept away all this time, and
made it clear that she did not wish my black hands

at her table. My father, no doubt, felt sure that, so far as I was concerned, she would soon or late relent. This, in fact, came about in midwinter, upon her asking my mother to send me to see her. My father observed that he had no will to make quarrels, or to keep them alive. My mother smiled demurely, knowing him as none other did, and bade me go with her.

In her own room she had laid out on the bed a brown coat of velveteen, with breeches to match, and stockings with brown clocks, and also a brown beaver, the back looped up, all of which she had, with sweet craftiness, provided, that I might appear well before my Aunt Gainor.

"Thou wilt fight no one on the way, Hugh. And now, what shall be done with his hands, so rough and so hard? Scrub them well. Tell Gainor I have two new lilies for her, just come from Jamaica. Bulbs they are; I will care for them in the cellar. I was near to forget the marmalade of bitter orange. She must send; I cannot trust Tom. Thy father had him whipped at the jail yesterday, and he is sulky. Put on thy clothes, and I will come again to see how they fit thee."

In a little while she was back again, declaring I looked a lord, and that if she were a girl she should fall in love with me, and then—"But I shall never let any woman but me kiss thee. I shall be jealous. And now, sir, a bow. That was better. Now, as I curtsey, it is bad manners to have it over before I am fully risen. Then it is permitted that *les beaux yeux se rencontrent. Comme ça. Ca va bien.* That is better done."

"What vanities are these?" said my father at the door she had left open.

She was nowise alarmed. "Come in, John," she cried. "He does not yet bow as well as thou. It would crack some Quaker backs, I think. I can hear Friend Waln's joints creak when he gets up."

"Nonsense, wife! Thou art a child to this day."

"Then kiss me, *mon père.*" And she ran to him and stood on tiptoe, so engaging and so pretty that he could not help but lift up her slight figure, and, kissing her, set her down. It was a moment of rare tenderness. Would I had known or seen more like it!

"Thou wilt ruin him, wife."

As I ran down the garden she called after me, "Do not thou forget to kiss her hand. To-morrow will come the warehouse; but take the sweets of life as they offer. Adieu." She stood to watch me, all her dear heart in her eyes, something pure, and, as it were, virginal in her look. God rest her soul!

It was late when I got to my aunt's, somewhere about eight, and the hum of voices warned me of her having company. As I entered she rose, expecting an older guest, and, as I had been bid, I bowed low and touched her hand with my lips, as I said:

"Dear Aunt Gainor, it has been so long!" I could have said nothing better. She laughed.

"Here is my nephew, Mr. Etherington"—this to an English major; "and, Captain Wallace of the king's navy, my nephew."

The captain was a rough, boisterous sailor, and the other a man with too much manner, and, as I heard later, risen from the ranks.

He saluted me with a lively thump on the shoulder, which I did not relish. "Zounds! sir, but you are a stout young Quaker!"

"We are most of us Quakers here, captain," said a quiet gentleman, who saw, I fancy, by my face that this rude greeting was unpleasant to me.

"How are you, Hugh?" This was the Master of the Rolls, Mr. John Morris. Then my aunt said, "Go and speak to the ladies—you know them;" and as I turned aside, "I beg pardon, Sir William; this is my nephew, Hugh Wynne." This was addressed to a high-coloured personage in yellow velvet with gold buttons, and a white flowered waistcoat, and with his queue in a fine hair-net.

"This is Sir William Draper, Hugh; he who took Manilla, as you must know." I did not, nor did I know until later that he was one of the victims of the sharp pen of Junius, with whom, for the sake of the Marquis of Granby, he had rashly ventured to tilt. The famous soldier smiled as I saluted him with my best bow.

"Fine food for powder, Mistress Wynne, and already sixteen! I was in service three years earlier. Should he wish for an ensign's commission, I am at your service."

"Ah, Sir William, that might have been, a year or so ago, but now he may have to fight General Gage."

"The gods forbid! Our poor general!"

"Mistress Wynne is a rank Whig," put in Mrs. Ferguson. "She reads Dickinson's 'Farmer's Letters,' and all the wicked treason of that man Adams."

"A low demagogue!" cried Mrs. Galloway. "I hear there have been disturbances in Boston, and that because one James Otis has been beaten by our officers, and because our bands play 'Yankee Doodle' on Sundays in front of the churches—I beg pardon, the meetings—Mr. Robinson, the king's collector, has had to pay and apologise. Most shameful it is!"

"I should take short measures," said the sailor.

"And I," cried Etherington. "I have just come from Virginia, but not a recruit could I get. It is like a nest of ants in a turmoil, and the worst of all are the officers who served in the French war. There is, too, a noisy talker, Patrick Henry, and a Mr. Washington."

"I think it was he who saved the wreck of the king's army under Mr. Braddock," said my aunt. "I can remember how they all looked. Not a wig among them. The lodges must have been full of them, but their legs saved their scalps."

"Is it for this they call them wigwams?" cries naughty Miss Chew.

"Fie! fie!" says her mamma, while my aunt laughed merrily.

"A mere Potomac planter," said Etherington, "'pon my soul—and with such airs, as if they were gentlemen of the line."

"Perhaps," said my aunt, "they had not had your opportunities of knowing all grades of the service."

The major flushed. "I have served the king as well as I know how, and I trust, madam, I shall have the pleasure to aid in the punishment of some of these insolent rebels."

"May you be there to see, Hugh," said my aunt, laughing.

Willing to make a diversion, Mrs. Chew said, "Let us defeat these Tories at the card-table, Gainor."

"With all my heart," said my aunt, glad of this turn in the talk.

"Come and give me luck, Hugh," said Mrs. Ferguson. "What a big fellow you are! Your aunt must find you ruffles soon, and a steenkirk."

With this I sat down beside her, and wondered to see how eager and interested they all became, and how the guineas and gold half-joes passed from one to another, while the gay Mrs. Ferguson, who was at the table with Mrs. Penn, Captain Wallace, and my aunt, gave me my first lesson in this form of industry.

A little later there was tea, chocolate, and rusks, with punch for the men; and Dr. Shippen came in, and the great Dr. Rush, with his delicate, clean-cut face under a full wig. Dr. Shippen was full of talk about some fine game-cocks, and others were busy with the spring races in Centre Square.

You may be sure I kept my ears open to hear what all these great men said. I chanced to hear Dr. Rush deep in talk behind the punch-table with a handsome young man, Dr. Morgan, newly come from London.

Dr. Rush said, "I have news to-day, in a letter from

Mr. Adams, of things being unendurable. He is bold
enough to talk of separation from England; but that
is going far, too far."

"I think so, indeed," said Morgan. "I saw Dr.
Franklin in London. He advises conciliation, and
not to act with rash haste. These gentlemen yonder make it difficult."

"Yes; there is no insolence like that of the soldier."
And this was all I heard or remember, for my aunt
bade me run home and thank my mother, telling
me to come again and soon.

The plot was indeed thickening, and even a lad
as young as I could scent peril in the air. At home
I heard nothing of it. No doubt my father read at
his warehouse the "Pennsylvania Journal," or more
likely Galloway's gazette, the "Chronicle," which was
rank Tory, and was suppressed in 1773. But outside
of the house I learned the news readily. Mr. Warder took papers on both sides, and also the Boston
"Packet," so that Jack and I were well informed, and
used to take the gazettes when his father had read
them, and devour them safely in our boat, when by
rare chance I had a holiday.

And so passed the years 1770, 1771, and 1772,
when Lord North precipitated the crisis by attempt-
ing to control the judges in Massachusetts, who were
in future to be paid by the crown, and would thus
pass under its control. Adams now suggested committees of correspondence, and thus the first step
toward united action was taken.

These years, up to the autumn of 1772, were not

without influence on my own life for both good and evil. I was, of course, kept sedulously at work at our business, and, though liking it even less than farriery, learned it well enough. It was not without its pleasures. Certainly it was an agreeable thing to know the old merchant captains, and to talk to their men or themselves. The sea had not lost its romance. Men could remember Kidd and Blackbeard. In the low-lying dens below Dock Creek and on King street, were many, it is to be feared, who had seen the black flag flying, and who knew too well the keys and shoals of the West Indies. The captain who put to sea with such sailors had need to be resolute and ready. Ships went armed, and I was amazed to see, in the holds of our own ships, carronades, which out on the ocean were hoisted up and set in place on deck; also cutlasses and muskets in the cabin, and good store of pikes. I ventured once to ask my father if this were consistent with non-resistance. He replied that pirates were like to wild beasts, and that I had better attend to my business; after which I said no more, having food for thought.

These captains got thus a noble training, were splendid seamen, and not unused to arms and danger, as proved fortunate in days to come. Once I would have gone to the Madeiras with Captain Biddle, but unluckily my mother prevailed with my father to forbid it. It had been better for me had it been decided otherwise, because I was fast getting an education which did me no good.

"Indeed," says Jack later on in his diary, "I was

much troubled in those seventies" (he means up to
'74, when we were full twenty-one) " about my friend
Hugh. The town was full of officers of all grades,
who came and went, and brought with them much
licence and contempt for colonists in general, and a
silly way of parading their own sentiments on all
occasions. Gambling, hard drinking, and all manner
of worse things became common and more openly
indulged in. Neither here nor in Boston could young
women walk about unattended, a new and strange
thing in our quiet town.

"Mistress Gainor's house was full of these gentlemen, whom she entertained with a freedom only
equalled by that with which she spoke her good
Whig mind. The air was full of excitement. Business fell off, and Hugh and I had ample leisure to
do much as we liked.

"I must honestly declare that I deserve no praise
for having escaped the temptations which beset
Hugh. I hated all excess, and suffered in body if I
drank or ate more than was wise. As regards worse
things than wine and cards, I think Miss Wynne was
right when she described me as a girl-boy; for the
least rudeness or laxity of talk in women I disliked,
and as to the mere modesties of the person, I have
always been like some well-nurtured maid.

"Thus it was that when Hugh, encouraged by his
aunt, fell into the company of these loose, swagger-
ing captains and cornets, I had either to give up
him, who was unable to resist them, or to share
in their vicious ways myself. It was my personal

disgust at drunkenness or loose society which saved
me, not any moral or religious safeguards, although
I trust I was not altogether without these helps. I
have seen now and then that to be refined in tastes
and feelings is a great aid to a virtuous life. Also I
have known some who would have been drunkards
but for their heads and stomachs, which so behaved as to be good substitutes for conscience. It
is sometimes the body which saves the soul. Both
of these helps I had, but my dear Hugh had neither.
He was a great, strong, masculine fellow, and if I
may seem to have said that he wanted refined feelings, that is not so, and to him, who will never read
these lines, and to myself, I must apologise."

I did come to see these pages, as you know. I
think he meant, that with the wine of youth and at
times of other vintages, in my veins, the strong paternal blood, which in my father only a true, if hard,
religion kept in order, was too much for me. If I
state this awkwardly it is because all excuses are
awkward. Looking back, I wonder that I was not
worse, and that I did not go to the uttermost devil.
I was vigorous, and had the stomach of a temperate
ox, and a head which made no complaints. The
morning after some mad revel I could rise at five, and
go out in my boat and overboard, and then home in
a glow, with a fine appetite for breakfast; and I was
so big and tall that I was thought to be many years
older than I was.

I should have been less able unwatched to go
down this easy descent, had it not been for a train

of circumstances which not only left me freer than I
ought to have been, but, in the matter of money, made
it only too possible for me to hold my own amid
evil or lavish company. My aunt had lived in London, and in a society which had all the charm of
breeding, and all the vices of a period more coarse
than ours. She detested my father's notions, and if
she meant to win me to her own she took an ill way
to do it. I was presented to the English officers, and
freely supplied with money, to which I had been
quite unused, so long as my father was the only
source of supply. We were out late when I was
presumed to be at my Aunt Gainor's; and to drink
and bet, or to see a race or cock-fight, or to pull
off knockers, or to bother the ancient watchmen,
were now some of my most reputable amusements.
I began to be talked about as a bit of a rake, and
my Aunt Gainor was not too greatly displeased; she
would hear of our exploits and say "Fie! fie!" and
then give me more guineas. Worse than all, my
father was deep in his business, lessening his ventures, and thus leaving me more time to sow the
seed of idleness. Everything, as I now see it, combined to make easy for me the downward path. I
went along it without the company of Jack Warder,
and so we drew apart; he would none of it.

When my father began to withdraw his capital my
mother was highly pleased, and more than once in
my presence said to him: "Why, John, dost thou
strive for more and more money? Hast thou not
enough? Let us give up all this care and go to our

great farm at Merion, and live as peaceful as our cattle." She did not reckon upon the force with which the habits of a life bound my father to his business.

I remember that it was far on in April, 1773, when my Aunt Gainor appeared one day in my father's counting-house. Hers was a well-known figure on King street, and even in the unpleasant region alongshore to the south of Dock street. She would dismount, leave her horse to the groom, and, with a heavily mounted, silver-topped whip in hand, and her riding-petticoat gathered up, would march along, picking her way through mud and filth. Here she contrived to find the queer china things she desired, or in some mysterious way she secured cordials and such liquors as no one else could get.

Once she took my mother with her, and loaded her with gods of the Orient and fine China pongee silks.

"But, Hugh," said the dear lady, "*il n'est pas possible de vous la décrire. Mon Dieu!* she can say terrible words, and I have seen a man who ventured some rudeness to me—no, no, *mon cher*, nothing to anger you; *il avait peur de cette femme.* He was afraid of her—her and her whip. He was so alarmed that he let her have a great china mandarin for a mere nothing. I think he was glad to see her well out of his low tavern."

"But the man," I urged; "what did he say to thee, mother?"

"*N'importe, mon fils.* I did want the mandarin. He nodded this way—this way. He wagged his head as a dog wags his tail, like Thomas Scattergood in the Meeting. *Comme çà.*" She became that man in a moment, turning up the edge of her silk shawl, and nodding solemnly. I screamed with laughter. Ever since I was a child, despite my father's dislikes, she had taught me French, and when alone with me liked me to chatter in her mother language. In fact, I learned it well.

On the occasion of which I began just now to speak, my Aunt Gainor entered, with a graver face than common, and I rising to leave her with my father, she put her whip across my breast as I turned, and said, "No; I want you to hear what I have to say."

"What is it, Gainor?"

"This business of the ship 'Gaspee' the Rhode Island men burned is making trouble in the East. The chief justice of Rhode Island, Hopkins, has refused to honour the order to arrest these Rhode-Islanders."

"Pirates!" said my father.

"Pirates, if you like. We shall all be pirates before long."

"Well, Gainor, is that all? It does not concern me."

"No; I have letters from London which inform me that the Lord North is but a puppet, and as the king pulls the wires he will dance to whatever tune the king likes. He was a nice, amiable young fellow when I stayed at his father's, my Lord Guilford's, and not without learning and judgment. But for the Exchequer—a queer choice, I must say."

"It is to be presumed that the king knows how to

choose his ministers. Thou knowest what I think,
Gainor. We have but to obey those whom the Lord
has set over us. We are told to render unto Cæsar
the things which are Cæsar's, and to go our ways in
peace."

"The question is, What are Cæsar's?" said my
aunt. "Shall Cæsar judge always? I came to tell
you that it is understood in London, although not
public, that it is meant to tax our tea. Now we do
not buy; we smuggle it from Holland; but if the
India Company should get a drawback on tea, we
shall be forced to take it for its cheapness, even with
the duty on it of threepence a pound."

"It were but a silly scheme, Gainor. I cannot
credit it."

"Who could, John? and yet it is to be tried, and
all for a matter of a few hundred pounds a year. It
will be tried not now or soon, but next fall when the
tea-ships come from China."

"And if it is to be as thou art informed, what of
it?"

"A storm—a tempest in a teapot," said she.

My father stood still, deep in thought. He had
a profound respect for the commercial sagacity of
this clear-headed woman. Moreover, he was sure,
as usual, to be asked to act in Philadelphia as a consignee of the India Company.

She seemed to see through her brother, as one sees
through glass. "You got into trouble when the
stamps came."

"What has that got to do with this?"

6

"And again when you would not sign the Non-importation Agreement in '68."

"Well?"

"They will ask you to receive the tea."

"And I will do it. How can I refuse? I should lose all their India trade."

"There will soon be no trade to lose. You are, as I know, drawing in your capital. Go abroad. Wind up your affairs in England; do the same in Holland. Use all your ships this summer. Go to Madeira from London. Buy freely, and pay at once so as to save interest; it will rise fast. Come home in the fall of '74 late. Hold the goods, and, above all, see that in your absence no consignments be taken. Am I clear, John?"

I heard her with such amazement as was shared by my father. The boldness and sagacity of the scheme impressed a man trained to skill in commerce, and ever given to courageous ventures.

"You must sail in October or before; you will need a year. No less will do."

"Yes—yes."

I saw from his look that he was captured. He walked to and fro, while my Aunt Gainor switched the dust off her petticoat or looked out of the window. At last she turned to me. "What think you of it, Hugh?"

"Mr. Wilson says we shall have war, aunt, and Mr. Attorney-General Chew is of the same opinion. I heard them talking of it last night at thy house. I think the king's officers want a war." I took refuge, shrewdly, in the notions of my elders. I had no wiser thing to say. "I myself do not know," I added.

"How shouldst thou?" said my father, sharply.

I was silent.

"And what think you, John?" .

"What will my wife say, Gainor? We have never been a month apart."

"Let me talk to her."

"Wilt thou share in the venture?" He was testing the sincerity of her advice. "And to what extent?"

"Five thousand pounds. You may draw on me from London, and buy powder and muskets," she added, with a smile.

"Not I. Why dost thou talk such folly?"

"Then Holland blankets and good cloth. I will take them off your hands at a fair profit."

"I see no objection to that."

My aunt gave me a queer look, saying, "The poor will need them. I shall sell them cheap."

It was singular that I caught her meaning, while my father, reflecting on the venture as a whole, did not.

"I will do it," he said.

"Then a word more. Be careful here as to debts. Why not wind up your business, and retire with the profit you will make?" It was the same advice my mother had given, as I well knew.

"Hast thou been talking to my wife?" he said.

"No," she replied, surprised; "may I?"

"Yes. As to going out of business, Gainor, I

should be but a lost man. I am not as well-to-do as thou dost seem to think."

"Stuff and nonsense!" cried my aunt. "I believe Thomas Willing is no better off in what you call this world's gear, nor Franks, nor any of them. You like the game, and, after all, what is it but a kind of gambling? How do you know what hands the ocean holds? Your ventures are no better than my guineas cast down on the loo-table." These two could never discuss anything but what it must end in a difference.

"Thou art a fool, Gainor, to talk such wicked nonsense before this boy. It is not worth an answer. I hear no good of Hugh of late. He hath been a concern to James Pemberton and to my friend, Nicholas Waln, and to me—to me. Thy gambling and idle redcoats are snares to his soul. He has begun to have opinions of his own as to taxes, and concerning the plain duty of non-resistance. As if an idle dog like him had any right to have an opinion at all!"

"Tut! tut!" cried Miss Wynne.

"I am not idle," I said, "if I am a dog."

He turned and seized me by the collar. "I will teach thee to answer thy elders." And with this he shook me violently, and caught up a cane from a chair where he had laid it.

And now, once again, that disposition to be merry came over me, and, perfectly passive, I looked up at him and smiled. As I think of it, it was strange in a young fellow of my age.

"Wouldst thou laugh?" he cried. "Has it gone

that far?" and he raised his stick. My Aunt Gainor
jerked it out of his hand, and, standing, broke it
over her knee as if it had been a willow wand.

He fell back, crying, "Gainor! Gainor!"

"My God! man," she cried, "are you mad? If I
were you I would take some heed to that hot Welsh
blood. What would my good Marie say? Why have
you not had the sense to make a friend of the boy?
He is worth ten of you, and has kept his temper like
the gentleman he is."

It was true. I had some queer sense of amusement
in the feeling that I really was not angry; neither
was I ashamed; but an hour later I was both angry
and ashamed. Just now I felt sorry for my father,
and shared the humiliation he evidently felt.

My aunt turned to her brother, where, having let
me go, he stood with set features, looking from her
to me, and from me to her. Something in his look
disturbed her.

"You should be proud of his self-command. Cannot you see that it is your accursed repression and
dry, dreary life at home that has put you two apart?"

"I have been put to scorn before my son, Gainor
Wynne. It is thy evil ways that have brought this
about. I have lost my temper and would have struck
in anger, when I should have reflected, and, after
prayer, chastised this insolence at home."

"I heard no insolence."

"Go away, Hugh, and thou, Gainor. Why dost
thou always provoke me? I will hear no more!"

"Come, Hugh," she said; and then: "It seems to

me that the boy has had a good lesson in meekness,
and as to turning that other cheek."

"Don't, Aunt Gainor!" said I, interrupting her.

"Oh, go!" exclaimed my father. "Go! go, both
of you!"

"Certainly; but, John, do not mention my news
or my London letter."

"I shall not."

"Then by-by! Come, Hugh!"

VI

HERE must have been in this troubled country many such sad scenes as I have tried to recall. Father and son were to part with hot words, brother to take sides against brother. My unpleasant half-hour was but prophetic of that which was to come in worse shape, and to last for years.

My Aunt Gainor said, "Do not tell your mother," and I assuredly did not.

"He will tell her. He tells her everything, soon or late. I must see her at once. Your father is becoming, as the French say, impossible. The times, and these wrangling Friends, with their stupid testimonies, irritate him daily until he is like a great, strong bull, such as the Spaniards tease to madness with little darts and fireworks. You see, Hugh, events are prickly things. They play the deuce with obstinate people. Your father will be better away from home. He has never been in England, and he will see how many, like Mr. Pitt and Colonel Barré, are with us. As for myself, I have been a bit of a fool about you, and your father is more or less right. We must abjure sack and take physic."

"What?" said I.

"To be plain, we must—that is, you must—play less and drink less, and in your father's absence look sharply, with my help, to his business."

I was to need other doctors before I mended my ways. I said my aunt was right, and I made certain good resolutions, which were but short-lived and never reached adult maturity of usefulness.

My aunt walked with me north between the warehouses, taverns, and ship-chandlers on the river-front, and so across the bridge over Dock Creek, and up to Third street. She said I must not talk to her. She had thinking to do, and for this cause, I suppose, turning, took me down to Pine street. At St. Peter's Church she stopped, and bade me wait without, adding, "If I take you in I shall hear of it; wait."

There was a midday service at this time, it being Lent. I waited idly, thinking of my father, and, as I before said, vexed and sorry and ashamed by turns. Often now I pause before I enter this sacred edifice, and think of that hour of tribulation. I could hear the fine, full voice of the Rev. Dr. Duché as he intoned the Litany. He lies now where I stood, and under the arms on his tomb is no record of the political foolishness and instability of a life otherwise free from blame. As I stood, Mrs. Ferguson came out, she who in days to come helped to get the unlucky parson into trouble. With her came my aunt.

"I said a prayer for thee, Hugh," she whispered. "No; no cards in Lent, my dear Bess. Fie! for shame! This way, Hugh;" and we went east, through Pine street, and so to the back of our garden, where we found a way in, and, walking under the peach-trees, came to where my mother sat beneath a plum-tree, shelling peas, her great Manx cat by her side.

She wore a thin cap on top of the curly head, which was now wind-blown out of all order. "Come, Gainor," she cried, seeing us; "help me to shell my peas. Thou shalt have some. They are come in a ship from the Bermudas. What a pretty pale green the pods are! I should like an apron of that colour."

"I have the very thing, dear. Shall it be the minuet pattern, or plain?"

"Oh, plain. Am I not a Friend? *Une Amie? Ciel!* but it is droll in French. Sarah Logan is twice as gay as I, but John does not love such vanities. *Quant à moi, je les adore.* It seems odd to have a colour to a religion. I wonder if drab goodness be better than red goodness. But what is wrong, Gainor? Yes, there is something. Hugh, thy collar is torn; how careless of me not to have mended it!"

Then my Aunt Gainor, saying nothing of my especial difficulty, and leaving out, too, her London news, related with remarkable clearness the reasons why my father should go overseas in the early fall and be gone for a year. The mother went on quietly shelling the peas, and losing no word. When Gainor had done, the bowl of peas was set aside, and my mother put back her curls, fixed her blue eyes on her sister-in-law, and was silent for a moment longer. At last she said, "It were best, for many reasons best. I see it," and she nodded her head affirmatively. "But my son? my Hugh?"

"You will have him with you at home. Everything will go on as usual, except that John will be amusing himself in London."

At this the little lady leaped up, all ablaze, so to speak. Never had I seen her so moved. "What manner of woman am I, Gainor Wynne, that I should let my husband go alone on the seas, and here and there, without me? I will not have it. My boy is my boy; God knows I love him; but my husband comes first now and always, and thou art cruel to wish to part us."

"But I never wished to part you. Go with him, Marie. God bless your sweet heart! Leave me your boy; he cannot go. As God lives, I will take care of him!"

Upon this the two women fell to weeping in each other's arms, a thing most uncommon for my Aunt Gainor. Then they talked it all over, as if John Wynne were not: when it would be, and what room I was to have, and my clothes, and the business, and so on—all the endless details wherewith the cunning affection of good women knows to provide comfort for us, who are so apt to be unthankful.

It amazed me to see how quickly it was settled, and still more to learn that my father did not oppose, but fell in with all their plans.

Now back of all my weaknesses and folly I had, as I have said, some of the sense of honour and proud rectitude of my father, who strictly abided by his

creed and his conscience. I returned no more that
day to the counting-house, but, saying to my mother
I had business, I went off, with a hunk of bread, to
my boat, and down the creek to the Delaware. I
pulled out, past our old playground on the island, and
far away toward the Jersey shore, and then, as the
sun fell, drifted with the tide, noting the ruddy lines
of the brick houses far away, and began to think.

The scene I had gone through had made a deep
impression. It has been ever so with me. Drinking, gaming, betting, and worse, never awakened my
conscience or set me reflecting, until some sudden,
unlooked-for thing took place, in which sentiment
or affection was concerned. Then I would set to
work to balance my books and determine my course.
At such times it was the dear mother who spoke in
me, and the father who resolutely carried out my
decision.

The boat drifted slowly with the flood-tide, and I,
lying on the bottom, fell to thought of what the day
had brought me. The setting sun touched the single
spire of Christ Church, and lit up yellow squares of
light in the westward-looking windows of the rare
farm-houses on the Jersey shore. Presently I was
aground on the south end of Petty's Island, where in
after-years lay rotting the "Alliance," the remnant ship
of the greatest sea-fight that ever was since Grenville
lay in the "Revenge," with the Spanish fleet about him.
I came to ground amid the reeds and spatter-docks,
where the water-lilies were just in bud. A noisy
orchestra of frogs, with, as Jack said, fiddles and

bassoons in their throats, ceased as I came, and pitched headlong off the broad green floats. Only one old fellow, with a great bass voice, and secure on the bank, protested loudly at intervals, like the owl in Mr. Gray's noble poem, which my Jack loved to repeat.

At last he—I mean my frog—whose monastery I had disturbed, so vexed me, who wanted stillness, that I smacked the water with the flat of an oar, which he took to be a hint, and ceased to lament my intrusion.

I was now well on to twenty, and old enough to begin at times to deal thoughtfully with events. A young fellow's feelings are apt to be extreme, and even despotic, so that they rule the hour with such strength of sway as may be out of proportion to the cause. I might have seen that I had no just cause to blame myself, but that did not help me. The mood of distressful self-accusation was on me. I had no repeated impulse to smile at what, in my father's conduct, had appeared to me a little while ago odd, and even amusing. I could never please him. I had grinned as I always did when risks were upon me. He never understood me, and I was tired of trying. What use was it to try? I had one of those minutes of wishing to die, which come even to the wholesome young. I was well aware that of late I had not, on the whole, satisfied my conscience; I knew this quite too well; and now, as I lay in the boat discontented, I felt, as the youthful do sometimes feel, as if I were old, and the ending of things were near.

It was but a mood, but it led up to serious thought. There are surely hours in youth when we are older than our years, and times in age when we are again young. Sometimes I wonder whether Jack was right, who used to say it may be we are never young or old, but merely seem to be so. This is the queer kind of reflection which I find now and then in Jack's diary, or with which he used to puzzle me and please James Wilson. Of course a man is young or is old. and there 's an end on 't, as a greater man has said. But Jack has imagination, and I have none.

I asked myself if I had done wrong in what I had said. I could not see that I had. With all my life-long fear of my father, I greatly honoured and respected him, finding in myself something akin to the unyielding firmness with which he stood fast when he had made up his mind.

That this proud and steadfast man, so looked up to by every one, no matter what might be their convictions religious or political, should have been humiliated by a woman, seemed to me intolerable; this was the chief outcome of my reflections. It is true I considered, but I fear lightly, my own misdoings. I made up my mind to do better, and then again the image of my father in his wrath and his shame came back anew. I turned the boat, and pulled steadily across the river to our landing.

My father was in the counting-house in his own room, alone, although it was full late. "Well?" he said, spinning round on his high stool. "What is it? Thou hast been absent, and no leave asked."

"Father," I said, "if I was wrong this morning I wish to ask thy pardon."

"Well, it is full time."

"And I am come to say that I will take the punishment here and now. I did not run away from that."

"Very good," he replied, rising. "Take off thy fine coat."

I wished he had not said this of my coat. I was in a heroic temper, and the sarcasm bit cruelly, but I did as I was bid. He went to the corner, and picked up a rattan cane. To whip fellows of nineteen or twenty was not then by any means unusual. What would have happened I know not, nor ever shall. He said, "There, I hear thy mother's voice. Put on thy coat." I hastened to obey him.

The dear lady came in with eyes full of tears. "What is this, John, I hear? I have seen Gainor. I could not wait. I shall go with thee."

"No," he said; "that is not to be." But she fell on his neck, and pleaded, and I, for my part, went away, not sorry for the interruption. As usual she had her way.

I remember well this spring of '73. It was early by some weeks, and everything was green and blossoming in April. My father and mother were not to sail until the autumn, but already he was arranging for the voyage, and she as busily preparing or thinking over what was needed.

When next I saw my Aunt Gainor, she cried out, "Sit down there, bad boy, and take care of my mandarin. He and my great bronze Buddha are my only counsellors. If I want to do a thing I ask Mr. Mandarin—he can only nod yes; and if I want not to do a thing I ask Buddha, and as he can neither say no nor yes, I do as I please. What a wretch you are!"

I said I could not see it; and then I put my head in her lap, as I sat on the stool, and told her of my last interview with my father, and how for two days he had hardly so much as bade me good-night.

"It is his way, Hugh," said my aunt. "I am sorry; but neither love nor time will mend him. He is what his nature and the hard ways of Friends have made him."

I said that this was not all, nor the worst, and went on to tell her my latest grievance. Our family worship at home was, as usual with Friends in those days, conducted at times in total silence, and was spoken of by Friends as "religious retirement." At other times, indeed commonly, a chapter of the Bible was read aloud, and after that my father would sometimes pray openly. On this last occasion he took advantage of the opportunity to dilate on my sins, and before our servants to ask of Heaven that I be brought to a due sense of my iniquities. It troubled my mother, who arose from her knees in tears, and went out of the room, whilst I, overcome with anger, stood looking out of the window. My father spoke to her as she opened the door, but she made no answer, nor even so much as turned her head. It brought to my memory a day of my childhood, when my father was vexed because she taught me to say the Lord's Prayer. He did not approve, and would have no set

form of words taught me. My mother was angry
too, and I remember my own amazement that any
one should resist my father.

When I had told my aunt of the indignity put
upon me, and of the fading remembrance thus
recalled, she said, "John Wynne has not changed,
nor will he ever." She declared that, after all, it was
her fault—to have treated me as if I were a man, and
to have given me too much money. I shook my head,
but she would have it she was to blame, and then said
of a sudden, "Are you in debt, you scamp? Did John
pray for me?" I replied that I owed no one a penny,
and that she had not been remembered. She was
glad I was not in debt, and added, "Never play unless you have the means to pay. I have been very
foolish. That uneasy woman, Bessy Ferguson, must
needs tell me so. I could have slapped her. They
will have thy sad case up in Meeting, I can tell thee."

"But what have I done?" I knew well enough.

"Tut! you must not talk that way to me; but it is
my fault. Oh, the time I have had with your mother!
I am not fit, it seems, to be left to take care of you.
They talk of leaving you with Abijah Hapworthy—
sour old dog! I wish you joy of him!"

"Good heavens!" I exclaimed; for among my aunt's
gay friends I had picked up such exclamatory phrases
as, used at home, would have astonished my father.

"Rest easy," said Mistress Wynne; "it is not to be.
I have fought your battle, and won it. But I have
had to make such promises to your father, and—woe
is me!—to your mother, as will damn me forever if

you do not help me to keep them. I can fib to your
father and not care a snap, but lie to those blue eyes
I cannot."

"I will try, Aunt Gainor; indeed I will try." Indeed, I did mean to.

"You must, you must. I am to be a sort of god-
mother-in-law to you, and renounce for you the world,
the flesh, and the devil; and that for one of our breed!
I shall be like a sign-post, and never go the way I
point. That was Bessy Ferguson's malice. Oh, I
have suffered, I can tell you. It is I, and not you, that
have repented."

"But I will; I do."

"That is all very well; but I have had my whip-
ping, and you got off yours."

"What do you mean, aunt?"

"What do I mean? Here came yesterday Sarah
Fisher, pretty gay for a Quaker, and that solemn
Master Savory, with his sweet, low voice like a nice
girl's tongue, and his gentle ways. And they are
friends of thy people, who are distressed at thy go-
ings on; and Nicholas Waln has seen thee with two
sons of Belial in red coats, come out of the coffee-
house last month at evening, singing songs such as
are not to be described, and no better able to take
care of yourself than you should be. They did think
it well and kind—hang 'em, Hugh!—to consider the
matter with me. We considered it—we did, indeed.
There be five people whose consciences I am to make
you respect. And not one of them do I care for,
but Mother Blue-eyes. But I must! I must! It was
7

all true, sir, what Friend Waln said; for you had reason enough left to come hither, and did I not put you to bed and send for Dr. Chovet, who grinned famously, and said, '*Je comprends,*' and went to call on your father on a hint from me, to declare you were *enrhumé*, and threatened with I know not what; in fact, he lied like a gentleman. You made a noble recovery, and are a credit to the doctor. I hope you will pay the bill, and are ashamed."

I was, and I said so.

"But that is not all. These dear Quakers were the worst. They were really sorry, and I had to put on my best manners and listen; and now everybody knows, and you are the talk of the town. Those drab geese must out with the whole naughtiness, despite the company which came in on us, and here were Mr. Montresor and that ape Etherington grinning, and, worst of all, a charming young woman just come to live here with her aunt, and she too must have her say when the Quakers and the men were gone."

"And what did she say?" I did not care much. "And what is her name?"

"Oh, she said the Quakers were rather outspoken people, and it was a pity, and she was sorry, because she knew you once, and you had taken her part at school."

"At school?"

"Yes. She is Darthea Peniston, and some kin of that Miss de Lancey, whom Sir William Draper will marry if he can."

"Darthea Peniston?" I said, and my thoughts

went back to the tender little maid who wept when
I was punished, and for whom I had revenged myself on Master Dove.

"Quite a Spanish beauty," said my Aunt Wynne;
"a pretty mite of a girl, and not more money than
will clothe her, they say; but the men mad about her.
Come and see her to-morrow if you are sober."

"O Aunt Gainor!"

"Yes, sir. I hear Mr. Montresor has leave from
Anthony Morris to invite you to 'The Colony in
Schuylkill' to-morrow. It is well your father has
gone to visit Mr. Yeates at Lancaster."

"I shall behave myself, Aunt Gainor."

"I hope so. The Fish House punch is strong."

I went home thinking of Miss Darthea Peniston,
and filled with desire to lead a wiser life. It was full
time. My aunt's lavish generosity had, as I have said,
given me means to live freely among the officers,
who were, with some exceptions, a dissolute set. To
be with them made it needful to become deceitful
and to frame excuses, so that, when I was supposed
to be at my aunt's, or riding, I was free that past winter to go on sleighing-parties or to frequent taverns,
pleased with the notice I got from men like Montresor and the officers of the Scotch Grays.

I have dwelt not at all on these scenes of dissipa-
tion. It is enough to mention them. My father was
wrapped up in his business, and full of cares both
worldly and spiritual; for now Friends were becoming politically divided, and the meetings were long
and sometimes agitated.

My good mother was neither deceived nor unconcerned. She talked to me often, and in such a way as brings tears to my eyes even now to think of the pain I gave her. Alas! it is our dearest who have the greatest power to wound us. I wept and promised, and went back to my husks and evil company.

I have no wish to conceal these things from my children. It is well that our offspring when young should think us angels; but it were as well that when they are older they should learn that we have been men of like passions with themselves, and have known temptation, and have fought, and won or lost, our battles with sin. It is one of the weaknesses of nations, as well as of children, that they come to consider their political fathers as saints. I smile when I think of the way people nowadays think of our great President, as of a mild genius, incapable of being moved to anger or great mirth, a man unspotted of the world. They should have heard him at Monmouth, when Lee failed him in a time of peril, or seen him, as I have seen him, soberly merry over his wine with Knox. But some day you shall see him as my friend Jack and I saw him, and you will, I trust, think no worse of him for being as human as he was just.

The day of my more honest repentance was near, and I knew not that it was to be both terrible and of lasting value. I sometimes reflect upon the curious conditions with which my early manhood was surrounded. Here was I, brought up in the strictest ways of a sect to which I do no injustice if I describe it as ascetic. At home I saw plain living, and no luxury, save as to diet, which my father would have of the best money could buy. I was taught the extreme of non-resistance, and absolute simplicity as to dress and language. Amusements there were none, and my father read no books except such as dealt with things spiritual, or things commercial. At my aunt's, and in the society I saw at her house, there were men and women who loved to dance, gamble, and amuse themselves. The talk was of bets, racing, and the like. To be drunk was a thing to be expected of officers and gentlemen. To avenge an insult with sword or pistol was the only way to deal with it. My father was a passive Tory, my aunt a furious Whig. What wonder that I fell a victim to temptation?

VII

HE next day, having seen to matters of business in the morning, I set out after dinner in my finest clothes to join my friends. I fear that I promised my mother to be careful, and to be at home by nine o'clock.

I met Captain Montresor at the London Coffeehouse, at High and Front streets, and, having taken a chaise, drove out through the woods to the upper ferry, and thence to Egglesfield, the seat of Mr. Warner, from whom the club known then as "The Colony in Schuylkill" held under a curious tenure the acre or two of land where they had built a log cabin and founded this ancient and singular institution. Here were met Anthony Morris, who fell at Trenton, Mr. Tench Francis, sometime Attorney-General, Mifflin, and that Galloway who later became a Tory, with Mr. Willing, and others of less note, old and young. I was late for the annual ceremony of presenting three fish to Mr. Warner, this being the condition on which the soil was held, but I saw the great pewter dish with the Penn arms, a gift from that family, on which the fish were offered.

It was a merry and an odd party ; for, clad in white

aprons, the apprentices, so called, cooked the dinner and served it; and the punch and Madeira went round the table often enough, as the "king's health" was drunk, and "success to trade," and "the ladies, God bless them!"

I liked it well, and, with my aunt's warning in mind, drank but little, and listened to the talk, which was too free at times, as was the bad custom of that day, and now and then angry; for here were some who were to die for their country, and some who were to fail it in the hour of need.

Despite my English friends, and thanks to Mr. Wilson and my Aunt Gainor, I was fast becoming an ardent Whig, so that the talk, in which I had small share, interested me deeply. At last, about seven, the pipes having been smoked and much punch taken, the company rose to go, some of them the worse for their potations.

We drove into town, and at the coffee-house put up and paid for our chaise. I said good-by to Mr. Montresor, who, I think, had been charged by Miss Wynne to look after me, when a Captain Small, whom I knew, stopped me. He was well known as one of the most reckless of the younger officers, a stout, short man, rather heroically presented long afterward, in Trumbull's picture of the "Death of Warren," as trying to put aside the bayonets. As I paused to reply, I saw Jack Warder standing on the other side of the street. He nodded, smiling, and made as if he were about to cross over. He had many times talked with me seriously this winter,

until I had become vexed, and told him he was a
milksop. After this I saw little of him. Now I was
annoyed at the idea that he was spying upon my
actions, and therefore, like a fool, merely nodded,
and, turning my back on him, heard Mr. Small say:
"You must not go yet, Mr. Wynne. We are to
have supper upstairs, and you will like to see a gentleman of your name, Mr. Arthur Wynne, of the Scots
Grays. He tells me he is of distant kin to you."

Montresor said I had better go home, but Etherington asked if I wanted my bottle and nurse; and
so at last, partly from pride and partly out of curiosity to see this other Wynne, I said I would remain
long enough to welcome the gentleman and take a
social glass. When we entered the room upstairs,
I found a supper of cold meats and, as usual, punch
and liquors. There were two dozen or more officers
in undress jackets, their caps and swords in the corners, and also two or three of the younger men of
the Tory or doubtful parties.

Several officers called to me to sit with them, for I
was a favourite, and could troll a catch or sing parts
fairly well. My companion, Small, said, "This way,
Wynne," and, followed by Montresor and the colonel
of the Scots Grays, whose name I forget, we moved
to a table remote from the door. Here Montresor,
pushing past Small, said: "Captain Wynne, I have
the honour to present to you Mr. Hugh Wynne, one
of your family, I hear."

Upon this there rose to greet me a gentleman in
the undress uniform of the Grays. He was tall and

well built, but not so broad or strong as we other
Wynnes; certainly an unusually handsome man.
He carried his head high, was very erect, and had
an air of distinction, for which at that time I should
have had no name. I may add that he was dressed
with unusual neatness, and very richly; all of which,
I being but a half-formed young fellow, did much
impress me.

He looked at me so steadily as we came near that
it gave me a rather unpleasant impression; for those
who do not meet the eye at all are scarcely less dis-
agreeable than those who too continually watch you,
as was this man's way. I was rather young to be a
very careful observer of men's faces, but I did see that
Captain Wynne's bore traces of too convivial habits.

As I recall his dark, regular features, I remember,
for we met often afterward, that the lower part of
his face was too thin, and that in repose his mouth
was apt not to remain fully shut, a peculiarity, as I
now think, of persons of weak will.

My first feeling of there being something unpleas-
ing about him soon left me. He rose, and, with gra-
ciousness and the ease and manner of one used to
the best society, moved around the table and took
my hand.

"I am but a far-away kinsman," he said, "but I
am charmed to make your acquaintance. You are
like the picture of old Sir Robert at Wyncote, where
I was last year for the otter-hunting."

I greeted him warmly. "And art thou living at
Wyncote?" I asked rather awkwardly.

"No, I do not live at home. I am but a cadet,
and yours is the elder branch." Then he added gaily,
"I salute you, sir, as the head of our old house. Your
very good health!" And at this, with a charm of manner I have seen but rarely, he put a hand on my
shoulder, and added, "We must be friends, Cousin
Wynne, and I must know your father, and above all
Mistress Wynne. Montresor never ceases talking of
her."

I said it would give me pleasure to present him;
then, delighted to hear of Wyncote, I sat down, and,
despite a warning look from Montresor, began to take
wine with this newly found kinsman.

Mr. Arthur Wynne was a man fully ten years my
senior. He had served in the Guards, and in the
Indies, and was full of stories of court and camp
and war, such as every young fellow of spirit likes
to hear.

Captain Montresor lingered awhile, and then, finding it vain to persist in his purpose, gave it up, and
fell to talking with one of his fellow-officers, while
I went on questioning my cousin as to the Wynnes
to their uttermost generation. Either he cared little
about them, or he knew little, for he seemed much
to prefer to tell queer stories about the court ladies,
and my Lord Chesterfield's boor of a son, who had
such small manners and such a large appetite, and
of Sir Guy Carleton, whom he was about to join in
Canada. He advised me to get a pair of colours as
my aunt had once desired, and seemed surprised
when I paraded my friend Mr. Wilson's opinions as

my own, and talked of taxation and the oppression under which commerce had to be carried on. In fact, as to this I knew something; but in this, as in other matters, he deferred to me as one does to a well-informed talker of one's own age, now setting me right with admirable courtesy, and now cordially agreeing.

What with his evident desire to be friendly, and the wine I was taking, I fell an easy prey to one who rarely failed to please when he was so minded. Too well amused to reflect that the hours were swiftly passing, I sat, taking glass after glass mechanically. As the night went on we had more punch, and the dice began to rattle on the tables, despite the landlord's remonstrance, who feared to fall into the hands of the law and lose his licence. But a lively major called out that here was licence enough, and hustled him out of the room, calling for more rum-punch, and stronger.

Meanwhile the smoke grew thick and thicker. Here and there a song broke out, and the clink of coin and the rattle of dice went on. Then, when at last Montresor came to our table and said he was going, and would I come too, I rose, and, bidding my kinsman good-by, went with the captain. I heard him swear as he found the door locked. No one seemed to know who had the key, and as for me, not ill-pleased, and past feeling regret, I turned back and stood over a table where some officers were throwing a main.

Then I saw in a corner a poor fellow who used to

be an usher at the academy, and who, having taken to drink, had lost his place. Now he was a sort of servitor in the coffee-house, and had gotten locked up in the room and could not escape. He had taken refuge in a corner at a deserted table, and, sitting unnoticed, was solacing himself with what was left of a bowl of punch. A sense of not altogether maudlin pity came upon me, and I went over and sat down beside him. No one took any heed of us. The air was heavy with pipe-smoke, oaths, mad catches of song, clink of glasses, and rattle of dice noisily cast, with here and there a toast cried; so that it was hard to see for the smoke, or to hear a man speak.

"Why, Savoy! How camest thou here?" I said.

"The devil fetched me, I guess."

He was far gone in liquor. "I am like Mr. Sterne's starling: 'I can't get out.' Ever read Mr. Sterne's—what is it?—oh, his 'Sentimental Journey'?"

Here was one worse than I, and I felt inclined to use what Friends call a precious occasion, a way being opened.

"This is a sad business, Savoy," I said.

"Dre'ful," he returned. "*Facilis descensus taverni.* No use to talk to me. I am tired of life. I am going to die. Some men shoot themselves, some like the rope, and some cold water. You know what Bishop what's-his-name—I mean Jeremy Taylor—says about ways to die: 'None please me.' But drink is the best. I mean to drink myself dead—dead—d—dead," and here he fell on to my shoulder. Letting him down easily, I loosed his neckerchief, and stood beside him, pitiful and shocked. Then in a moment I felt that I was drunk. The room whirled, and with an èffort I got to the open window, stumbling over legs of men, who looked up from their cards and cursed me.

Of what chanced after this I knew for a time but little, until I was in one instant sobered. This was an hour later, and nigh to twelve o'clock. What took place I heard from others; and, as it concerns a turning-point in my life, I shall try to relate it as if I myself had been conscious all the while.

The better for air, I went over to a table in the centre of the room not far from the door. Leaning heavily on Captain Small's shoulder, I threw on the table the last gold joe my aunt had given me with her final lesson in morals.

"Best in three, Etherington."

"Take it," he cried.

I threw double sixes, he threes, and I deuce ace. Then he cast some numbers as good. Certainly the devil meant to have me. I threw a third time; a six and a five turned up, and he an ace and a four. I had won. "Double or quits," I said; "one throw." I won again, and at this I went on until the pile of gold grew beneath my eyes, amid laughter, curses, and all manner of vileness. Presently I heard the colonel exclaim, "This won't do, gentlemen," and I felt some one trying to draw me from the table. It was Captain Wynne. I cried out, "Hands off! no liberties with me! I am the head of thy house; thou art only a cadet." He laughed as I pushed him aside.

"You said double or quits," cried the stout major. How he got into the game I knew not.

"It is a mere boy! for shame!" cried the colonel. "I forbid it."

"I am a gentleman," I said. "Thou canst order thy officers; thou canst not order me," and as I spoke I cast so hard that I crushed the box. I heard some one cry, "A damn pretty Quaker! By George, he has lost! A clean hundred pounds!" Even in this drunken revel there was a pause for a moment. I was, after all, but a tipsy lad of twenty, and some were just not far enough gone to feel that it might look to others an ugly business. The colonel said something to Major Milewood as to disrespect, I hardly know what; for at this moment there was a loud knocking at the door. In the lull that followed I heard the colonel's voice.

Then the tumult broke out anew. "By Jove, it is a woman!" cried Wynne. "I hear her. Wine and women! A guinea to a guinea she's pretty!"

"Done!" cried some one.

"Here's the key," said the major; "let's have her in."

"*Place aux dames*," hiccoughed a cornet.

The colonel rose, but it was too late. Wynne, seizing the key, unlocked the door and threw it wide open, as my mother, followed by Jack Warder, entered the room, and stood still a moment, dazed.

Captain Wynne, leering and unsteady, caught at her waist, exclaiming, "By George! she might be younger, but I've won. A toast! a toast! A Quaker, by George!"

Whether I was sobered or not, I know not. I can only say that of a sudden I was myself, and strangely quiet. I saw the dear lady, brave, beautiful, and with her curls falling about her neck, as she shrank back from the man's touch.

"Come, Hugh," she said.

"Yes, mother," I said; "but first—" and I struck Captain Wynne full in the face, so that, unprepared as he was, he fell over a table and on to the floor.

Every one started up. There was instant silence.

In a moment he was on his feet, and, like myself, another man. Turning, he said, with amazing coolness, wiping the blood away, for I was strong, and had hit hard, "Madam, I beg your pardon; we have been behaving like beasts, and I am fitly punished. As to you, Mr. Wynne, you are a boy, and have undertaken to rough it with men. This shall go no further."

"It shall go where I please," I cried.

"No, no; Hugh, Hugh!" said my mother.

"We will talk it over to-morrow," said the captain; and then, turning, "I mean, gentlemen, that this shall stop here. If any man thinks I am wrong, let him say so. I shall know how to settle accounts with him."

"No, no," said the colonel; "you are right, and if any officer thinks otherwise, I too am at his service." In the silence which came after he added, "Permit me, madam;" and offering his arm to my mother, we following, they went downstairs, Jack and I after them, and so into the street and the reproachful calm of the starlit April night.

.

VIII

"EVEN so far away as now," says Jack, writing in after-days, "it grieves me to think of that winter, and of this mad scene at the London Coffee-house. When I saw Hugh go in with the officers, I waited for an hour, and then went away. Returning later, I learned that he was still upstairs. I felt that if I stayed until he came forth, although he might not be in a way to talk to me, to know that I had waited so long might touch him and help him to hear me with patience. I walked to and fro until the clock had struck twelve, fearful and troubled like a woman. Sometimes I think I am like a woman in certain ways, but not in all.

"There were many people who loved Hugh, but, save his mother, none as I did. He had a serious kindliness in his ways, liking to help people, and for me at certain times and in certain crises a reassuring directness of swift dealing with matters in hand, most sustaining to one of my hesitating nature. His courage was instinctive, mine the result of obedience to my will, and requiring a certain resolute effort.

"I think of him always as in time of peril, throwing his head up and his shoulders back, and smiling,

112

with very wide-open eyes, like his mother's, but a deeper blue. The friendship of young men has often for a partial basis admiration of physical force, and Hugh excelled me there, although I have never been considered feeble or awkward except among those of another sex, where always I am seen, I fear, to disadvantage.

"Just after twelve I saw a woman coming hastily up Front street. As she came to a pause in the light which streamed from the open door, I knew her for Madam Marie, as she had taught me to call her. She wore a *calèche* hood, fallen back so that I saw her hair, half tumbled from under the thin gauze cap worn on the top of the head by most Quakers. She was clad quite too slightly, and had for wrap only a light, gray silk shawl.

"'*Mon Dieu!*' she exclaimed, 'I had to come. Jack, is he here? *Il faut que je monte*, I must go upstairs.' In excitement she was apt to talk French, and then to translate. 'Let me go,' said I; but she cried out, 'No, no! come!'

"There were many rough folks without, and others called together by the noise above, and no wonder. I said, 'Come in; I will go up with thee.' She pushed me aside, and, with staring eyes, cried, '*Où est l'escalier?*' As we went through the coffee-room, the loungers looked at her with surprise. She followed me without more words, ran by me on the stairs, and in a moment beat fiercely on the door, crying, '*Ouvrez!* open! quick!' Then there was that madhouse scene."

And this was how it came about, as Jack has here

8

told, that, still hot and angry, but much sobered, I, her son, walked beside my mother till we came to our door, and Jack left us, saying:

"Wilt thou see me to-morrow?"

I said, "Yes. God bless thee! Thou art the real son," and we entered.

Then it was sweet to see her; she said no word of reproach except, "*Il ne faut pas me donner ton baiser du soir.* No, no; I am not to be kissed." And so I went, sorrowful and still dizzy, up to my sleepless couch.

At the first gray light of dawn I rose, and was soon away half a mile from shore in my boat. As I came up from my first plunge in the friendly river, and brushed the water from my eyes, I do assure you the world seemed different. The water was very cold, but I cared nothing for that. I went home another and a better man, with hope and trust and self-repose for company. That hour in the water at early morn forever after seemed to me a mysterious separation between two lives, like a mighty baptismal change. Even now I think of it with a certain awe.

I pulled home as the sun rose, and lingered about until our servants came in for the early worship of the day. Soon I had the mother's kiss, and underwent a quick, searching look, after which she nodded gaily, and said, "*Est-ce que tout est bien, mon fils?* Is all well with thee, my son?" I said, "Yes—yes." I heard her murmur a sweet little prayer in her beloved French tongue. Then she began to read a chapter. I looked up amazed. It was the prodigal's story.

I stood it ill, thinking it hard that she should have made choice of that reproachful parable. I stared sideways out at the stream and the ships, but lost no word, as, with a voice that broke now and then, she read the parable to its close. After this should have come prayer, silent or spoken; but, to my surprise, she said, "We will not pray this morning," and we went in to breakfast at once.

As for me, I could not eat. I went out alone to the garden and sat down. I knew she would come to me soon. It seemed to me a long while. I sat on the grass against a tree, an old cherry, as I remember, and waited.

I can see her coming toward me under the trees, grave and quiet and sweet. The great beauty, Sarah Lukens, who married in mid-war the gallant Lennox, used to say of my mother that she put some sugar into all her moods; and it was true. I have seen her angry. I had rather have faced my father in his wildest rage than her. Why was she not angry now? She had vast reason for displeasure. After men have become wise enough to understand woman, I protest there will remain the mother, whom no man will ever comprehend.

"What a beautiful day, Hugh! And you had a good swim? was it cold? Why may not girls swim? I should love it."

Next she was beside me on the grass, my head on her bosom, saying, with a little sob, as if she had done some wrong thing:

"I—I did not choose it, dear; indeed I did not. It

came in order with the day, as your father reads;
and I—I did not think until I began it, and then I
would not stop. It is strange for it to so chance. I
wonder where that prodigal's mother was all the
while? Oh, you are better than that wicked, wicked
prodigal. I never would have let him go at all—
never if I could have helped it, I mean. *Mon Dieu!*
I think we women were made only for prayer or for
forgiveness; we can stop no sin, and when it is done
can only cry, ' Come back! come back! I love you!'"

If I cried on that tender heart, and spoke no word,
and was but a child again, I am sure that it was of
all ways the best to tell her that never again should
she be hurt by any act of mine.

" See, there is Judith at the door, wondering where
I am," she said, "and what is to be for dinner. I
must go and get ready the fatted calf. Ah, I would
not have left one alive. Yes, yes, I can jest, because
I am no more afraid, *mon fils*, nor ever shall be."

Upon this I would have said something of my
deep shame, and of the swine among whom I had
wallowed.

"No," she cried; "*c'est fini, mon cher*. It is all
over. The swine will eat alone hereafter." And
so would hear no more, only adding, "As for me,
I want to be told once how brave I was. Jack said
so; indeed he did. I *was* brave, was I not?"

"Don't, dear mother! please! I cannot bear it."
Somehow this plea, so childlike, to be praised for
what must have cost so much, quite overcame me.

"Yes, yes," she said; "I understand thee, and I

shall always. How strong thou art, *mon fils !* I was proud of thee, even in that sty of pigs in red coats. And he behaved like a gentleman, and hath wondrous self-command. I would see him again; who is he ?"

I told her his name.

" *Que c'est drôle.* That is curious. Thy cousin ! No doubt we shall see him to-day, and thy father. I shall tell him all—all. He must know."

"Yes, he must know," I said; "but I will tell him myself."

" He will be angry, but that is part of thy punishment."

Then I told her, too, I had lost an hundred pounds, as I believed, and she said :

" That is, after all, the least. There are pearls of my sister's I never wear. Thy aunt must take them and pay this debt. Go now to thy business as if nothing had happened, and I will send thee the pearls by Tom. No, no; it is to be as I say; I must have my way."

What could I do ? I kissed her, and we parted. I made no promises, and she asked for none. I like to think of how, after all, I left with her this sense of quiet trust.

I have said that the daily march of events never so influenced my life as did critical occasions. This was surely one of them. I do not now regret the knowledge of a baser world which I thus acquired. It has been of use to me, and to some with whose lives I have had to deal.

Of the wrath of my father, when I humbly con-

fessed my sins, it is not needful to speak at length.
For business calamities he was ready enough, and
lacked not decision; but in this matter he was, as
I could see, puzzled. He strode up and down, a great
bulk of a man, opening and shutting his hands, a
trick he had in his rare moments of doubt or of
intense self-repression.

"I know not what to do with thee," he said over
and over; "and thou didst strike the man, thy cousin?
Well, well! and hurt him, I am told? And he did
not return the blow!"

I had not said so. Thus I knew that other busy
tongues had been at work. For my life, I could not
see whether he looked upon the blow as my worst
iniquity, or deep in his heart was hardly grieved at it.

"Thou didst strike him? I must consider of thee;
I must take counsel. Go! thou wilt bring my gray
hairs in sorrow to the grave." And so I left him,
still striding to and fro, with ever the same odd
movement of his hands. He took counsel, indeed,
and for me and for him the most unwise that ever
a troubled man could have taken. It was some days
before this unpleasant scene took place, and meanwhile I had seen my aunt.

She was taking snuff furiously when I entered,
and broke out at once, very red in the face, and
walking about in a terrible rage. My mother used
to say that the first thing one saw of my Aunt
Gainor was her nose. It had been quite too much
of a nose for the rest of her face, until gray hair and
some change wrought by time in the architecture of

her fine head helped to make it more in harmony with the rest of her features. Somehow it arrested my attention now, and Heaven knows why it seemed to me more odd than ever.

"This is a fine repentance indeed! What are you staring at, you fool? Here has been that wild curlew, Bess Ferguson, with an awful tale of how you have gambled and lost an hundred pounds, and half killed an unlucky cousin. Who the deuce is the man? A nice godchild you are! A proper rage I am in, and Dr. Rush tells me I am never to get excited! You should hear Mrs. Galloway; duels and murder are the least of her talk; and, upon my word, you know no more of the small sword than of—I know not what. I must send you to Pike for lessons. When is it to be?"

"My dear aunt," I cried, "I wish all these Tory cats of yours were dead!"

At this she broke into laughter, and sat down.

"Cats! and did n't they miaow! That sweet girl-boy, Jack Warder, has been here too; sent, I suppose, by that dear Jesuit, your mother. How he blushes! I hear you behaved like a gentleman even in your cups. I like the lad; I did not use to. He is a manly miss. Sit down, and tell me all about it. Bless me! how hot I am!"

Upon this I knew I had won my battle, and went on to tell the whole story. When I produced my pearls, of which I was horribly ashamed, she broke out anew, declaring we were all mere traders, and did we think her a pawnbroker? and ended by giving me an hundred pounds, and bidding me to be careful and pay at once, as it was a debt of honour. "As to the pearls, let Madam Marie keep them for thy wife."

Thus ended a sorry business. It was to be told, and I have told it; but none, not even my mother or Jack, knew how deep a mark it left upon my character, or how profoundly it affected my life.

My friend Jack shall say the requiescat of this chapter of my life, which I have so unwillingly recorded. There was one more thing needed to complete its misery. Says Jack:

"Hugh Wynne and I fell apart this last winter of '72 and '73. It was my fault." This I do not understand. "Came then that hideous night in April, and all the rest; and Hugh I saw the day after, and begged him to forgive me because I had so easily deserted him. I took him later a kind message from Mr. James Wilson; for our small city knew it all. Friends looked at him as one disgraced, except Friend Rupert Forest, who, to my amusement, seemed to enjoy to hear the whole story, saying, 'Alas! alas!' and yet, as I saw, far more pleased than distressed. It brought to my mind the battle he had set us to fight out when we were boys. For a week or two Hugh was dispirited, but after that, when the colonel had called, and his cousin, Arthur Wynne, began to be more and more with him, he took heart, and faced our little world, and would let no one, except myself, say a word to him of the time of his downfall; this I think I never did, save perhaps once, and that long after.

"There was no need to preach. Converted devils make the best saints. I never was as good as Hugh, because I lacked courage to be wicked. Hugh was no saint, but he drank no more for a long while, and was ever after moderate. As to cards and dice, it was much the same."

What Jack has here written is all nonsense. He was a better man than I, and never was nor could have been a bad one.

IX

HAVE said that one event had to be recorded before I completed the story of that episode of which I was weary of hearing. My father—and it was against all his habits in regard to most matters —reminded me almost daily of my misdeeds. He hoped I did not drink any more, and he would even look at the square flasks on the shelf to see, as I suspected, if they had been used. To be prayed for was worst of all, and this he did more than once. It was all of it unwise, and but for my mother I should have been even more unhappy. I can see now that my father was this while in distress, feeling that he must do something, and not knowing what to do.

In his business life there had always been a way opened, as Friends say. He did not see that what I needed was what it was not in his nature to give, and thus it came about that we drew apart, and perhaps neither then nor at any later time were, or could ever have been, in the kindlier relation which makes the best of friendships that of the grown-up son with the elderly father.

At last, after a month or more, when it was far

on in June, he ceased to trouble me, and to walk up
and down, opening and shutting his hands, as he
recounted my sins. He had reached an unfortunate
decision, of which I was soon to feel the results.

In the mean time my cousin, Mr. Arthur Wynne,
had come into very close intimacy with all our family
circle. As he had much to do with my later life, it
is well to return a little, and to detail here what followed after the night of my mother's visit to the
coffee-house.

Next day, in the evening, came the colonel of the
Scots Grays, and desired to see me in the sitting-
room, my father being still in Lancaster.

"Mr. Wynne," he said, "Captain Wynne has
asked me to call in reference to that unhappy business of last night. He begs to make his excuses
to Mrs. Wynne in this letter, which may I ask
you to deliver? And after this action on his part
I trust you will see your way to regret the blow you
struck."

I was quiet for a moment, feeling that I must be
careful what answer I made. "I cannot feel sorry,"
I said; "I do not regret it."

"That is a pity, Mr. Wynne. You should remember that Mr. Arthur Wynne could not have known
who the lady was. A blow is a thing no gentleman can, as a rule, submit to; but this has been discussed by Sir William Draper and myself, and we
feel that Mr. Arthur Wynne cannot challenge a boy
of eighteen."

"I am twenty," I replied.

"Pardon me—of twenty, who is his cousin. That is the real point I would make. You have the best of it. You were right, quite right; but, by St. George, you are a hard hitter! Mr. Wynne would have come in person, but he is hardly fit to be seen, and a sign-painter is just now busy painting his eyelids and cheek, so as to enable him to appear out of doors."

The colonel treated me with the utmost respect, and, as a young fellow naturally would be, I was embarrassed more than a little, but not at all dissatisfied with the condition of my cousin. I said awkwardly that if he was willing to forget it I supposed I ought to be.

"I think so," said the colonel. "Suppose you leave it with me, and in a day or two talk it over with him. Indeed, he is a most charming gentleman, and a worthy member of a good old house."

I said I would leave it with the colonel, and upon this he said, "Good-by, and come and dine with the mess some day, but don't hit any more of us;" and so, laughing, he went away, leaving me flattered, but with the feeling that somehow he had gotten the better of me.

My mother declared it was a beautiful letter, writ prettily, but ill-spelled (neither George the king nor our own George could spell well). She would not let me see it. I did years afterward. In it he spoke of me as a boy, and she was cunning enough to know that I should not like that.

It was a week before we saw Mr. Arthur Wynne.

My father had meanwhile vented his first wrath on
me, and I was slowly getting over the strong sense of
disgust, shame, contrition, and anger, and had settled down earnestly to my work. I hardly recognised
the man who came in on us after supper, as my
mother and I sat in the orchard, with my father in a
better humour than of late, and smoking a churchwar-
den, which, you may like to know, was a long clay
pipe. The smoke sailed peacefully up, as I sat looking at its blue smoke-rings. How often since have
I seen them float from the black lips of cannon, and
thought of my father and his pipe!

We discussed the state of trade, and now and then
I read aloud bits from the Boston "Packet" of two
weeks back, or my mother spoke of their September
voyage, and of what would be needed for it, a voyage
being looked upon as a serious affair in those times.

"I found your doors hospitably open," said the
captain, appearing, "and the servant said I should find
you here; so I have taken my welcome for granted,
and am come to make my most humble excuses to
Mrs. Wynne."

We all rose as he drew near, my mother saying
in my ear as he approached, "It is Arthur Wynne.
Now, Hugh, take care!"

This newly found cousin was, like all of us, tall,
but not quite so broad as we other Wynnes. He
was of swarthy complexion from long service in the
East, and had black hair, not fine, but rather coarse.
I noticed a scar on his forehead. He shook hands,
using his left hand, because, as I learned, of awkward-

ness from an old wound.   But with his left he was
an expert swordsman, and, like left-handed swords-
men, the more dangerous.

"We are glad to see thee, Cousin Wynne," said
my mother.

Seeing the marks of my handiwork still on his
cheek, I took his greeting with decent cordiality, and
said, "Sit down; wilt thou smoke a pipe, Cousin
Arthur?"

He said he did not smoke, and set himself, with
the address of a man used to a greater world than
ours, to charm those whom no doubt he considered
to be quite simple folk.   In a few minutes the un-
pleasantness of the situation was over.   He and my
father were at one about politics, and I wisely held
my peace.   He let fall a discreet sentence or two
about the habits of soldiers, and his own regrets,
and then said, laughing:

"Your son is not quite of your views as a Friend
in regard to warfare."

"My son is a hasty young man," said my father,
and I felt my mother's touch on my arm.

Our cousin was in no way upset by this.   He said,
"No, no, cousin; he is young, but not hasty.   I was
fitly dealt with.   We are hot-blooded people, we
Wynnes.   The ways of Friends are not our ways of
dealing with an injury; and it was more—I wish to
say so—it was an insult.   He was right."

"There is no such thing as insult in the matter,"
said my father.   "We may insult the great Master,
but it is not for man to resent or punish."

"I fear as to that we shall continue to differ." He spoke with the utmost deference. "Do you go to Wyncote? I hear you are for England in the autumn."

"No; I shall be too full of business. Wyncote has no great interest for me."

"Indeed? It might perhaps disappoint you—a tumble-down old house, an embarrassed estate. My brother will get but a small income when it falls to him. My father fights cocks and dogs, rides to hounds, and, I grieve to say, drinks hard, like all our Welsh squires."

I was surprised at his frank statement. My mother watched him curiously, with those attentive blue eyes, as my father returned:

"Of a certainty, thou dost not add to my inducements to visit Wyncote. I should, I fear, be sadly out of place."

"I am afraid that is but too true, unless your head is better than mine. We are a sad set, we Wynnes. All the prosperity, and I fear much of the decency of the family, crossed the ocean long ago."

"Yet I should like to see Wyncote," said I. "I think thou didst tell me it is not thy home."

"No; a soldier can hardly be said to have a home; and a younger brother, with a tough father alive, and an elder brother on an impoverished estate, must needs be a wanderer."

"But we shall make thee welcome here," said my father, with grave kindness. "We are plain people, and live simply; but a Wynne should always find, as we used to say here, the latch-string outside."

With a little more talk of the Wynnes, the captain, declining to remain longer, rose, and, turning to me, said, "I hear, Cousin Hugh, that you refused to say that you were sorry for the sharp lesson you gave me the other night. I have made my peace with your mother."

"I shall see that my son behaves himself in future. Thou hast heard thy cousin, Hugh?"

I had, and I meant to make it up with him, but my father's effort as a peacemaker did not render my course the more easy. Still, with the mother-eyes on me, I kept my temper.

"I was about to say thou hast done all a man can do," said I.

"Then let us shake hands honestly," he replied, "and let bygones be bygones."

I saw both my parents glance at me. "I should be a brute if I did not say yes, and mean it, too; but I cannot declare that I am sorry, except for the whole business." And with this I took his left hand, a variety of the commonplace ceremony which always, to my last knowledge of Captain Wynne, affected me unpleasantly.

He laughed. "They call us in Merionethshire the wilful Wynnes. You will find me a good friend if you don't want the things I want. I am like most younger brothers, inclined to want things. I thank you all for a pleasant hour. It is like home, or better." With this he bowed low to my mother's curtsey, and went away, chatting as I conducted him to the door, and promising to sail with me, or to fish.

Naturally enough, on my return I found my parents discussing our newly found relative. My mother thought he talked much of himself, and had been pleasanter if he had not spoken so frankly of his father. My father said little, except that there seemed to be good in the young man.

"Why should we not forgive that in him which we must forgive in our own son?"

My father had some dreadful power to hurt me, and to me only was he an unjust man; this may have been because my wrong-doing troubled both his paternal and his spiritual pride. I was about to say that there was little likeness between my sin and that of my cousin; but I saw my mother, as she stood a little back of my father's great bulk, shake her head, and I held my tongue. Not so she.

"If thou hadst been a woman in my place, John Wynne, thou wouldst be far from saying the thing thou hast said."

Never had I heard or seen in our house a thing like this. I saw, in the fading light, my father working his hands as I have described, a signal of restrained anger, and, like anything physically unusual in one we love, not quite pleasant to see. But my mother, who knew not fear of him nor of any, went on, despite his saying, "This is unseemly—unseemly, wife."

"Thou art unjust, John, to my son."

"Thy son?"

"Yes; mine as well as thine. I have faith that thou, even thou, John, wouldst have done as my boy did."

9

"I? I?" he cried; and now I saw that he was disturbed, for he was moving his feet like some proud,
restrained horse pawing the grass. At last he
broke the stillness which followed his exclamations:
"There is but one answer, wife. Both have been
brutes, but this boy has been kept near to godly
things all his life. Each First-day the tongues of
righteous men have taught him to live clean, to put
away wrath, to love his enemies; and in a day—a
minute—it is gone, and, as it were, useless, and I the
shame of the town."

I hoped this was all; but my mother cried, "John!
John! It is thy pride that is hurt. No, it is not
seemly to dispute with thee, and before thy son. And
yet—and yet—even that is better than to let him go
with the thought that he is altogether like, or no better
than, that man. If thou hast a duty to bear testimony, so have I." And thus the mother of the prodigal son had her say. No doubt she found it hard,
and I saw her dash the tears away with a quick hand,
as she added, "If I have hurt thee, John, I am sorry."

"There is but one answer, wife. Love thy enemy;
do good to them that despitefully use thee. Thou
wilt ruin thy son with false kindness, and who shall
save him from the pit?"

I turned at last in a storm of indignation, crying,
"Could I see my mother treated like a street-wench
or a gutter-drab, and lift no hand? I wish I had
killed him!"

"See, wife," said my father. "Yes, even this was
to be borne."

"Not by me!" I cried, and strode into the house, wondering if ever I was to be done with it.

The day after no one of us showed a sign of this outbreak. Never had I seen the like of it among us; but the Quaker habit of absolute self-repression, and of concealment of emotion again prevailed, so that at breakfast we met as usual, and, whatever we may have felt, there was no outward evidence of my mother's just anger, of my father's bitterness, or of my own disgust.

X

I WAS not yet to see the end of my iniquity, and was to feel the consequences in ways which, for many a day, influenced my life and actions.

It was toward the end of June. The feeling of uneasiness and dread was becoming more and more felt, not only in commerce, which is so sensitive, but also in the social relations of men. The king's officers were more saucy, and, like all soldiers, eager for active service, imagining an easy victory over a people untrained in war. Such Tory pamphleteers as the foul-tongued Massachusetts writer, Daniel Leonard, were answering "Vindex" (Mr. Adams) and the widely read letters of "An American Farmer." The plan of organised correspondence between the colonies began to be felt in some approach to unity of action, for at this time the outspoken objection to the views of the king and his facile minister was general, and even men like Galloway, Chew, the Allens, and John Penn stood with varying degrees of good will among those who were urging resistance to oppression. As yet the too mighty phantom of independence had not appeared on the horizon of our stormy politics, to scare the timid, and to consolidate our own resistance.

I worked hard with my father at our lessening and complicated business, riding far into the country to collect debts, often with Jack, who had like errands to do, and with whom I discussed the topics which were so often, and not always too amiably, in question at my Aunt Gainor's table. I was just now too busy to be much with my old favourites, the officers. Indeed, I was wise enough to keep away from them.

My cousin I saw often, both at my aunt's, as I shall relate, and elsewhere; for he came much to our house, and my father found it agreeable to talk over with him the news of the day. My mother did not like him as well, but she held her peace, and, like every other man, he was attracted by her gaiety, and quaint way of looking at men and things.

Mr. Wilson I saw at times, as he still had, I know not why, a fancy for me, and loved well to sail with me of evenings over to Kaighn's Point to fish, or down to Gloucester to bob for crabs. I owed him much. A profound knowledge of law, variety of reading, and a mind which left broadly on our after-history the marks of his powerful intellect, were at my service. He used to caution me how I spoke of his opinions to others, and he would then discuss with freedom politics and the men whose figures were fast rising into distinctness as leaders to be listened to and trusted. Many of them he knew, and thus first I heard clearly what manner of persons were Patrick Henry and the Adamses, Dickinson, Peyton Randolph, and others less prominent. In this way I came to be more and more confirmed in the opinions my Aunt Gainor so resolutely held, and also more careful how I expressed them. Indeed, although but twenty years of age, I was become quite suddenly an older and graver man. Mr. Wilson surprised me one day by saying abruptly, as he pulled up a reluctant crab, " Do you never think, Hugh, that we shall have war ? "

I was indeed amazed, and said so. Then he added, " It will come. My place will not be in the field, but, whether you like it or not, you will see battles. You were made for a soldier, Hugh, Quaker or no Quaker."

I thought it odd that two people as different as my Aunt Gainor and he should have the same belief that we were drifting into war. She had said to me the night before that she had known Lord North as a boy, and that the king was an obstinate Dutchman, and would make his minister go his way, adding, " When it comes you will be in it; you can't escape."

No one else whom I knew had any such belief. Wilson's views and prediction sent me home thoughtful enough.

That evening my father said to me, " We go to Merion the day after to-morrow." It was there we spent our summers. "To-morrow will be Fourthday. It is our last day of Meeting in the town. There will, perhaps, be some wise words said as to present confusions, and I wish thee to hear them, my son."

I said, "Yes; at seven, father?" I was, however,

astonished; for these occasional night Meetings in the middle of the week were but rarely attended by the younger Friends, and, although opened with such religious observances as the society affected, were chiefly reserved for business and questions of discipline. I had not the least desire to go, but there was no help for it.

Our supper took place at six on this Wednesday, a little earlier than usual, and I observed that my father drank several cups of tea, which was not his habit. Few people took tea since the futile tax had been set upon it; but my father continued to drink it, and would have no concealment, as was the custom with some Whigs, who in public professed to be opposed to the views of the crown as to the right to collect indirect taxes.

Seeing that I did not drink it, and knowing that I liked nothing better than a good dish of tea, he asked me why I did not partake of it. Not willing to create new trouble, I said I did not want any. He urged the matter no further, but I saw he was not well pleased. We set off soon after in silence, he walking with hands behind his back clasping his gold-headed cane, his collarless coat and waistcoat below his beaver, and the gray hair in a thick mass between. He wore shoes, fine drab short-clothes, and black silk stockings, all without buckles; and he moved rapidly, nodding to those he met on the way, to the Bank Hill Meeting-house, in Front street, above Arch.

It was a simple, one-story, brick building, set a

few feet above the level of the roadway. The gables
and shutters were painted white, as was also the
plain Doric doorway, which had a pillar on each
side. I judged by the number of both sexes entering that it was an unusual occasion. There were
many drab-coated men, and there were elderly women,
in gowns of drab or gray, with white silk shawls
and black silk-covered cardboard bonnets. Here and
there a man or woman was in gayer colours or wore
buckles, and some had silver buttons; but these were
rare. The Meeting-room was, so to speak, a large
oblong box with whitewashed walls. A broad
passage ran from the door to the farther end; on
the right of it sat the men, on the left the women;
against the remoter wall, facing the rude benches,
were three rows of seats, one above the other. On
these sat at the back the elders, and in front of
them the overseers. The clerk of the Meeting had
a little desk provided for him. Over their heads
was a long sounding-board.

To me the scene had been familiar for years; but
to-day it excited my attention because of an air of
expectation, and even of excitement, among the few
more youthful Friends. I saw, as we entered, furtive
glances cast at my father and myself; but as to this
I had grown to be of late more or less indifferent, and
had no anticipation of what was to follow later.

I had become, since my sad downfall, a more serious
and thoughtful young man, and far better fitted to
feel the beauty and the spirituality of these Meetings
than I had been before. When the doors were closed

I sat silent in prayer; for some ten minutes increasing stillness came upon one and all of the three or four hundred people here met together.

As I waited, with long-trained patience, for full twenty minutes, a yet deeper quiet fell on the figures seated on each side of the aisle. For a time none of the men uncovered, but soon a few took off their broad hats, having remained with them on their heads long enough to satisfy custom by this protest against the ways of other men. The larger number kept their hats on their heads. Then a strange incident took place: a woman of middle age, but gray, her hair fallen about her shoulders, entered noisily, and, standing before the elders, cried out in a loud voice, as though in affliction and sore distress, " See to your standing; the Lord is about to search and examine your camp. Ho! ye of little faith and less works, the hand of God is come upon you—the mighty hand of punishment." As she spake thus wildly she swayed to and fro, and seemed to me disordered in mind. Finally she passed across the space in front of the overseers, to the women's side, and then back again, repeating her mad language. My Aunt Gainor's great bronze Buddha was not more motionless than they who sat on the elders' seats. At last the woman faced the Meeting, and went down the aisle, waving her hands, and crying out, " I shall have peace, peace, in thus having discharged my Lord's errand." The many there met did justice to their discipline. Scarce a face showed the surprise all must have felt. No one turned to see her go out, or seemed to hear the door banged furiously after her. The covered heads remained silent and undisturbed; the rows of deep bonnets were almost as moveless. Fully ten minutes of perfect silence followed this singular outburst. Then I saw the tall, gaunt figure of Nicholas Waln rise slowly, a faint but pleasant smile on his severe face, while he looked about him and began:

"Whether what ye have heard be of God I cannot say. The time hath troubled many souls. The woman, Sarah Harris, who hath, as some are aware, borne many sweet and pleasing testimonies to Friends in Wilmington, I know not. Whether what ye have heard be of God or but a rash way of speech, let us feel that it is a warning to Friends here assembled that we be careful of what we say and do. It hath been borne in upon me that Friends do not fully understand one another, and that some are moved to wrath, and some inclined to think that Friends should depart from their ways and question that which hath been done by the rulers God hath set over us. Let us be careful that our General Epistles lean not to the aiding of corrupt and wicked men, who are leading weak-minded persons into paths of violence." And here he sat down.

A moment later got up Thomas Scattergood, grim and dark of visage. None of his features expressed the slightest emotion, although even from the beginning he spoke with vehemence and his body rocked to and fro.

"The days are darkening; the times are evil. Our master, set over us by God, has seen fit to tax cer-

tain commodities, that means may be raised for the
just government of these colonies, where we and our
fathers have prospered in our worldly goods, under
a rule that has left us free to worship God as seems
best to us. And now we are bid by men, not of our
society, ungodly self-seekers, sons of darkness, to
unite with them in the way of resistance to the law.
There have even been found here among us those
who have signed agreements to disobey such as are
set over us, unmindful of the order to render to Cæsar
that which is his. Let there be among Friends neither
fear nor any shortcoming. Let us bear testimony
against evil-doers, whether they be of us or not. Let
us cut down and utterly cast forth those who depart
from righteousness. Are they not of the scum which
riseth on the boiling pot? There is a time for Friends
to remonstrate, and a time to act. I fear lest these
too gentle counsels of Friend Waln be out of time
and out of place. Away with those who, hearing,
heed not. Let them be dealt with as they should be,
with love for the sinner, but with thought as to the
evil which comes of unscourged examples, so that
when again we are met in the Quarterly Meeting there
shall be none among us to stir up discord, and we can
say to other Meetings, 'As we have done, so do ye.
Make clean the house of the Lord.'"

The night was now upon us, and the ringing tones
of the speaker were heard through the darkness before he sat down. While all waited, two Friends
lit the candles set in tin sconces against the pillars
of the gallery, and, in the dim light they gave, the
discussion went on.

Then I saw that Arthur Howell was about to speak.
This able and tender-minded man usually sat in
Meeting with his head bent, his felt hat before his
eyes, wrapped in thought, and lifted above all consideration of the things of this earth. As he began,
his rich, full voice filled the space, and something in
its pleading sweetness appealed to every heart. He
spoke as one who, having no doubt, wondered that
any one else should doubt, and he brought the discussion to a decisive point at once.

"It is well," he said, "that all should be convinced
by those who, from age and influence among Friends,
have the best right of speech. Nevertheless, since
this is a Meeting for discipline, let all be heard with
fairness and order. Men have gone astray. They
have contended for the asserting of civil rights in
a manner contrary to our peaceable profession and
principles, and, although repeatedly admonished, do
not manifest any disposition to make the Meeting a
proper acknowledgment of their outgoings. Therefore it is that we bear our testimony against such
practices, and can have no unity with those who follow them until they come to a sense of their errors.
Therefore, if this be the sense of our Meeting, let
the clerk be moved to manifest the feelings of the
Meeting to these members, signing on our behalf,
for the matter hath already been before us twice,
and hath been deeply and prayerfully considered by
ourselves; and I am charged to tell Friends that these
members who have thus gone astray are unwilling
to be convinced by such as have sought to bring them

to a better mind. This hath been duly reported, and overseers having thus failed, it doth only remain to abide by the sense of our Meeting. But this I have already said: the matter hath been prayerfully considered."

After this, others spoke, but all elder Friends understood that the business had been disposed of, and little attention was given to those who rose after Friend Howell sat down. Indeed, that they were ill-advised to speak at all was plainly to be read in the countenances of many.

This was my first experience of an evening Meeting, and, even to one acquainted with all the ways of Friends, the scene was not without its interest. The night was now dark outside. The tallow dips ran down and flared dismally. A man with snuffers went to and fro, and the pungent odours of candles, burned out and to be replaced, filled the room.

In the quiet which followed Arthur Howell's refined and distinct accents, I looked at the row of placid faces where the women sat, some rosy, some old, all in the monastic cell of the bonnet, which made it as impossible to see, except in front, as it is for a horse with blinders. I wondered how this queer head-gear came to have been made, and recalled my aunt's amusement at the care exercised as to its form and material. Few there, I think, let their thoughts wander, and in front of me the row of drab coats and wide felt or beaver hats remained almost motionless.

At last James Pemberton, the esteemed clerk of the Meeting, rose. "I am moved," he said, "by the

Spirit to declare that the sense, and also the weight, of the Meeting is that Cyrus Edson and William Jameson be advised, in accordance with the instructed wish of Friends."

He then sat down. There was no vote taken. Even had a majority of those present been hostile to the proposed action, it is improbable that any protest would have been made. · The clerk's statement that the weight of the Meeting was affirmative, would have been held to settle the matter, as it appeared best to a limited number of those recognised, through their piety and strict living, to be competent to decide for the rest.

I was now assured that this was all, and looked to see two of the elders shake hands, which is the well-recognised signal for the Meeting to break up; but as the elders did not move, the rest sat still and waited. By and by I saw Nicholas Waln extend his hand to my father, who, looking steadily before him, made no sign of perceiving this intention to dismiss Friends. A still longer pause followed. As I learned afterward, no further speaking was anticipated. No one stirred. For my part, I was quite ready to go, and impatiently awaited the signal of dismissal. A minute or two passed; then I was aware of a short, neatly built man, who rose from a bench near by. His face was strong, irregular of feature, and for some reason impressed me. I could see even in the indistinct light that he flushed deeply as he got up on his feet. He received instant attention, for he went past me, and, standing in the passageway, was quiet for a moment. He was, I think, not over thirty, and seemed embarrassed at the instant attention he received. For a few minutes he appeared to seek his words, and then, quite suddenly, to find them in eloquent abundance.

"It is not usual," he said, "for disowned members of the society to openly protest. Neither are these our brothers here to-day. Nor, were they with us, are they so skilled with the tongue as to be able to defend themselves against the strong language of Thomas Scattergood or the gentle speech of Arthur Howell. I would say a word for them, and, too, for myself, since nothing is more sure than that I think them right, and know that ye will, before long, cast out me, to whom your worship is sweet and lovely, and the ways of Friends for the most part such as seem to me more acceptable than those of any other Christian society. Whether it be that old memories of persecution, or too great prosperity, have hardened you, I do not know. It does seem to me that ye have put on a severity of dress and life that was not so once, and that undue strictness hath destroyed for us some of the innocent joys of this world. I also find unwholesome and burdensome that inner garment of self-righteousness in which ye clothe yourselves to judge the motives of your fellow-men.

"So far as the law went against such views as you entertained, none did more resist them, in your own way, than did you; but now the English across the seas tell us that the liberty our fathers sought on these shores is to be that which pleases a corrupt and

pliant ministry, and not that which is common to
men of English blood. Some brave men of our society say, 'Let us make a stand here, lest worse things
come. Let us refuse to eat, drink, or wear the articles they assume to tax, whether we will or not.'
There is no violence. Believe me, there will be none
if we are one throughout the colonies. But if not—
if not—if grave old men like you, afraid of this mere
shadow of passive resistance, dreading to see trade
decay and the fat flanks of prosperity grow lean—
if you are wholly with our oppressors, passively with
them, or, as some believe, actively, then—then, dear
friends, it will be not the shadow, but the substance,
of resistance that will fall in blood and ruin on you
and on all men—on your easy lives and your ac-
cumulated gains.

"Aye, look to it! There is blood on the garments
of many a man who sits fearfully at home, and thinks
that because he does nothing he will be free of guilt
when the great account is called."

On this a rare exception to the tranquillity of Meeting occurred. Daniel Offley, by trade a farrier, rose
and broke in, speaking loudly, as one used to lift his
voice amid the din of hammers: "Wherefore should
this youth bring among us the godless things of
worldly men?" His sonorous tones rang out through
the partial obscurity, and shook, as I noticed, the
scattered spires of the candle flames. "This is no
time for foolish men to be heard, where the elders
are of a mind. The sense of the Meeting is with us.
The weight of the Meeting is with us. The king is

a good king, and who are we to resist? Out with those who are not of our ways! Let the hammer fall on the unrighteous, lest the sheep be scattered, and the Shepherd leave them."

At this queer mixture of metaphors I saw the previous speaker smile, as he stood in the aisle. Next I heard the gentle voice of James Pemberton break in on the uncouth speech of the big farrier.

"It is the custom of Friends that all men who feel to be moved to tell us aught shall be heard. Friend Wetherill, we will hear thee to an end." He spoke with the courteous ease of a well-bred gentleman, and the smith sat down.

Friend Wetherill paused a moment, looking to left and right along the lines of deeply interested and motionless faces. Then he continued: "On what you and others do in these days depends what shall come upon us. Let no man deceive you, not even the timid counsel of gray hairs or the wariness of wealth. The guinea fears; the penny fights; and the poor penny is to-day deeply concerned. You take shelter under the law of Christ, to live, as far as possible, at peace with all men. As far as possible? It should at times be felt that Paul's limitation is also a command. Do not resist him who would slay a child or wrong a woman—that is how you read the law of God.

"It is extremes which bring ruin to the best Christian societies, and if the mass of men were with you civil order would cease, and the carefully builded structure of civilisation would perish. You are already undergoing a process of dry decay, and as you

10

dry and dry, you harden and shrink, and see it not.
A wild woman has told you to set your camp in order.
See to it, my friends; see to it!"

For not less than a minute the speaker remained
silent, with bended head, still keeping the wonderfully steady attention of this staid assembly.
Very slowly he lifted his face, and now, as he began
again, it was with a look of tender sweetness: "It
was far back in Second-month, 1771, I began to be
encompassed by doubts as to the course Friends were
taking. To-day I am assured in spirit that you are
wrong in the support you gave, and, let me say, are
giving, to an unjust cause. I think I take an innocent liberty to express myself on this occasion, also
according to the prospect I have of the matter.
There is something due to the king, and something
to the cause of the public. When kings deviate from
the righteous law of justice in which kings ought to
rule, it is the right, aye, and the religious duty, of the
people to be plain and honest in letting them know
where. I am not a person of such consequence as
to dictate; but there is in me and in you a court, to
which I confidently appeal. I *have* appealed to it in
prayer, as to what my course shall be. I obey my
conscience. Take heed that you do not act rashly."

Here again, after these calm words, he paused, and
then said, with emphatic sternness, "As my last
words, let me leave with you the admonition of the
great founder of this colony. 'I beseech you,' he
says, 'for the sake of Christ, who so sharply pro-
hibited making others suffer for their religion, that

you have a care how you exercise power over other men's consciences. My friends, conscience is God's throne in man, and the power of it His prerogative!' These are solemn words. Whether you leave me to live among you, free to do what seems right to me, or drive me forth, who have no wish to go, now and always I shall love you. That love you cannot take away, nor weaken, nor disturb."

I was sorry when the melody of this clear voice ceased. The speaker, wiping the moisture from his brow, stood still, and, covering his face with his hands, was lost in the prayer which I doubt not followed.

A long interval of absence of all sound came after he ceased to speak. No one replied. The matter was closed, a decision reached, and the clerk instructed. I knew enough to feel sure that those manly tones of appeal and remonstrance had failed of their purpose.

At this moment I saw an elderly man on the seat before me rise, and with deliberateness kneel in prayer; or, as Friends say, Israel Sharpless appeared in supplication. At first, as he began to be heard, Friends rose here and there, until all were afoot and all uncovered. The silence and reverent bended heads, and the dim light, affected me as never before. Many turned their backs on the praying man, an odd custom, but common. As he prayed his voice rose until it filled the great room; and of a sudden I started, and broke out in a cold sweat, for this was what I heard:

" O Lord, arise, and let Thine enemies be scattered

Dip me deeper in Jordan. Wash me in the laver of
regeneration. Give me courage to wrestle with ill-
doers. Let my applications be heard.

"Father of mercy, remember of Thy pity those of
the young among us who, being fallen into evil ways,
are gone astray. We pray that they who have gambled and drunk and brought to shame and sorrow
their elders may be recovered into a better mind,
and sin no more. We pray Thee, Almighty Father,
that they be led to consider and to repent of deeds
of violence, that those among us whom the confusion
of the times has set against the law and authority of
rulers be better counselled; or, if not, strengthen us
so to deal with these young men as shall make pure
again Thy sheepfold, that they be no longer a means
of leading others into wickedness and debauchery."
I heard no more. This man was a close friend of my
father. I knew but too well that it was I who was
thus reproved, and thus put to shame. I looked this
way and that, the hot blood in my face, thinking to
escape. Custom held me. I caught, as I stared,
furtive glances from some of the younger folk. Here
and there some sweet, gentle face considered me a
moment with pity, or with a curiosity too strong for
even the grim discipline of Friends. I stood erect.
The prayer went on. Now and then I caught a phrase,
but the most part of what he said was lost to me. I
looked about me at times with the anguish of a
trapped animal.

At last I saw that my gentle-voiced speaker, Wetherill, was, like myself, rigid, with upheld head, and

that, with a faint smile on his face, he was looking toward me. Minute after minute passed. Would they never be done with it? I began to wonder what was going on under those bent gray hats and black bonnets. I was far away from penitence or remorse, a bruised and tormented man, helpless, if ever a man was helpless, under the monotonous and silent reproach of some hundreds of people who had condemned me unheard. It did seem as if it never would end.

At last the voice died out. The man rose, and put on his hat. All resumed their seats and their head-coverings. I saw that Friend Scattergood extended a hand to my father, who was, as I have not yet stated, an elder. The grasp was accepted. Elders and overseers, both men and women, rose, and we also. I pushed my way out, rudely, I fear. At the door James Pemberton put out his hand. I looked him full in the face, and turned away from the too inquisitive looks of the younger Friends. I went by my father without a word. He could not have known what pain his method of saving my soul would cost me. That he had been in some way active in the matter I did not doubt, and I knew later that my opinion was but too correct.

Hastening down Front street with an overwhelming desire to be alone, I paused at our own door, and then, late as it was, now close to ten, I unmoored my boat, and was about to push off when I felt a hand on my shoulder. It was Samuel Wetherill.

"Let me go with thee, my boy," he said. "We should talk a little, thou and I."

I said, "Yes. Thou art the only man I want to see to-night."

There were no more words. The moon was up as I pulled down Dock Creek and out on my friendly river.

"Let thy boat drift," he said. "Perhaps thou art aware, Hugh Wynne, how grieved I was; for I know all that went before. I somehow think that thou hast already done for thyself what these good folk seemed to think was needed. Am I right?"

"Yes," I said.

"Then say no more. James Wilson has spoken of thee often. To be loved of such a man is much. I hear that thou hast been led to think with us, and that, despite those wicked wild oats, thou art a young man of parts and good feelings, thoughtful beyond thy years."

I thanked him almost in tears; for this kindly judgment was, past belief, the best remedy I could have had.

"I saw thy great suffering; but in a year, in a month, this will seem a thing of no import; only, when thou art calm and canst think, hold a Meeting in thy own heart, and ask thy quiet judgment, thy conscience, thy memory, if prayer be needed; and do it for thyself, Hugh."

I said, "Thank thee," but no more. I have ever been averse to talking of my relations to another world, or of what I believe, or of what I am led thereby to do in hours of self-communion. I sat wishing my father were like this, a tender-hearted yet resolute man.

Seeing me indisposed to speak, he went on: "If we could but keep the better part of Friends' creed, and be set free to live at peace with the law, to realise that to sit down quietly under oppression may be to serve the devil, and not God! Thou knowest, as well as I, that divers Friends have publicly avowed the ministry, and allege that whatever they may do is a just punishment of rebellion. We are going to have a serious settlement, and it will become us all, Hugh, young and old, to see that we are on the right side, even if we have to draw the sword. And thou and I shall not be alone of Friends. There are Clement and Owen Biddle, and Christopher Marshall, and more."

I was surprised, and said so.

"Yes, yes," he said; "but I talk to thee as to a man, and these things are not to be spread abroad. I trust I have been to thee a comfort; and, now the moon is setting, let us go home."

I thanked him as well as I knew how. He had indeed consoled me.

When I came in my father had gone to bed, but my mother was waiting to see me. She caught me in her arms, and, weeping like a child, cried, "Oh, I have heard! He did not tell me beforehand, or I should have forbade it. Thou shouldst never have gone! never! It was cruel! *Mon Dieu!* how could they do it!"

It was I who now had to comfort, and this helped me amazingly, and yet added to my just anger; for why must she, who was innocent, be thus made

to suffer? My father, when he came in, had asked
for me. He had met my cousin, who had seen me
going down Front street, and had hinted that I meant
to find comfort at the coffee-house among the officers.
She knew better, and had said her mind of this kinsman and his ways; upon which my father had gone
angry to his bed. I was beginning to have an increasing distrust and dislike of Arthur, and the
present news did not lessen either feeling. So at
last here was an end of the consequences of my sad
night at the coffee-house.

XI

HE next day we went to our farm in Merion. My father said no word of the Meeting, nor did I. The summer of '73 went on. I rode in to my work daily, sometimes with my father, who talked almost altogether of his cattle or of his ventures, never of the lowering political horizon. He had excused himself from being a consignee of the tea, on the score of his voyage, which was now intended for September.

My aunt lived in summer on the farther slope of Chestnut Hill, where, when the road was in order, came her friends for a night, and the usual card-play. When of a Saturday I was set free, I delighted to ride over and spend Sunday with her, my way being across country to one of the fords on the Schuylkill, or out from town by the Ridge or the Germantown highroad. The ride was long, but, with my saddle-bags and Lucy, a new mare my aunt had raised and given me, and clad in overalls, which we called tongs, I cared little for the mud, and often enough stopped to assist a chaise out of the deep holes, which made the roads dangerous for vehicles.

Late one day in August, I set out with my friend

Jack to spend a Sunday with my Aunt Gainor.
Jack Warder was now a prime favourite, and highly
approved. We rode up Front street, and crossed the
bridge where Mulberry street passed under it, and is
therefore to this day called Arch street, although few
know why. The gay coats of officers were plentiful,
farmers in their smocks were driving in with their
vegetables, and to the right was the river, with here
and there a ship, and, beyond, the windmill on the
island. We talked of the times, of books, of my father's
voyage, and of my future stay with my aunt.

Although Jack's father was a Quaker, he was too
discreet a business man not to approve of Jack's
visits to my aunt, and too worldly not to wish for
his son a society to which he was not born; so Mrs.
Ferguson and Mrs. Galloway made much of Jack,
and he was welcome, like myself, at Cliveden, where
the Chews had their summer home.

The Tory ladies laughed at his way of blushing
like a girl, and, to Jack's dismay, openly envied his
pink-and-white skin and fair locks. They treated
him as if he were younger than I, although, as it
chanced, we were born on the same day of the same
year; and yet he liked it all—the gay women, the
coquettish Tory maids, even the "genteel" Quaker
dames, such as Mrs. Sarah Logan or Mrs. Morris,
and the pretty girls of the other side, like Sarah
Lukens and the Misses Willing, with their family
gift of beauty. These and more came and went at my
aunt's, with men of all parties, and the grave Drs. Rush
and Parke, and a changing group of English officers.

In the little old house at Belmont, the Rev. Richard
Peters was glad to sit at cards with the Tory ladies,
whose cause was not his, and still less that of Richard,
his nephew. At times, as was the custom, sleigh-
ing parties in winter or riding-parties in summer
used to meet at Cliveden or Springetsbury, or at a
farm-house where John Penn dwelt while engaged
in building the great house of Lansdowne, looking
over trees to the quiet Schuylkill.

We rode out gaily this August afternoon, along
the Germantown road, admiring the fine farms, and
the forests still left among the cultivated lands.
Near Fisher's Lane we saw some two or three people in the road, and, drawing near, dismounted.
A black man, who lay on the ground, groaning with
a cut head, and just coming to himself, I saw to be
my aunt's coachman Cæsar. Beside him, held by a
farmer, was a horse with a pillion and saddle, all
muddy enough from a fall. Near by stood a slight
young woman in a saveguard petticoat and a sad-
coloured, short camlet cloak.

"It is Miss Darthea Peniston," said Jack.

"Miss Peniston," I said, dismounting, "what has
happened?"

She told me quietly, that, riding pillion to stay
with my aunt, the horse had fallen and hurt Cæsar,
not badly, she thought. She had alighted on her
feet, but what should she do? After some discussion, and the black being better, we settled to
leave him, and I proposed that Jack, the lighter
weight, should ride my Aunt Gainor's horse, with

Miss Peniston on the pillion behind him. Upon this Jack got red, at the idea, I suppose, of Miss Darthea's contemplating the back of his head for four miles. The young woman looked on with shy amusement.

At this moment Cæsar, a much pampered person, who alone of all her house dared give my aunt advice, declared he must have a doctor. Jack, much relieved, said it was inhuman to leave him in this case, and put an end to our discussion by riding away to fetch old Dr. de Benneville.

Miss Darthea laughed, said it was a sad thing a woman should have no choice, and pretended to be in misery as to my unfortunate lot. I said nothing, but, after looking Cæsar's horse over, I gave my saddle to be kept at the farmer's, and put the coachman's saddle on my mare Lucy, with the pillion behind made fast to the saddle-straps arranged for this use. Then I looked well to the girths, and mounted to see how Lucy would like it. She liked it not at all, and was presently all over the road and up against the fence of the old graveyard I was to see again in other and wilder days.

I saw the little lady in the road watching me with a smiling face, by no means ill pleased with the spectacle. At last I cried, "Wait!" and putting Miss Lucy down the road for a mile at a run, soon brought her back quite submissive.

"Art thou afraid?" I said.

"I do not like to be asked if I am afraid. I am very much afraid, but I would die rather than not get on your mare." So a chair was fetched, Miss Penis-

ton put on her linen riding-mask, and in a moment
was seated behind me. For ten minutes I was fully
taken up with the feminine creature under me. At
last I said:

"Put an arm around my waist. I must let her
go. At once!" I added; for the mare was getting to
rear a little, and the young woman hesitated. "Do
as I tell thee!" I cried sharply, and when I felt her
right arm about me, I said, "Hold fast!" and gave
the mare her head. A mile sufficed, with the double
burden, so to quiet her that she came down to her
usual swift and steady walk.

When there was this chance to talk without having every word jolted out in fragments, the young
person was silent; and when I remarked, "There
is now an opportunity to chat with comfort," said:

"I was waiting, sir, to hear your excuses; but perhaps Friends do not apologise."

I thought her saucy, for I had done my best; and
for her to think me unmannerly was neither just nor
kind.

"If I am of thy friends—"

"Oh, Quakers, I meant. Friends with a large F,
Mr. Wynne."

"It had been no jesting matter if the mare had
given thee a hard fall."

"I should have liked that better than to be ordered
to do as your worship thought fit."

"Then thou shouldst not have obeyed me."

"But I had to."

"Yes," I said. And the talk having fallen into these

brevities, Miss Peniston was quiet awhile, no doubt pouting prettily ; her face was, of course, hid from me.

After a while she said something about the milestones being near together, and then took to praising Lucy, who, I must say, had behaved as ill as a horse could. I said as much, whereon I was told that mares were jealous animals; which I thought a queer speech, and replied, not knowing well how to reply, that the mare was a good beast, and that it was fair flattery to praise a man's horse, for what was best in the horse came of the man's handling.

"But even praise of his watch a man likes," said she. "He has a fine appetite, and likes to fatten his vanity."

She was too quick for me in those days, and I never was at any time very smart at this game, having to reflect too long before seeing my way. I said that she was no doubt right, but thus far that I had had thin diet.

Perhaps saying that Lucy was gay and well bred and had good paces was meant to please the rider. This woman, as I found later, was capable of many varieties of social conduct, and was not above flattering for the mere pleasure it gave her to indulge her generosity, and for the joy she had in seeing others happy.

Wondering if what she had said might be true, held me quiet for a while, and busied with her words, I quite forgot the young woman whose breath I felt now and then on my hair, as she sat behind me.

Silence never suited Miss Peniston long in those

days, and especially not at this time, she being in a
merry mood, such as a little adventure causes. Her
moods were, in fact, many and changeful, and, as I
was to learn, were too apt to rule even her serious
actions for the time; but under it all was the true
law of her life, strongly charactered, and abiding
like the constitution of a land. It was long before I
knew the real woman, since for her, as for the most
of us, all early acquaintance was a masquerade, and
some have, like this lady, as many vizards as my
Aunt Gainor had in her sandalwood box, with her
long gloves and her mitts.

The mare being now satisfied to walk comfortably,
we were going by the Wister house, when I saw saucy
young Sally Wister in the balcony over the stoop,
midway of the penthouse. She knew us both, and
pretended shame for us, with her hands over her
face, laughing merrily. We were friends in after-
life, and if you would know how gay a creature
a young Quakeress could be, and how full of mischief, you should see her journal, kept for Deborah
Logan, then Miss Norris. It has wonderful gaiety,
and, as I read it, fetches back to mind the officers
she prettily sketches, and is so sprightly and so full
of a life that must have been a joy to itself and to
others, that to think of it as gone and over, and of
her as dead, seems to me a thing impossible.

It was not thought proper then for a young woman
to go on pillion behind a young man, and this Miss
Sally well knew. I dare say she set it down for the
edification of her young friend.

"The child" (she was rather more than that) "is saucy," said my lady, who understood well enough what her gestures meant. "I should like to box her ears. You were very silent just now, Mr. Wynne. A penny is what most folks' thoughts are bid for, but yours may be worth more. I would not stand at a shilling."

"Then give it to me," said I. "I assure thee a guinea were too little."

"What are they?"

"Oh, but the shilling."

"I promise."

"I seem to see a little, dark-faced child crying because of a boy in disgrace—"

"Pretty?" she asked demurely.

"No, rather plain."

"You seem to have too good a memory, sir. Who was she?"

"She is not here to-day."

"Yes, yes!" she cried. "I have her—oh, somewhere! She comes out on occasions. You may never see her; you may see her to-morrow."

I was to see her often. "My shilling," I said.

"That was only a jest, Mr. Wynne. My other girl has stolen it, for remembrance of a lad that was brave and—"

"He was a young fool! My shilling, please."

"No, no!"

At this I touched the mare with my spur. She, not seeing the joke, pranced about, and Miss Darthea was forced to hold to my waist for a minute.

"The mare is ill broke," she cried. "Why does she not go along quietly?"

"She hates dishonesty," I said.

"But I have not a penny."

"Thou shouldst never run in debt if thou art without means. It is worse than gambling, since here thou hast had a consideration for thy money, and I am out of pocket by a valuable thought."

"I am very bad. I may get prayed over in Meeting, only we do not have the custom at Christ Church."

I was struck dumb. Of course every one knew of my disaster and what came of it; but that a young girl should taunt me with it, and for no reason, seemed incredible. No one ever spoke of it to me, not even Mistress Ferguson, whose daily food was the saying of things no one else dared to say. I rode on without a word.

At last I heard a voice back of me quite changed —tender, almost tearful. "Will you pardon me, Mr. Wynne? I was wicked, and now I have hurt you who was once so good to me. Your aunt says that I am six girls, not one, and that— Will you please to forgive me?"

"Pray don't; there is nothing to forgive. I am over-sensitive, I suppose. My friend Mr. Wilson says it is a great thing in life to learn how to forget wisely. I am learning the lesson; but some wounds take long to heal, and this is true of a boy's folly. Pray say no more." I put the mare to trotting, and we rode on past Cliveden and Mount Airy, neither speaking for a while.

11

I wondered, as we rode, at her rashness of talk and
her want of consideration; and I reflected, with a
certain surprise, at the frequent discovery, of late,
on how much older I seemed to be. It was a
time which quickly matured the thoughtful, and I
was beginning to shake off, in some degree, the lifelong shackles of limitation as to conduct, dress, and
minor morals, imposed upon me by my home surroundings. In a word, being older than my years, I
began to think for myself. Under the influence of
Mr. Wetherill I had come, as without him I could not
have done, to see how much there was of the beautiful and noble in the creed of Fox and Penn, how
much, too, there was in it to cramp enterprise, to
limit the innocent joys of life, to render progress
impossible, and submission to every base man or
government a duty.

I had learned, too, in my aunt's house, the ways
and manners of a larger world, and, if I had yielded
to its temptations, I had at least profited by the bitter lesson. I was on the verge of manhood, and had
begun to feel as I had never done before the charm
of woman; this as yet I hardly knew.

As we breasted the hill, and saw beneath us
the great forest-land spread out, with its scattered
farms, an exclamation of delight broke from my
companion's lips. It was beautiful then, as it is to-
day, with the far-seen range of hills beyond the river,
where lay the Valley Forge I was to know so well, and
Whitemarsh, all under the hazy blue of a cool August
day, with the northwest wind blowing in my face.

Within there were my aunt and some young women, and my Cousin Arthur, with explanations to be
made, after which my young woman hurried off to
make her toilet, and I to rid me of my riding-dress.

It was about seven when we assembled out of doors
under the trees, where on summer days my Aunt
Gainor liked to have supper served. My Cousin
Wynne left Mrs. Ferguson and came to meet me.
We strolled apart, and he began to ask me questions
about the tea cargoes expected soon, but which came
not until December. I said my father's voyage would
prevent his acting as consignee, and this seemed to
surprise him and make him thoughtful, perhaps because he was aware of my father's unflinching loyalty.
He spoke, too, of Mr. Wilson, appearing—and this
was natural enough—to know of my intimacy with
the Whig gentleman. I was cautious in my replies,
and he learned, I think, but little. It was a pity, he
said, that my father would not visit Wyncote. It
seemed to me that he dwelt overmuch on this matter,
and my aunt, who greatly fancied him, was also of this
opinion. I learned long after that he desired to
feel entirely assured as to the certainty of this visit
not being made. I said now that I wished I had my
father's chance to see our Welsh home, and that I
often felt sorry my grandfather had given it up.

"But he did," said my cousin, "and no great thing,
either. Here you are important people. We are
petty Welsh squires, in a decaying old house, with
no money, and altogether small folk. I should like
to change places with you."

"And yet I regret it," said I. My Aunt Gainor
had filled me full of the pride of race.

I spoke as we approached the group about my
aunt, and I saw his face take an expression which
struck me. He had a way of half closing his eyes,
and letting his jaw drop a little. I saw it often afterward. I suspect now that he was dealing intensely
with some problem which puzzled him.

He seemed to me to be entirely unconscious of this
singular expression of face, or, as at this time, to be
off his guard; for the look did not change, although
I was gazing at him with attention. Suddenly I
saw come down the green alley, walled with well-
trimmed box, a fresh vision of her who had been
riding with me so lately. My cousin also became
aware of the figure which passed gaily under the
trees and smiled at us from afar.

"By George! Hugh," said Arthur, "who is the
sylph? what grace! what grace!"

For a moment I did not reply. She wore a silken
brocade with little broidered roses here and there, a
bodice of the same, cut square over a girl-like neck,
white, and not yet filled up. Her long gloves were
held up to the sleeve by tightens of plaited white
horsehair, which held a red rosebud in each tie; and
her hair was braided with a ribbon, and set high in
coils on her head, with but little powder. As she
came to meet us she dropped a curtsey, and kissed
my aunt's hand, as was expected of young people.

I have tried since to think what made her so unlike other women. It was not the singular grace

which had at once struck my cousin; neither was
she beautiful. I long after hated Miss Chew for an
hour because she said Darthea Peniston had not one
perfect feature. She had, notwithstanding, clear,
large brown eyes, and a smile which was so variously eloquent that no man saw it unmoved. This
was not all. Her face had some of that charm of
mystery which a few women possess—a questioning
look; but, above all, there was a strange flavour of
feminine attractiveness, more common in those who
are older than she, and fuller in bud; rare, I think,
in one whose virgin curves have not yet come to
maturity. What she was to me that summer evening she was to all men—a creature of many moods,
and of great power to express them in face and voice.
She was young, she loved admiration, and could be
carried off her feet at times by the follies of the
gay world.

If you should wonder how, at this distant day, I
can recall her dress, I may say that one of my aunt's
lessons was that a man should notice how a woman
dressed, and not fail at times to compliment a gown,
or a pretty fashion of hair. You may see that I had
some queer schoolmasters.

I said to my cousin, "That is Miss Darthea Peniston."

"Darthea," he repeated. "She looks the name.
Sad if she had been called Deborah, or some of your
infernally idiotic Scripture names."

He was duly presented, and, I must say, made the
most of his chances for two days, so that the elder

dames were amused at Darthea's conquest, my cousin
having so far shown no marked preference for any
one except the elder Miss Franks, who was rich and
charming enough to have many men at her feet,
despite her Hebrew blood.

In truth he had been hit hard that fatal August
afternoon, and he proved a bold and constant wooer.
With me it was a more tardy influence which the fair
Darthea as surely exerted. I was troubled and disturbed at the constancy of my growing and ardent
affection. At first I scarce knew why, but by and
by I knew too well; and the more hopeless became
the business, the more resolute did I grow; this is
my way and nature.

During the remaining weeks of summer I saw
much of Miss Peniston, and almost imperceptibly
was made at last to feel, for the first time in my life,
the mysterious influence of woman. Now and then
we rode with my aunt, or went to see the troops re-
viewed. I thought she liked me, but it soon became
only too clear that at this game, where hearts were
trumps, I was no match for my dark, handsome
cousin, in his brilliant uniform.

XII

N September 1, 1773, and earlier than had been meant, my father set sail for London with my ever dear mother. Many assembled to see the "Fair Trader" leave her moorings. I went with my people as far as Lewes, and on account of weather had much ado to get ashore. The voyage down the Delaware was slow, for from want of proper lights we must needs lay by at night, and if winds were contrary were forced to wait for the ebb.

While I was with them my father spoke much to me of business, but neither blamed my past, nor praised my later care and assiduity in affairs. He was sure the king would have his way, and, I thought, felt sorry to have so readily given up the consigneeship of the teas. I was otherwise minded, and I asked what was to be done in the event of certain troubles such as many feared. He said that Thomas, his old clerk, would decide, and my Aunt Gainor had a power of attorney; as to the troubles I spoke of, he well knew that I meant such idle disturbances of peace as James Wilson and Wetherill were doing their best to bring about.

"Thy Cousin Arthur is better advised," he said,

"and a man of sound judgment. Thou mightst seek worse counsel on occasion of need."

I was surprised at this, for I should have believed, save as to the king, they could not have had one opinion in common.

Far other were those sweeter talks I had with my mother, as we sat on the deck in a blaze of sunlight. She burned ever a handsome brown, without freckles, and loved to sit out, even in our great heats. She would have me be careful at my aunt's not to be led into idleness; for the rest I had her honest trust; and her blue eyes, bright with precious tears, declared her love, and hopeful belief. I must not neglect my French—it would keep her in mind; and she went on in that tongue to say what a joy I had been in her life, and how even my follies had let her see how true a gentleman I was. Then, and never before, did she say a thing which left on my mind a fear that life had not brought and kept for her throughout all the happiness which so good and noble a creature deserved.

"There is much of thy father in thee, Hugh. Thou art firm as he is, and fond of thine own way. This is not bad, if thou art thoughtful to see that thy way is a good way. But do not grow hard. And when thou art come to love some good woman, do not make her life a struggle."

"But I love no woman, *ma mère*," I cried, "and never shall, as I love thee. It is the whole of my love thou hast, *chère, chère maman ;* thou hast it all."

"Ah, then I shall know to divide with her, Hugh;

and I shall be generous too. If thou hast any little
fancies that way, thou must write and tell me. Oh,
mon fils, thou wilt write often, and I must know
all the news. I do hear that Darthea Peniston is in
thy aunt's house a good deal, and Madam Ferguson,
the gossip, would have me believe thou carest for her,
and that Arthur Wynne is taken in the same net. I
liked her. I did not tell thee that thy Aunt Gainor
left her with me for an hour while she went into
King street to bargain for a great china god. What
a gay, winning creature it is! She must needs tell
me all about herself. Why do people so unlock
their hearts for me?"

I laughed, and said she had a key called love; and
on this she kissed me, and asked did I say such pretty
things to other women? Darthea was now to live
with her aunt, that stiff Mistress Peniston, who was
a fierce Tory. "She will have a fine bargain of the
girl. She has twenty ways with her, real or false,
and can make music of them all like a mocking-bird.
Dost thou like her, Hugh?—I mean Darthea."

I said, "Yes."

"And so do I," she ran on. "I loved her at sight.
But if ever thou dost come to love her—and I see
signs, oh, I see signs—if ever,—then beware of thy
Cousin Wynne. I heard him once say to thy father,
'If there is only one glass of the Madeira left, I want
it, because there is only one.' And there is only one
of a good woman. What another wants that man
is sure to want, and I do not like him, Hugh. Thou
dost, I think. He has some reason to linger here.

Is it this woman? Or would he spy out the land to
know what we mean to do? I am sure he has orders
to watch the way things are going, or why should not
he have gone with Sir Guy Carleton to Quebec? It
is a roundabout way to go through Philadelphia."

I said I did not know; but her words set me to
thinking, and to wondering, too, as I had not done
before. Another time she asked me why Arthur
talked so as to disgust my father out of all idea of
going to see the home of his ancestors. I promised
to be careful as to my cousin, whom, to tell the truth,
I liked less and less as time ran on.

At Lewes we parted. Shall I ever forget it?
Those great blue eyes above the gunwale, and then
a white handkerchief, and then no more. When I
could no longer see the ship's hull I climbed a great
sand-dune, and watched even the masts vanish on
the far horizon. It was to me a solemn parting.
The seas were wide and perilous in those days, the
buccaneers not all gone, and the trading ship was
small, I thought, to carry a load so precious.

As the sun went down I walked over the dunes,
which are of white sand, and forever shifting, so as
at one time to threaten with slow burial the little
town, and at another to be moving on to the forest.
As they changed, old wrecks came into view, and I
myself saw sticking out the bones of sailors buried
here long ago, or haply cast ashore. A yet stranger
thing I beheld, for the strong northwest wind, which
blew hard all day and favoured the "Fair Trader," had
so cast about the fine sand that the buried snow of

last winter was to be seen, which seemed to me a
thing most singular. When I told Jack, he made
verses about it, as he did sometimes, but would
show them only to me. I forget entirely what
he wrote; how a man can make verses and dig
rhymes out of his head has always been to me a
puzzle.

At the town inn, "The Lucky Fisherman," I saw,
to my surprise, Jack on horseback, just arrived. He
said he had a debt to collect for his father. It was
no doubt true, for Jack could not tell even the
mildest fib and not get rose-red. But he knew how
I grieved at this separation from my mother, and, I
think, made an occasion to come down and bear me
company on my long ride home. I was truly glad to
have him. Together we wandered through the great
woodlands Mr. Penn had set aside to provide fire-
wood forever for the poor of Lewes.

The next day we sent Tom on ahead with our sacks
to Newcastle, where we meant to bait ourselves and
our horses. But first we rode down the coast to
Rehoboth, and had a noble sea-bath; also above the
beach was a bit of a fresh-water lake, most delicious
to take the salt off the skin. After this diversion,
which as usual dismissed my blue devils, we set out
up the coast of the Bay of Delaware, and were able
to reach Newcastle that evening, and the day after
our own homes.

This ride gave us a fine chance for talk, and we
made good use of it.

As we passed between the hedges and below the

old Swede church nigh to Wilmington, Jack fell into
talk of Darthea Peniston. Why we had not done so
before I knew not then; we were both shy of the
subject. I amused myself by insisting that she was
but a light-minded young woman with no strong
basis of character, and too fond of a red coat. It
did amuse me to see how this vexed Jack, who
would by no means accept my verdict. We con-
versed far longer on the stormy quarrels of the
colonies and their stepmother England, who seemed
to have quite forgot of what blood and breed they
were.

Concerning my Cousin Wynne, with whom at first
I had been much taken, Jack was not inclined to
speak freely. This I foolishly thought was because
Arthur laughed at him, and was, as he knew, of
some folks' notion that Jack was a feminine kind of
a fellow. That he had the quick insight and the
heart of a woman was true, but that was not all of
my dear Jack.

My aunt came back to town early in September,
and I took up my abode in her town house, where a
new life began for me. Letters went and came at long
intervals. Our first reached me far on in October.

My mother wrote: "There is great anger here in
London because of this matter of the tea. Lord
Germaine says we are a tumultuous rabble; thy
father has been sent for by Lord North, and I fear
has spoken unadvisedly as to things at home. It is
not well for a wife to differ with her husband, and
this I will not; nevertheless I am not fully of his

way of thinking as to these sad troubles; this, however, is not for any eye or ear but thine. Benjamin Franklin was here to see us last week. He seems to think we might as well, or better, pay for the tea, and this suited thy father; but after thus agreeing they went wide apart, Franklin having somewhat shed his Quaker views. I did fear at times that the talk would be strong.

" When he had gone away, thy father said he never had the Spirit with him, and was ever of what creed did most advantage him, and perhaps underneath of none at all. But this I think not. He hath much of the shrewd wisdom of New England, which I like not greatly; but as to this, I know some who have less of any wisdom, and, after all, I judge not a man so wise, and so much my elder.

" General Gage, lately come hither on a visit, we are told assured the king that no other colony would stand by Massachusetts, and that four regiments could put an end to the matter. I am no politician, but it makes me angry to hear them talk of us as if we were but a nursery of naughty children. It seems we are to pay for the tea, and until we do no ships may enter Boston harbour. Also all crown officers who may commit murder are to be tried in England ; and there is more, but I forget."

This was most of it fresh news to us. Meanwhile Hutchinson, the governor of the rebel State, was assuring Lord North that to resist was against our interest, and we, being " a trading set," would never go to extremes. " As if," said Wilson, " nations, like men, had not passions and emotions, as well as day-books and ledgers."

Meanwhile at home our private affairs were rapidly wound up and put in good condition. My father found it difficult to collect his English debts, and so had to limit his purchases, which we stowed as they came over, declining to sell. As business failed, I was more and more at leisure, and much in the company of my cousin, whom to-day I disliked, and to-morrow thought the most amusing and agreeable of companions. He taught me to shoot ducks at League Island, and chose a good fowling-piece for me.

On Sundays I went to hear my aunt's friend, the Rev. Mr. White, preach at Christ Church, and would not go to Meeting, despite Samuel Wetherill, whose Society of Free Quakers did not come to life until 1780. Meanwhile by degrees I took to wearing finer garments. Cards I would never touch, nor have I often, to this day.

One morning, long after my parents left, my Aunt Gainor looked me over with care, pleased at the changes in my dress, and that evening she presented me with two fine sets of neck and wrist ruffles, and with paste buckles for knees and shoes. Then she told me that my cousin, the captain, had recommended Pike as a fencing-master, and she wished me to take lessons; "for," said she, "who knows but you may some day have another quarrel on your hands, and then where will you be?"

I declared that my father would be properly furious; but she laughed, and opened and shut her fan, and said he was three thousand miles away, and that she was my guardian, and responsible for my education. I was by no means loath, and a day later went to see the man with my Cousin Arthur, who asked, as we went, many questions about my mother, and then if my father had left England, or had been to Wyncote.

I had, as he spoke, a letter in my pocket writ in the neat characters I knew so well; our clerk coming from New York had just given it to me, and as I had not as yet read it, liking for this rare pleasure to taste it when alone, I did not mention it to my cousin. I told him I was sure my father would not go to Wales, both because of business, and for other reasons; but I hoped when he came back to get leave to be a year away, and then I should be sure to visit our old nest.

My cousin said, " A year—a year," musingly, and asked when my parents would return.

I said, "About next October, and by the islands," meaning the Madeiras.

To this Arthur Wynne returned, in an absent fashion, " Many things may happen in a year."

I laughed, and said his observation could not be contradicted.

" What observation ?" he replied, and then seemed so self-absorbed that I cried out:

" What possesses thee, Cousin Wynne ? Thou art sad of late. I can tell thee the women say thou art in love."

" And if I were, what then ?"

This frankness in a man so mature seemed to me odd, when I thought how shy was the growing tenderness my own heart began to hide. His words troubled me. It could only be Darthea Peniston. After a silence, such as was frequent in my cousin, he added, "I fear that blushing friend of yours is fluttering about a certain bright candle. A pity the lad were not warned. You are my cousin, and of course my friend. I may have to go away soon, and I may ask you to do a certain thing for me when I am gone. No man nor lad shall stand in my way, and you must hold your tongue too."

I was puzzled and embarrassed. I said cautiously, "We shall see." But as to Jack Warder, I liked not what he said, and for two reasons. I knew that, living next door to Darthea, he was with her almost daily; and here was a new and terrible fear, for who could help but love her? Nor could I hear with patience Jack so contemptuously put aside as a child.

"Cousin Arthur," I said, "thou art mistaken in Warder. There is no more resolute or courageous man. Jack's shy ways and soft fashions make him seem like a timid girl, but I would advise no one to count on this." I went on, hesitating, "He is an older friend than thou, and—holloa, Jack!" for here was the dear fellow himself, smiling and blushing; and where had the captain been of late? and that awkward left hand was taken, and Jack would come with us and see us play with the small sword, and would like to go after the ducks to-morrow. He seemed happy and pleased to meet us.

Pike was a little man who had a room among the shops on Second street. He wore, as I had often seen, a laced cocked hat, and was clad in a red coat, such as none wore except creoles from the French settlements, or gentlemen from the Carolinas. He had the straight figure and aggressive look all men carry who teach the sword, and a set belief that no man could teach him anything—a small game-cock of a fellow, who had lost one eye by an unlucky thrust of a foil.

I will let Jack's journal, not writ till long after, tell the story for a while. He saw more than I at the time, even if he understood it all as little.

"I saw Hugh strip," he writes, "and was amused to see Pike feel his muscles and exclaim at his depth of chest. Then he showed him how to wear the wire mask, while the captain and I sat by and looked on.

"Hugh was awkward, but he had a wrist of steel, and when once he had caught the ideas of Pike, who talked all the time in a squeaky voice, his guard was firm. Pike praised him, and said he would learn soon. The thing so attracted me that I was fain to know how it felt to hold a foil; and saying as much, the captain, who fenced here daily, said: 'It is my breathing-time of day, as Prince Hamlet says. By George! you should see Mr. Garrick in that fencing scene! I will give Mr. Warder a lesson. I have rather a fancy for giving young men lessons.'

"In a minute I saw my foil fly six feet away
12

with such a wrench of the wrist as made my arm tingle.

"'Hold the foil lightly. Not so stiff,' said Pike, and we began again. Of course I was as a child before this man, and again and again he planted a button where he pleased, and seemed, I thought, to lunge more fiercely than is decent, for I was dotted with blue bruises that evening.

"At last I gave up, and the captain and Pike took the foils, while we sat and watched them. He was more than a match for Pike, and at last crying, 'Take care! here is a *botte* you do not know,' caught him fair in the left chest.

"'By George! Mr. Wynne, that is a pretty piece of play! I remember now Major Montresor tried to show it to me. He said it was that way you killed Lord Charles Trevor.'

"I was shocked to know he had killed a man, and Hugh looked up with his big mother-eyes, while the captain said coolly:

"'Yes; a sad business, and about a woman, of course. It is dreadful to have that kind of a disposition, boys, that makes you dangerous to some one who wants what you want. He was very young too. A pity! a pity!'

"Hugh and I said nothing; but I had the odd notion that he was threatening us. One gets these ideas vaguely in youth, and sometimes after-events justify them. However, the fancy soon took me to fence with Hugh in his room, for I dared not risk asking my father's leave. As Hugh got his lessons both from Pike and the captain, and became very expert, I got on pretty nearly as fast as he.

" At times we practised in our shirt-sleeves in the garden at Miss Wynne's, or fenced with Graydon, who was later the most expert small sword we had in the army. Hugh soon became nearly as skilful, but I was never as clever at it."

One day we were busy, as Jack has described, when who should come out into the garden but Mistress Wynne and Darthea, and behind them the captain. We dropped our points, but Miss Peniston cried out, " Go on! go on!" and, laughing, we fell to again.

Presently I, a bit distracted, for I was facing Darthea's eyes, felt Jack's foil full on my chest. Darthea clapped her hands, and, running forward, would pin a bunch of red ribbons she took from her shoulder on Jack's sleeve. Jack fell back, as red as the ribbons, and my aunt cried out, " Darthea, you are too forward!"

The young woman flushed, and cast down the bow, and as Arthur Wynne bent to pick it up set her foot on it. I saw the captain rise, and stand with the half-shut eyes and the little drop of the jaw I have already mentioned. My aunt, who liked the girl well, went after her at once as she left us in a pet to return to the house. I saw my aunt put a hand on her shoulder, and then the captain, looking vexed, followed after. An hour later I went to look for the ribbon. It was gone, and for years I knew not where, till, in a little box in Jack's desk, I came upon it neatly tied up.

Young as I was, I began to see that here were
Captain Wynne, and possibly my friend, in the toils
of a girl,—she was but seventeen,—and I, alas! no
better off; but of this I breathed not a word to any.
Jack hung about her and fell back when any less
shy man wanted his place. I felt that he was little
likely to have his way, and that neither he nor I
had much chance in such a game against a man like
my cousin. He had played with hearts before, and
the maid listened like Desdemona to this dark-browed
soldier when he talked of courts and kings, and far-
away Eastern battles, and the splendour of the Orient.
My aunt, whom nothing escaped, looked on much
amused. Perhaps she did not take as serious the
love-affairs of lads like Jack and me. We were like
enough to have a dozen before we were really captured. That I was becoming at twenty-one more
thoughtful and resolute than far older people, she did
not see, and she was sometimes vexed at my sober
ways. I was at times gay enough, but at others she
would reproach me with not taking more pains to
please her guests. Society, she said, had duties as well
as pleasures. My friend Jack no one fully understood
in those days, nor knew the sweet manhood and the
unselfishness that lay beneath his girl-like exterior.

One day, late in November, my aunt and I were,
for a wonder, alone, when she dropped the cards with
which she was playing, and said to me: "Hugh, there
is something serious between that mischievous kitten
and your cousin. They are much talked of. If you
have a boy-fancy that way, get rid of it. I don't see

through the man. He has been telling her about the fine house at Wyncote, and the great estate, and how some day he will have it, his elder brother being far gone in a phthisis."

"There must be some mistake," I said. "Thou knowest what he told my father."

"Yes; I don't like it," she went on; "but the girl is caught. He talks of soon having to join Sir Guy Carleton in Canada. And there is my dear girl-boy trapped too, I fear. But, really, he is such a child of a fellow it hardly matters. How many does she want in her net? The fish may squabble, I fear. A sweet thing she is; cruel only by instinct; and so gay, so tender, so truthful and right-minded with all her nonsense. No one can help loving her; but to-day she has one mood, and to-morrow another. There will be a mad massacre before she is done with you all. Run away, Hugh! run! Make love to Kitty Shippen if you want to get Miss Darthea."

I laughed, but I had little mirth in my heart.

"Aunt Gainor," I said, "I love that woman, and no other man shall have her if I can help it."

"If? if? Stuff! you can't help it. Don't be a fool! The sea is full of fish. This is news indeed."

"The land has but one Darthea," said I. "I am a boy no longer, Aunt Gainor. Thou hast made me tell thee, and, now it is out, I may as well say I know all about my cousin. He as good as told me, and in a way I did not like. The man thinks I am a boy to be scared out of going my own way. I have told

no one else; but if I can get her I will, and it is no
laughing matter."

"I am sorry, Hugh," she said. "I knew not it
was so serious. It is hard to realise that you are no
more a boy, and must have the sorrows my sex pro-
vides for you. I like her, and I would help you if I
could, but you are late." And she went on shuffling
the cards, while I took up a book, being inclined to
say no more.

That evening two letters came by the New York
packet. One from my father I put aside. It was
dated outside, and was written two weeks later than
my mother's, which I read first. I opened it with
care.

"MY OWN DEAR SON: Thy last sweet letter was a
great refreshment to me, and the more so because I
have not been well, having again my old ache in the
side, but not such as need trouble thee. I blush to
hear the pretty things thy letters say; but it is love
that holds thy pen, and I must not be too much set
up in my own esteem. How much love I give thee
in return thou knowest, but to pay in this coin will
never beggar us. I love thee because thou art all I
can desire, and again because thou lovest me, and
again for this same dear reason which is all I can
say to excuse my mother-folly. Thy father is well,
but weary of this great town; and we both long to
be at home."

Then there was more about my Aunt Wynne, and
some woman-talk for her friends about the new

fashions, which do not concern her, she being not of this world. "Am I not?" she says. "I love it all—the sea, even the sea, and flowers, and our woods, and, dear me! also gay gowns. I hope the last I got here will not disturb the Meeting, and my new muff,—very big it is,—and a green joseph to ride in. I mean to ride with thee next spring often—often." And so on, half mother, half child, with bits of her dear French, and all about a new saddle for me, and silver spurs. The postscript was long.

"I saw last week a fair Quaker dame come out of Wales. I asked her about the Wynnes. She knew them not, but told me of their great house, and how it was a show-place people went to see, having been done over at great cost; and how a year or two since coal was found on the estate, and much iron, so that these last two years they were rich, and there was some talk of making the present man a baronet. Also that the elder brother is ill, nigh to death. It seems strange after what thy cousin said so often. Thy father is away in Holland. I will tell him when he is come back. Be cautious not to talk of this. I never liked the man."

I sat back in my chair to read it all over again, first giving my aunt my father's letter. In a few minutes I heard a cry, and saw my aunt, pale and shaken, standing up, the letter in her hand.

"My God!" I cried, "what is it? Is it my mother?"

"Yes, yes!" she said. "Be strong, my boy! She is—dead!"

For a moment I saw the room whirl, and then, as my Aunt Gainor sat down, I fell on my knees and buried my face in her lap. I felt her dear old hands on my head, and at last would have the letter. It was brief.

"MY SON: The hand of God has fallen heavily upon me. Thy mother died to-day of a pleurisy which none could help. I had not even the consolation to hear her speak, since, when I came from Holland, she was wandering in talk of thee, and mostly in French, which I know not. I seek to find God's meaning in this chastisement. As,yet I find it not. It is well that we should not let bereavements so overcome us as to make us neglect to be fervent in the business of life, or to cease to praise Him who has seen fit to take away from us that which it may be we worshipped as an idol. What more is to say I leave until I see thee. My affairs are now so ordered that I may leave them. I shall sail in a week for home in the ship in which I came out, and shall not go, as I did mean, to the islands."

It seemed to me, as I read and re-read it, a cold, hard letter. I said as much to my aunt some days after this; but she wisely urged that my father was ever a reticent man, who found it difficult to let even his dearest see the better part of him.

I have no mind to dwell on this sad calamity. I went to and fro, finding neither possibility of repose nor any consolation. I saw as I rode, or lay in my boat, that one dear face, its blue-eyed tenderness, its smile of love. I could never thus recall to sight any other of those who, in after-years, have left me; but this one face is here to-day as I write, forever smiling and forever young.

And so time ran on, and nigh to Christmas day my father came home. The weather was more mild than common, and his ship met no delay from ice. I joined him off Chester Creek. He was grayer, older, I thought, but not otherwise altered, having still his erect stature, and the trick I have myself of throwing his head up and his shoulders back when about to meet some emergent occasion. I saw no sign of emotion when we met, except that he opened and shut his hands as usual when disturbed. He asked if I were well, and of my Aunt Gainor, and then, amid the tears which were choking me, if I were satisfied as to the business, and if the tea had arrived. I said yes, and that the ship had been sent away without violence. He said it was a silly business, and the king would soon end it; he himself had been too hasty—with more to like effect.

It seemed to me while we talked as though he had just come from my mother's death-bed, whereas a long time had elapsed, and he had been able to get over the first cruel shock. My own grief was still upon me, and I wondered at his tranquillity. A little later he said:

"I see thou hast taken to the foolishness of black garments. This is thy aunt's doings." In fact, it was her positive wish. I made no reply, but only looked him in the face, ready to cry like a child.

"Why hast thou no answers, Hugh? Thy tongue used to be ready enough. Thou hast thy mother's eyes. I would thou hadst them not."

This was as near as he ever came to speech of her, whom, to my amazement, he never again mentioned. Was it a deeper feeling than I knew, that so silenced him, or did he wish to forget her? I know not. Some deal thus with their dead. He bade my aunt take away my mother's clothes, and asked no questions as to how she disposed of them; nor for a month did he desire my return home.

What then passed between him and my Aunt Gainor I do not know; but he said nothing more of my dress, although I wore mourning for six months. Nor did he say a word as to my exactness and industry, which was honestly all they should have been. At meals he spoke rarely, and then of affairs, or to blame me for faults not mine, or to speak with cold sarcasm of my friends.

Except for Jack, and my Aunt Gainor, and Wilson and Wetherill, of whom I saw much, I should have been miserable indeed. Captain Wynne still came and went, and his strange intimacy with my father continued. I thought little of it then, and for my own part I liked to hear of his adventurous life, but the man less and less; and so the winter of '73 and '74 went by with fencing and skating and books, which now I myself ordered to suit me, or found in Mr. Logan's great library, of which I was made free.

In March my cousin left us for Canada and the army. Once I spoke before him of the news in my

mother's postscript; but he laughed, saying he had
heard some such rumours, but that they were not
true. They did not much trouble a hungry beggar
of a younger son with letters; still if there had
been such good news he should have heard it. He
wished it might be so; and as to his brother, poor
devil! he would last long enough to marry and have
children. Were the ducks still in the river? He
said no more to me of Darthea, or of what I was to do
for him, but he found a way at need, I am sure, to get
letters to her, and that without difficulty. At last,
as I have said, he was gone to join Sir Guy. I was
not sorry.

Mrs. Peniston, Darthea's aunt, usually talked little, and then of serious matters as if they were
trivial, and of these latter as if they were of the
utmost importance. With regard to this matter of
Darthea and my cousin, she was free of speech and
incessant, so that all the town was soon assured of the
great match Darthea would make. The fine house
at Wyncote grew, and the estate also. Neither Jack
nor I liked all this, and my friend took it sadly to
heart, to my Aunt Gainor's amusement and Mrs.
Ferguson's, who would have Dr. Rush set up a ward
in the new hospital for the broken-hearted lovers of
Darthea. When first Jack Warder was thus badg-
ered, he fell into such a state of terror as to what the
madcap woman would say next that he declined all
society for a week, and ever after detested the Tory
lady.

I became, under the influence of this much-talked-of

news, as mute as Jack; but, while he had only a deep
desire toward sadness, and to stay away from her
who had thus defeated his love, I, neither given over
to despair nor hope, had only a fierce will to have
my way; nor, for some reason or for none, did I consider Jack's case as very serious,—my aunt it much
amused,—so little do we know those who are most
near to us.

No sooner was the redcoat lover gone awhile
than, as Miss Chew declared, Darthea put off mourning for the absent.　Indeed, the pretty kitten began
once more to tangle the threads of Jack's life and
mine.　For a month Jack was in favour, and then
a certain captain, but never I, until one day late in
April.　She was waiting among my aunt's china for
her return, and had set the goggle-eyed mandarin to
nodding, while, with eyes as wide as his, she nodded
in reply, and laughed like a merry child.

I stood in the doorway, and watched this delicious
creature for a minute while she amused herself—and
me also, although she knew it not.　"Say No!" she
cried out to the great china nobleman; quite a foot
high he was.　But, despite her pretence at altering
his unvaried affirmative, it still went on.　My lady
walked all around him, and presently said aloud:
"No! no!　It must be No!　Say No!" stamping a
foot, as if angry, and then of a sudden running up
to the mandarin and laughing.　"He has a crack in
his head.　That is why he says Yes! Yes!　I must be
a female mandarin, and that is why I say No! No!　I
wonder does he talk broken China?"

At this moment she saw my tall black figure in a corner mirror, and made some exclamation, as if startled; an instant later she knew it was I, but as if by magic the laughing woman was no longer there. What I saw as she came toward me was a slight, quiet nun with eyes full of tears.

I was used to her swift changes of mood, but what her words, or some of them, meant I knew not; and as for this pitying face, with its sudden sadness, what more did it mean? Major André said of her later that Mistress Darthea was like a lake in the hills, reflecting all things, and yet herself after all. But how many such tricksy ways, pretty or vexing, she was to show some of us in the years to come did not yet appear.

In a moment I seemed to see before me the small dark child I first knew at school. Why was she now so curiously perturbed? "Mr. Wynne," she said, "you never come near me now—oh, not for a month! And to-day your aunt has shown me a part of the dear mother's letter, and—and—I am so sorry for you! I am indeed! I have long wanted to say so. I wish I could help you. I do not think you forget easily, and—and—you were so good to me when I was an ugly little brat. I think your mother loved me. That is a thing to make one think better of one's self. I need it, sir. It is a pretty sort of vanity, and how vain you must be, who had so much of her love!"

"I thank thee," I said simply. Indeed, for a time I was so moved that say more I could not. "I thank

thee, Miss Peniston. There is no one on earth whom
I would rather hear say what thou hast said."

I saw her colour a little, and she replied quickly, "I
am only a child, and I say what comes to my lips; I
might better it often if I stayed to think."

"No!" I cried. Whenever she got into trouble—
and she was ready to note the tenderness in my
voice—this pretty pretext of the irresponsibility of
childhood would serve her turn. "No," said I; "I
like dearly to hear my mother praised,—who could
praise her too much?—but when it is thou who
sayest of her such true things, how shall I tell thee
what it is to me who love to hear thee talk—even
nonsense?"

"I talk nonsense? Do I?"

"Yes, sometimes. I—want thee to listen to me.
I have cared for thee—"

"Now please don't, Mr. Wynne. They all do it,
and—I like you. I want to keep some friends."

"It is useless, Darthea. I am so made that I must
say my say. Thou mayest try to escape, and hate it
and me, but I have to say I love thee. No, I am not
a boy. I am a man, and I won't let thee answer me
now."

"I do not want to. It would hurt you. You must
know; every one knows. It was his fault and my
aunt's, all this gossip. I would have kept it quiet."

"It will never be," I broke out. "Thou wilt never
marry that man!" I knew when I said this that
I had made a mistake. I had learned to distrust
Arthur; but I had too little that was of moment to

say against him to make it wise to speak as I had done. I was young in those days, and hasty.

"Who?" says my lady, all on fire. "What man? Jack Warder? And why not? I do not know what I shall do."

"It is not my dear Jack," I cried. "Why dost thou trifle with me?"

"Your dear Jack, indeed! How he blushes! *I* might ask *him*. He never would have the courage."

"It is my cousin, Arthur Wynne, as thou well knowest. And thou art wicked to mock at an honest gentleman with thy light talk. Thou dost not know the man, this man, my cousin."

"Only a boy would be so foolish or so unfair as to speak thus of one behind his back, and to a woman too, who—" And she paused, confused and angry.

I could not tell her what was only suspicion or hearsay as to my cousin's double statements concerning his father's estate, or how either she or we were deceived. I had, in fact, lost my head a little, and had gone further than was wise. I would not explain, and I was too vexed to say more than that I would say the same to his face. Then she rejoined softly:

"Tell it to me. You are as mysterious as Miss Wynne; and have I not a right to know?"

"No," I said; "not now, at least. Thou mayest tell him if thou wilt."

"If I will, indeed! Every one is against him—you and Mistress Wynne and that impudent boy, Jack Warder, despite his blushes. Oh, he can be bold enough. Isn't he a dear fellow?"

How could one deal with a woman like this? I hesitated, and as I did so, not having ready anything but sad reproaches of her levity, my aunt appeared in the doorway.

"Are you two children quarrelling?" she said, in her outspoken way. "You will have time to repent. Here has been your father, sir, to-day, and his affairs in Jamaica are all in a nice pickle, and you and the old clerk are to up and away in the packet for Kingston, and that to-morrow."

"Indeed!" I cried. I was not sorry.

"I envy you," said my lady, as demure as you please. "You will fetch me a feather fan, and come back soon. I hate all those cornets and captains, and now I shall have no one but Jack."

My aunt looked on amused. Her news was true indeed, and with no chance to talk to any one, except to say a mere good-by to Jack, I spent the evening with my father and our head clerk over the business which took me away so hastily. At early morning on a cold day at the close of April, 1774, we were gliding down the Delaware with all sail set.

The voyage was long, the winds contrary. I had ample leisure to reflect upon my talk with Darthea. I was sure she must have known she was to me not as other women. Except for the accident of this chance encounter, I might long have waited before finding courage to speak. I had made nothing by it, had scarce had an answer, and should, like enough, have fallen back into the coldness of relation, by which she had so long kept me at a distance. I had been foolish and hasty to speak of my cousin at all; it did but vex her.

Of my errand in Jamaica there is little to be said. My father's letters were of business only. Of these long months and of what went on at home I heard but little from him, and with my request to have the gazettes he had evidently no mind to comply; nor were the chances of letters frequent. I heard, indeed, from my aunt but twice, and from Jack thrice; but he said nothing of Darthea. Years after I found in his record of events:

"Hugh left us the last of April. It may be he cares too much for that wayward witch, Darthea."

I should say that it was at this time or soon after my dear friend began to keep a somewhat broken diary of events. What he says of former years was put on paper long afterward.

"If I did but know," writes Jack, "that he is seriously taken, I should understand, alas! what not to do. But as to some things Hugh is a silent man. I think, as Mr. Wilson says, some men are made for friends, and some for lovers. I fear the latter is not my rôle. Is there—can there be—such a thing as revering a woman too much to make successful love? I think I see what Darthea is more truly than does my dear Hugh. There must come a day when she will show it. Sometimes I can hardly trust myself with her; and I yearn to tell her that I alone know her, and that I love her. I must watch myself. If it really be that Hugh cares for her, and yet I were to be the fortunate man, how could I face him again,

13

having had the advantage of his long absence? It
seems strange that I should ask myself if I am more
her lover than his friend. He does not talk of her
to me.

"It is now September, '74, and Hugh must soon
return. Mr. Gage is fortifying Boston Neck, and
we have had the mischievous Boston Port Bill,
and Virginia up in a rage, which I do not understand. We, who have our commerce crippled by
foolish laws, may well be on the side of resistance;
but why the planters should put in peril their only
tobacco market I see less well. A Continental Congress is to meet here on the fifth day of this month,
and already the town is alive with gentlemen from
the South and North.

"No doubt Darthea has letters from Mr. Arthur
Wynne. I think Mr. Wilson judges that man correctly. He says he is selfish, and more weak as to
morals than really bad, and that he will be apt to
yield to sudden temptation rather than to plan deliberate wickedness. Why should he have need
to plan at all? Mistress Wynne says he does not
like Hugh. How could any not like my Hugh, and
how do women see the things which we do not?

"It is sad to see my father's state of mind. Yesterday he was with me to visit Mr. Hancock, very
fine in a purple velvet coat with gold buttons, and
a flowered waistcoat. He is our correspondent in
Boston. My father came home a hot Whig; and to-
morrow is Meeting-day, and he will be most melancholy, and all for the king if this and that should

happen. John Wynne can turn him which way he likes. If my Hugh remains of a Whig mind—and who less like to change?—he will have a hot time with his father, I fear."

Is it any wonder I, his friend, loved this man? He seemed so gentle that all but I, even James Wilson, misunderstood him. No more obstinate fellow ever was or will be. I ought to say "determined," for there was always a reason of head or heart for what he would or would not do, and I really think that in all his noble life he had but one hour of weakness, of which by and by I may have to tell.

XIII

WAS to have come home earlier, but in June I got letters from my father instructing me to await a vessel which would reach Jamaica in June, and sail thence to Madeira. There were careful instructions given as to purchase of wines, and the collection of delayed payments for staves, in the wine islands.

I did not like it, but I was young, and to travel had its charm after all. Had there been no Darthea, I had been altogether pleased. The excuse of this new business made me smile. It was clear my father was using that pretext to keep me out of the mischief which was involving most young men of courage, and creating in them a desire to train as soldiers in the organisations which were everywhere being formed. He was unwise enough to say that my cousin, from whom he had heard, sent his love, and was glad I was out of our disloyal and uneasy country.

There was no help for it, and thus it chanced that not until September did I see the red brick houses of my native city. Late news I had almost none, for none reached me, and I was become wild with desire to learn what the summer months had brought forth.

On the fifth day of September, 1774, at seven in the morning, I saw my Jack in a boat come out to meet me as we came to anchor in the stream. He looked brown and handsome, reddening with joy as he made me welcome. All were well, he said. I did not ask for Darthea.

My father was on the slip, and told me that business might wait until the evening. My aunt had not been well, and would see me at once. This really was all, and I might have been any one but his son for what there was in his mode of meeting me. I walked with Jack to my Aunt Gainor's, where he left me. I was pleased to see the dear lady at her breakfast, in a white gown with frills and a lace tucker, with a queen's nightcap such as Lady Washington wore when I first saw her. Mistress Wynne looked a great figure in white, and fell on my neck and kissed me; and I must sit down, and here were coffee and hot girdle-cakes and blueberries, and what not. Did I like Jamaica? And had I fetched some fans? She must have her choice; and rum, she hoped, I had not forgot. How well I looked, and my eyes were bluer than ever! Was it the sea had got into them? and so on.

I asked about the Congress, and she was off in a moment. Mr. John Adams had been to see her, and that cat, Bessy Ferguson, had been rude to him. An ill-dressed man, but clear of head and very positive; and the members from Virginia she liked better. Mr. Peyton Randolph had called; and I would like Mr. Pendleton; he had most delightful manners. Mr. Livingston had been good enough to remember me, and had asked for me. He thought we must soon choose a general, and Mr. Washington had been talked of.

"Has it come to that?" said I.

"Yes; all the North is up, and Gage has more troops and is at work intrenching himself, he who was to settle us with three regiments. Mrs. Chew was here, and behaved like the lady she is. But they are all in a nice mess, Master Hugh, and know not what to do. I hate these moderates. Mr. Washington is a man as big as your father, and better builded. I like him, although he says little and did not so much as smile at Bessy Ferguson's nonsense. And Darthea—you do not ask about Darthea. She is playing the mischief with Jack and her captain. She will not let me talk about him. He is in Boston with Mr. Gage, I hear. Why don't you tell me about yourself?"

"How could I, Aunt Gainor? Thou—" and I laughed.

Then she became grave. "You will have to declare yourself and take sides; and how can I counsel you to resist your father? You must think it over and talk to Mr. Wilson. He is of the Congress. Poor Mr. Wetherill the Meeting has a mind to bounce, and he takes it hard. Come back at eleven, and we will go to Chestnut street, where they meet, and see the gentlemen go into the Carpenters' Hall. I came to town on purpose. And now go; I must dress."

At half-past ten—my aunt very splendid—we drove

down Second street and up Chestnut, where was a
great crowd come to look on. Dr. Rush, seeing my
aunt's chariot, got in at Second street, and, being one
of the members, enabled us to get near to Carpenters'
Alley, where at the far end, back from the street, is
the old building in which the Congress was to be held.
Jack met us here, and got up beside the coachman.
I think none had a better view than we. Andrew
Allen came to speak to us, and then Mr. Galloway,
not yet scared by the extreme measures of which few
as yet dreamed, and which by and by drove these and
many other gentlemen into open declarations for the
crown.

I saw James Pemberton looking on sadly, and
near him other Friends with sour aspects. Here and
there militia uniforms were seen amid the dull grays,
the smocks of farmers and mechanics, and the sober
suits of tradesmen, all come to see.

"The Rev. Dr. Duché passed us," says Jack, whom
now I quote, "in a fine wig and black silk small-
clothes. He was to make this day the famous prayer
which so moved Mr. Adams." And later, I may
add, he went over to the other side. "Soon others
came. Some we knew not, but the great Dr. Rush
pointed out such as were of his acquaintance.

"'There,' he said, 'is Carter Braxton. He tells
me he does not like the New England men—either
their religion or their manners; and I like them
both.' The doctor was cynical, I thought, but very
interesting. I set down but little of what he said
or I saw; for most of it I forget.

"'There is the great Virginia orator, Mr. Patrick Henry,' said the doctor. He was in simple dress, and looked up at us curiously as he went by with Pendleton and Mr. Carroll. 'He has a great estate —Mr. Carroll,' said the doctor. 'I wonder he will risk it.' He was dressed in brown silk breeches, with a yellow figured waistcoat, and, like many of them, wore his sword. Mr. Franklin was not yet come home, and some were late.

"Presently the doctor called, and a man in the military dress of the Virginia militia turned toward us. 'Colonel Washington,' said our doctor, 'will permit me to present him to a lady, a great friend of liberty. Mistress Wynne, Colonel Washington.'

"'I have already had the honour,' he said, taking off his hat—a scrolled beaver.

"'He is our best soldier, and we are fortunate that he is with us,' said the doctor, as the colonel moved away."

The doctor changed his mind later, and helped, I fear, to make the trouble which came near to costing Conway his life. I have always been a great admirer of fine men, and as the Virginia colonel moved like Saul above the crowd, an erect, well-proportioned figure, he looked taller than he really was. Nor was he, as my aunt had said, nearly of the bigness of my father.

"He has a good nose," said my Aunt Gainor, perhaps conscious of her own possessions in the way of a nasal organ, and liking to see it as notable in another; "but how sedate he is! I find Mr. Peyton

Randolph more agreeable, and there is Mr. Robert Morris and John Dickinson."

Then the lean form of Mr. Jefferson went by, a little bent, deep in talk with Roger Sherman, whom I thought shabbily dressed; and behind them Robert Livingston, whom my aunt knew. Thus it was, as I am glad to remember, that I beheld these men who were to be the makers of an empire. Perhaps no wiser group of people ever met for a greater fate, and surely the hand of God was seen in the matter; for what other colony—Canada, for example—had such men to show? There, meanwhile, was England, with its great nobles and free commons and a splendid story of hard-won freedom, driving madly on its way of folly and defeat.

Of what went on within the hall we heard little. A declaration of rights was set forth, committees of correspondence appointed, and addresses issued to the king and people of Great Britain. Congress broke up, and the winter went by; Gage was superseded by Sir William Howe; Clinton and Burgoyne were sent out, and ten thousand men were ordered to America to aid the purposes of the king.

The cold season was soon upon us, and the eventful year of '75 came in with a great fall of snow, but with no great change for me and those I loved. A sullen rage possessed the colonies, and especially Massachusetts, where the Regulation Acts were quietly disregarded. No counsellors or jurymen would serve under the king's commission. The old muskets of the French and Indian wars were taken from the

corners and put in order.　Men drilled, and women
cast bullets.

Failing to corrupt Samuel Adams and Hancock,
Gage resolved to arrest them at Concord and to seize
on the stores of powder and ball.　" The heads of trai-
tors will soon decorate Temple Bar," said a London
gazette; and so the march of events went on.　In
the early spring Dr. Franklin came home in despair
of accommodation; he saw nothing now to do but to
fight, and this he told us plainly.　His very words
were in my mind on the night of April 23d of this
year of '75, as I was slowly and thoughtfully walking over the bridge where Walnut crossed the Dock
Creek, and where I stayed for a moment to strike flint
and steel in order to light my pipe.　Of a sudden I
heard a dull but increasing noise to north, and then
the strong voice of the bell in the state-house.　It was
not ringing for fire.　Somewhat puzzled, I walked
swiftly to Second street, where were men and women in groups.　I stopped a man and asked what
had chanced.　He said, " A battle! a battle! and
General Gage killed."　Couriers had reached the
coffee-houses, but no one on the street seemed to
have more than this vague information; all were
going toward Chestnut street, where a meeting was
to be held, as I learned, and perhaps fuller news
given out.

I pushed on, still hearing the brazen clamour of the
bell.　As I crossed High street I came upon James
Wilson and Mr. Graydon.　They stopped me to tell
of the great tidings just come by swift post-riders

of the fight at Lexington. After giving me the full
details, Wilson left us. Said Graydon, very serious:
"Mr. Wynne, how long are you to be in deciding?
Come and join Mr. Cadwalader's troop. Few of us
ride as well as you."

I said I had been thinking.

"Oh, confound your thinkings! It is action now.
Let the bigwigs think."

I could not tell a man I then knew but slightly
how immense was my reluctance to make this complete break with the creed of my father, and to absolutely disobey him, as I knew I must do if I followed
my inclinations; nor did I incline to speak of such
other difficulties as still kept me undecided. I said
at last that if I took up arms it would be with Macpherson or Cowperthwaite's Quakers.

"Why not?" he said. "But, by George! man, do
something! There are, I hear, many Friends among
the Cowperthwaite Blues. Do they give orders with
'thou' and 'thee,' I wonder?"

I laughed, and hurried away. The town was already in a state of vast excitement, women in tears,
and men stopping even those they did not know to ask
for news. I ran all the way to my aunt's, eager to
tell it. In the hall I stood a minute to get my breath,
and reflect. I knew full well, as I recognised various voices, that my intelligence would mean tears
for some, and joy for others.

My long-taught Quaker self-control often served
me as well as the practised calm I observed to be the
expression assumed by the best-bred officers of the

army on occasions that caused visible emotion in others. I went in quietly, seeing a well-amused party of dames and younger folk, with, over against the chimneypiece, the great Benjamin Franklin, now in the full prime of varied usefulness, a benevolent face, and above it the great dome of head, which had to me even then a certain grandeur. He was talking eagerly with Mistress Wynne—two striking figures.

Mr. Galloway was in chat with his kinsman, Mr. Chew. The younger women, in a group, were making themselves merry with my friend Jack, who was a bit awkward in a fine suit I had plagued him into buying. And what a beauty he was, as he stood, half pleased with the teasing, blushing now and then, and fencing prettily in talk, as I knew by the laughter! At the tables the elder women were gambling, and intent on their little gains and losses, while the vast play of a nobler game was going on in the greater world of men.

To my surprise, I saw among the guests an English lieutenant. I say "to my surprise," for the other officers had gone of their own accord, or had been ordered to leave by the Committee of Safety. This one, and another, were, as I learned afterward, on their way through the town to join General Gage. There was evidently some dispute as to the cards. I heard high-pitched voices, and "spadille," "basto," "matador"—all the queer words of quadrille, their favoured game.

The lieutenant was bending over Mrs. Ferguson's chair. He was a fellow I had seen before and never liked, a vulgar-featured man, too fat for his years, which may have been some twenty-eight. He played the best hand of all of them, and, as my aunt declared, that was quite enough; for the rest she could keep any man in order. I held back in the gloom of the hall, looking at their busy gaiety, and wondering what they would say to my news.

As I went in I heard Woodville, the lieutenant, say, "The king—play the king, Mrs. Ferguson."

"No advice!" cried Mrs. Galloway.

"But I am betting," said he. "The king forever! We have won, madam. The king is always in luck."

I could not resist saying, "The king has lost, ladies."

My aunt turned, and knew I meant something. I suppose my face may have been more grave than my words. "What is it, Hugh?"

"I have strange news, Aunt Gainor."

"News? and what?" As she spoke the talk ceased, and every one looked up.

"There has been a fight at Lexington. Major Pitcairn is beat, and my Lord Percy. The farmers were all up to hinder them as they were on their way to seize our powder, and to take Mr. Hancock. The king has lost some three hundred men, and we under a hundred."

"Good heavens!" said Mr. Galloway. "But it cannot be true."

A pause came after, as I said there was no doubt of it.

Dr. Franklin asked if I was sure. I said, "Yes; I have it of James Wilson, and the town is already

in an uproar over it." The great philosopher remained deep in thought a moment, while the women
sat or stood in fear, or whispering excitement. At
last he said he must go, and that it was the beginning
of war, and welcome too. Then he bowed gravely
and went out. As he left, the stillness which had
prevailed for a time was broken.

A dozen questions fell on me from all sides. I
could only repeat my story, as Jack went by me to
go out and hear, if possible, more of the news than I
had to tell.

At last Mr. Chew said thoughtfully, "If it be true,
it is a sad business; but, really, how can it be, Hugh?
How could a lot of farmers, without good arms and
discipline, put to rout a body of trained men, well
armed?"

"I think," said Galloway, "we shall have quite
another version to-morrow. How does it strike you,
Mr. Woodville?"

"Oh, quite absurd," said the officer. "You may
reassure yourselves, ladies; such a loss, too, would be
incredible, even in regular war. I think we may go
on with our game, Mrs. Ferguson." He was very
pompous, but none seemed inclined to take his advice.

"And yet I don't like it," said a lady of the Tory
side.

"And I do," said Mistress Wynne. "It is as good
news as I have heard this many a day."

"It is nonsense!" said the officer; "sheer nonsense! You have strange notions, madam, as to
what is good news. It is only another rebel lie."

"I think not," said I, venturing to add that men who could kill squirrels would rarely miss a man, and that many of the older farmers had fought Indians and French, and had, I suspected, picked off the officers.

"How horrid!" said Darthea.

Had a stray bullet found my cousin I should not have grieved profoundly.

"You see where all your neutrality and loyalty have brought you," said Mistress Wynne. "I wish King George were with Mr. Gage; he might learn wisdom. 'T is but the beginning of a good end."

"May I remind you," said Woodville, very red in the face, "that I am his Majesty's officer?"

"No, you may not remind me. A fig for his Majesty!" cried my aunt, now in one of her tantrums.

"Shame!" cried Mrs. Ferguson, rising, as did the rest, some in tears and some saying Mrs. Ferguson was right, or the Lord knows what—not at all a pleasant scene; the men very silent, or vexed, or troubled.

My Aunt Gainor, as they filed out, made them each her finest curtsey. Darthea stood still, looking grave enough. Mr. Woodville, the lieutenant, lingered, made his adieus very decently, and went out, I showing him the way. On the step he said: "I do not quarrel with women; but I have heard that in Mistress Wynne's house, to which, as an officer of his Majesty, I cannot submit."

"Well?" I said; and my abominable propensity to grin got the better of me.

"You seem amused, sir," he said.

I was by no means amused.

"I suppose you are responsible," he added. "Miss Wynne might have better manners, and her nephew more courage. However, I have said what ought to be enough with English gentlemen. Good-evening."

"I have half a mind to give thee a good honest thrashing," said I.

"I dare say. You are big enough, Master Quaker; but I presume that about the weapons common among men of honour you know as much as I know of making horseshoes."

I was now cool enough and angry enough to have killed him. "Thy friend can find me here," said I. "I trust I shall be able to satisfy thee."

With this he went away, and I stood looking after his stumpy figure. I was again in a broil, not of my making; just a bit of ill luck, for here was a nice business. I went in, and was caught on my way upstairs by my Aunt Gainor, who called me into the sitting-room.

Still too furious to be prudent, she broke out before Darthea. "Insolent idiots! I hope I made Mr. Galloway understand, and the rest of them too! I trust Bessy Ferguson will never darken my doors again!" She walked up and down, and at last upset the big mandarin, who came head down on the hearth.

"I wish he were Mr. Gage!" said my aunt, contemplating the fragments.

"I dare say he was a Tory," says Darthea, who

feared no one. "And I am a Tory too, Miss Wynne, I would have you to know."

"I dare say," said my aunt; "it does n't matter much what you think, or what you are. You had some words with that stupid man, sir; I saw you. He looked as if he did not like it. Oh, I heard you, too."

I vainly shook my head at her.

"Are you two going to fight? I am not sorry! I wish I could have that cat Ferguson out."

"I hope—oh—I am sure, Mr. Wynne, it cannot be. How dreadful!" said Darthea.

"Nonsense!" cried my aunt. "A man cannot stand everything like a woman."

I said plainly, seeing how vain my aunt had made concealment, that there had been some words, but that I trusted no harm would come of it.

"But there will! there will!" said Miss Peniston.

"Mercy upon us!" cried my aunt; for here was Darthea on the floor, and burnt feathers and vinegar at hand, servants running about, my aunt ordering "Cut her stay-strings!" as I was turned out, hearing my aunt declare, "I do believe she is in love with *all* the men. Is it you or the captain? What a shameless monkey to tumble all of a heap that way! It is hardly decent. Do go away, you goose! 'T is a way she has Did never you see a woman faint?"

I never did, and I was scared faint myself. What between Darthea's fainting spell, and this quarrel not of my seeking, I was uncomfortable enough. I had no one but Jack to appeal to; and here was a pair of Quaker lads, just over twenty-two, in a proper

14

scrape. I had not the least intention of getting out of it, save in one way. The sneer at my aunt was more than I could endure. What my father would think was another matter.

Mr. Wilson used to say : "When you are in difficulties dispose of the worst first ;" and so I resolved, as I must fight the man, and that was the imminent matter, to set aside all thought of my parent, until I was done with Mr. Woodville. Jack I took for granted, and so left a note with the servant asking my opponent's friend to call on Jack at an hour when he was like to be alone. Before I could leave to warn him of what was on hand my aunt came to me.

"I sent that girl home in the chaise. It was her fear lest some one may be hurt, but she really has no excuse. She talked quite wild as she came to— I mean of you and Arthur Wynne—just mere babble. And, O Hugh! I am a drivelling old maid, and have taught you all manner of nonsense, and now I have got you into trouble. Don't let him kill you, Hugh. Cannot it be stopped? I told Darthea to hold her tongue, and I am so miserable, Hugh ; and when I think of your dead mother, and all I promised, what shall I do?" And the kind old lady penitently wept over me, as if I were run through already.

I felt, as you may imagine, the embarrassment and doubt a young man feels when about to protest by a single act against the creed of conduct which he has been taught to follow since he could remember. I smiled, too, as I recalled our first school duel, and how Jack and I ran away.

My aunt, seeing there was nothing more to be done, and having said quite enough, retired, I am sure to pray for me, and for herself as the main cause of my coming risk. She would have liked to see me well out of the affair, but I do believe would not have had me excuse myself to my lieutenant, let what might occur. Indeed, she did her best to keep Miss Darthea from betraying what, but for my aunt's rash outburst, would not have gone beyond those immediately concerned.

It was late in the afternoon, when I found Jack writing in his father's house. I must have looked grave, for he rose quickly and, coming to meet me, set a hand on each of my shoulders—a way he had, but only with me.

"What is it?" he said; "not the news?"

"No." In fact, it had clean gone out of my mind. "I have had trouble with Mr. Woodville, and now I must fight him." And on this I related the whole adventure, Jack listening intently.

"Thou shouldst have an older man than I, Hugh. These affairs may often be mended, I learn, without coming to violence." He seemed a little embarrassed, and reddened, hesitating as he spoke, so that, stupidly not comprehending him as I should have done, I said hastily that the man had insulted my aunt, and that there was but one way out of it, but that I could try to get some one else, if to act as my friend was not to his taste.

"At this time," he writes, "when Hugh came so near to hurting me, I was really going through in

my mind what he had already disposed of in his. At
Pike's we heard of nothing but duels. I had long
been Pike's pupil. The duel had come to seem to us,
I fear, the natural and inevitable ending of a quarrel. Such was the belief of my good friend Mistress
Wynne's set, and of the officers whose opinions as to
social matters we had learned to regard as final.

"And yet the absurdity of two Quaker lads so
trapped struck me as it did not Hugh. The man
must surely have thought him older than he was, but
so did most. I feared that I should not do my friend
justice; and then I thought of dear Mistress Gainor,
whom I now loved, and for whom to lose Hugh
would be as death in life; and so, quickly turning it
over for one mad moment, I wondered if I could
not someway get this quarrel on to my own shoulders. When I answered Hugh I must have made him
misunderstand me, or so I think from what he said.
When he exclaimed he could get some one else, I
made haste to put myself right. We had little time,
however, to discuss the matter, for at this moment
came a Captain Le Clere with Hugh's note.

"Hugh was now in one of his quiet, smiling
moods, when from his face you would have said
there was some jest or wager in question, and from
his talk, which had a kind of intensity of distinct
articulation, that it was, as I thought it, most serious.
He was coldly civil to Mr. Le Clere, and to me apart
said, 'Small swords, and the governor's woods by
the spring,' as if he were arranging a quite familiar
and every-day affair.

"I frankly declared that I was new to an office of this kind, and must trust to Mr. Le Clere's honour and courtesy. He seemed pleased at this, and thought a pity of so young a man to have such a difficulty, expressing his hopes of accommodation, which I knew Hugh too well to think possible.

"As soon as we had arranged the needed preliminaries, and Mr. Le Clere had gone, I went to borrow small swords of Pike, arranging to come for them after dark. Duels were common enough even in our Quaker town, especially among gentlemen of his Majesty's service. Although illegal, so strongly was it felt that for certain offences there was no other remedy possible, that it was difficult to escape the resort to weapons if those involved were of what we who are of it like to call the better class.

"At daybreak Hugh and I were waiting in the woods where—near to what Mr. Penn meant as a public square, a little east of Schuylkill-Eighth street—was an open space, once a clearing, but now disused, and much overgrown. We were first on the ground, and I took occasion to tell Hugh of Pike's counsels—for he had at once guessed what we were about—to watch his opponent's eyes, and the like. Hugh, who was merry, and had put aside such thoughts of the future as were troubling me, declared that it was the mouth a man should watch, which I think is the better opinion. I said, of course, nothing of what Pike told me as to Mr. Woodville being a first-rate player, and only advised my friend to be cautious.

"Mr. Woodville, who came with Le Clere and a surgeon, was a short lump of a man, and an odd contrast to his friend, who was long and lank. The pair of them looked like Don Quixote and his squire. The short man I felt quite confident Hugh could handle, and was surprised, seeing his build, that Pike should have declared him a good blade. Mr. Le Clere was very civil, and I followed his directions, knowing, as I have said, but little of such affairs.

"Our men being stripped to the shirt, and ready, Mr. Le Clere and I drew away some twenty feet. Then, to my surprise, the lean officer said to me, 'Mr. Warder, shall I have the honour to amuse you with a turn? Here are our own swords of a length, as you see.'

"I was anything rather than amused. I had heard of this foolish English custom of the friends also engaging. I knew that it was usual to make the offer, and that it was not needful to accept; but now, as I saw my Hugh standing ready with his sword upon the ground, I began to shake all over, and to colour. Such hath always been my habit when in danger, even from my boyhood. It is not because I am afraid. Yet, as it seems to another like fear, to feel it sets me in a cold rage, and has many times, as on this occasion, led me into extremes of rashness.

"I suppose Mr. Le Clere saw my condition, and unhappily let loose on his face a faint smile. 'At your service,' I said, and cast off my coat.

"'It is not necessary, sir,' he replied, a bit ashamed

to engage a fellow like me, who shook and blushed, and looked to be about seventeen.

"'We are losing time,' said I, in a fury, not over-sorry to be thus or in any way distracted from Hugh's peril. In truth, I need have had small fear for him. For two years Hugh and I had fenced almost daily, and what with Pike and Arthur Wynne, knew most of the tricks of the small sword.

"The next moment Le Clere cried, 'On guard, gentlemen!' and I heard the click of the blades as they met. I had my hands full, and was soon aware of Le Clere's skill. I was, however, as agile as a cat, and he less clever with his legs than his arm. Nor do I think he desired to make the affair serious. In a few minutes—it seemed longer—I heard an oath, and, alarmed for Hugh, cast a glance in his direction. I saw his foe fall back, his sword flying some feet away. My indiscretion gave my man his chance. His blade caught in my rolled-up sleeve, bent, and, as I drove my own through his shoulder, passed clean through the left side of my neck. With a great jet of blood, I fell, and for a little knew no more."

This account from Jack's journal is a better state-ment of this sad business than I could have set down. I saw with horror Jack and Le Clere salute, and then was too full of business to see more, until I had dis-armed Mr. Woodville, badly wounding his sword-hand, a rare accident. And here was my Jack dead, as I thought. I think I can never forget that scene; Mr. Le Clere, gaunt and thin, lifting his late foe, the surgeon kneeling and busy, my own man hot and wrathful, cursing like mad, and wrapping his hand about with a handkerchief, clearly in pain, and I waiting for the word of death or life.

At last the doctor said, "It is bad—bad, but not fatal. How came it, Le Clere? You told me that neither you nor Mr. Woodville meant anything serious."

I was kneeling by Jack, and was not intended to hear what all were too hot and excited to guard by bated breath.

"Damn it, doctor!" returned Le Clere. "It is no use to talk. I never imagined that youngster would take me at my word."

"You will be in hot water here," said the doctor. "I would advise you to get away, and soon."

"And we shall supply amusement to every mess in the army," said Woodville, with an abundance of bad language. "Quakers indeed!"

Jack's eyes opened, and he said, "Thou art not hurt, Hugh?"

"No, no!" I answered, and, relieved a little, turned to Mr. Le Clere: "We shall, I fear, have to ask thy chaise of thee. We came afoot. I will send it back at once."

Le Clere said, "Of course; with all my heart."

"Thou wilt pardon me," said I, "if I advise thee to accept the doctor's advice, and get away with all speed. I should be sorry if thou wert arrested. The feeling against gentlemen of thy profession is unhappily strong just now."

Le Clere looked me over with a quick glance of something like curiosity, and said, as he gave his hand, "You are a gallant gentleman, Mr. Wynne. You will permit an older man to say so. I trust we may meet again. Are all Quakers as clever at sword-play?"

I said a civil word, seeing Jack smile as he lay with my bloody coat under his head. Then, as I remembered that perhaps Mr. Woodville might not be satisfied, I went up to him and said, "I am at thy service, sir, if thou art not contented to let us be quit of this matter."

"It must needs rest now," he replied. "Damn your tricks!"

"Sir!" said I.

"Holloa!" says Le Clere; "this won't do. Keep your temper. This way, Mr. Wynne." And he drew me aside.

It was full time; I was beginning to get my blood up, and was in a rage.

"This comes," he said, "of going out with a fellow that has risen from the ranks. Why do your ladies receive every one who wears a red coat? Let me help you with your friend. I am most sorry. For my share, I have a neat reminder in the shoulder. Mr. Warder has the wrist of a blacksmith"—which was true, and for good reason.

There is no need to tell of the wrath and incapacity of poor Jack's father. I got away as soon as Dr. Rush arrived, and, promising to return in an hour, went off with a smile from my Jack, and a "Thank

God! Hugh, that it was not thou who had the worst of it."

It was about seven as I knocked at my aunt's door, and, passing the black page, ran upstairs. My aunt was in the breakfast-room; she came to meet me in a morning gown, and to my astonishment was very tranquil, but with eyes that looked anxious, and far more red than common.

"Sit down, sir. I want to hear about this ridiculous business."

"It may seem so to thee," said I; "I am glad if it amuses thee."

"Stuff! Talk decent English, man. That was like your father. Is—are you—is any one hurt?"

I said that was what we went for, and so told her the whole sorry business.

"And it was for me, sir!" she cried; "for me! And my dear brave girl-boy! Is it dangerous?"

I hoped not. We had both left our marks on the English officers. That she liked. Then she was silent awhile.

"Here is come a note from the kitten. Will you have it? It may be all you will ever get of her. She says she has held her tongue; I can't—I don't believe her—and asks me to let her know if any are hurt. I will. Does she suppose gentlemen go out just to look at one another? Ridiculous!"

I spoke at last of my father; of how he would take this matter, of his increasing acerbity, and of my own unhappy life, where I found nothing to replace my mother's love. My last disaster and poor

Jack's wound seemed like enough to widen the gap between me and my parent, and my Aunt Gainor was troubled.

"You must be first to tell him," said my aunt. "I think he will say but little. He has given you up as a sheep lost in the darkness of iniquity, and too black to be found easily."

I begged her not to jest. I was sore and sick at heart.

"Eat your breakfast," she said, "and get it over with your father."

I hurried through the meal, and went upstairs, to find my sleeve full of blood, although no harm had been done but what was easily set right by what Dr. Rush called a bit of diachylon plaster. (I think I spell it correctly.)

As I went by Darthea's home I cast a glance up at the open window, and saw my lady looking out. She was pale, and as she called to me I could not but go in, for, indeed, she ran herself to open the door.

"Come in! Oh, just a moment!" she cried. "Your aunt has written me a note, and it tells me almost nothing—nothing."

I was in no very kindly humour with Miss Darthea. Since our talk about my cousin she had been very high and mighty, and would have little to say to me except unpleasant things about the angry politics of the day. I said I was glad to have heard she had told no one of what my aunt's rash speech had let slip. I had better have held my own tongue. Darthea was in another mood to-day, and all at once became quiet and dignified.

"I gave my word, Mr. Wynne. When you know me better you will learn that I can keep it. Is—is Mr. Warder much hurt?"

"Yes," I said; "he is in great peril." I saw how anxious she was, and was vexed enough to want to hurt her.

"Oh, you men! you men!" she cried. "Will he die, do you think? Poor boy!" She sat down and began to cry. "He must not die; why did you lead him into such wicked trouble?"

It was vain to explain how little I had to do with the matter. Did she love Jack? I little knew in those days how tender was this gentle heart, how it went out, tendril-like, seeking it knew not what, and was for this reason ever liable to say too much, and to give rise to misapprehension.

"O Darthea!" I cried. "Dost thou love my Jack? I shall be the last to come in his way. I have said I love thee myself, and I can never change. But how can it be? how can it be? And my cousin? O Darthea!"

"I love no one, sir. I love everybody. I—I think you are impertinent, Mr. Wynne. Is it your business whom I love? My God! there is blood on your hand! Are you hurt?"

It was true; a little blood was trickling down my wrist. She was all tenderness again. I must not go; here was her handkerchief; and so on—till I longed to take her in my arms, she made me so sorry for her.

I said it was of no moment, and I must go.

"You will come soon again, and tell me about Jack."

I went away, not wondering that all the world should love her.

I hastened to Jack's home, and there found Dr. Rush and Dr. Glentworth, who was later to be the physician of Mr. Washington. My aunt, preceding me, had taken possession. Mr. Warder was reduced to a condition of abject obedience, and for a month and more my aunt hardly left her girl-boy's pillow. Indeed, it was long before I was let to see him, and then he was but a spectre of himself, with not enough blood to blush with. Our officers very promptly left for New York the day after our fight, and we heard no more of them.

It would have been of little use to tell this long story but for the consequences to me and to others. I should have done well to see my father at once; but I could not get away, and sat till noon, asking every now and then what I could do, and if Jack were better, despite the fact that I was told he was doing well.

Mr. Warder was one of those people who, once a crisis seems over, must still be doing something, and to be rid of him he was sent by my aunt to get certain articles the doctors did or did not need. It seemed wise to this gentleman, having completed his errands, to pay a visit of condolence to my father, and thus it was that greater mischief was made.

About two I got away, and set forth to see my parent. Already the news was out, and I was stopped

over and over to explain what had happened. It was
the hour of dinner; for Friends dined at two, but
my aunt and the gayer set at four.

My father turned from his meal, and coldly looked
me all over,—my arm was in a sling, on which Dr.
Rush had insisted,—and last into my eyes. "Well,"
he said, "thou art come at last. Fortunately, Friend
Warder has been here, and I know thy story and the
mischief into which thou hast led his poor lad. It is
time we had a settlement, thou and I. Hast thou fear
neither of God nor of man? A rebellious son, and
a defier of authority! It is well thy mother is dead
before she saw thee come to this ruin of soul and
body."

"My God! father," I cried; "how canst thou
hurt me thus! I am in sorrow for Jack, and want
help. To whom should I go but to thee? O mother,
mother!" I looked around at the bare walls, and
down at the sanded floor, and could only bury my
face in my hands and weep like a baby. What with
all the day had brought, and Darthea and Jack, and
now this grand old man silent, impassive, unmoved
by what was shaking me like a storm,—although I
loved him still for all his hardness,—I had no refuge
but in tears.

He rose, and I sat still, thinking what I should say.
"When thou art ready to turn from thy sin and ask
pardon of God and of me, who am brought to shame
on thy account, I will talk with thee."

Upon this I set myself between him and the door.
"We cannot part this way. It is too terrible."

"That was a matter thou hadst been wise to consider long ago, Hugh."

"No!" I cried. I was as resolved as he. "I must be heard. How have I offended? Have I neglected thy business? who can say so? I was insulted in Meeting, and I went where men do not trample on a penitent boy, and if I have gone the way of my aunt's world, is it my fault or thine? I have gone away from what, in thy opinion, is right as regards questions in which the best and purest side with me. Am I a child, that I may not use my own judgment?" It was the first time in my life that I had plainly asserted my freedom to think and to act.

To my surprise, he stood a moment in silence, looking down, I as quiet, regarding him with eager and attentive eyes. Then he said, seeking my gaze, "I am to blame; I have too much considered thy chances of worldly gain. I know not whence thou hast thy wilfulness." As I looked in the face of this strong, rock-like man, I wondered; for he went on, "Not from me, Hugh, not from me—"

"Stop!" I said. "Thou hast said enough." I feared lest again he should reproach her of whose sweetness I had naught but a gift of the blue eyes that must have met his with menace. I saw, as his hands shook, tapping the floor with his cane, how great were both his anger and his self-control.

"It were well, my son, that this ended. I hope thou wilt see thy way to better courses. Thy cousin was right. He, too, is a man not of my world, but he saw more clearly than I where thou wert going."

"What!" I cried, "and thou canst think this? Thou hast believed and trusted Arthur Wynne! What did he say of me?"

"I will not be questioned."

"The man lied to thee," I cried,—"why, I do not know,—and to others also. Why did he deceive us as to Wyncote? What reason had he? As he lied about that, so does he seem to have lied about me. By heaven! he shall answer me some day."

"I will hear no profanity in my house. Stand aside! Dost thou not hear me? Am I to be disobeyed in my own house?"

I but half took in his meaning, and stood still. The next moment he seized me by the lapels of my coat, and, spinning me round like a child, pushed me from him. I fell into the great Penn chair he had turned from the table when he rose. He threw open the door, and I saw him walk quickly down the hall and out into the orchard garden.

For a week he did no more than speak to me a word when business made it needful, and then the monotonous days went on as before in the gray, dismal home, out of which the light of life's gladness departed when those dear mother-eyes were closed in death.

XIV

HILE, throughout that sad summer, my Jack was slowly coming back to health, even the vast events of the war now under way moved me but little. My Aunt Gainor would think of no one but her young Quaker. Her house was no longer gay, nor would she go to the country, until Mr. Warder agreed that she should take Jack with us to the Hill Farmhouse, where, in the warm months, she moved among her cattle, and fed the hens, and helped and bullied every poor housewife far and near.

In a bright-tinted hammock I fetched from Madeira, Jack used to lie under the apple-trees that June and July, with my aunt for company; better could hardly have been. When I came from town in June, with news of what the farmers and their long rifles had done at Bunker Hill, it was a little too much for Jack's strength, and he burst into tears. But Dr. Rush declared that self-control was an affair of physical health, and that he who had too little blood—and Jack was lily-white—could be neither courageous, nor able to contain his emotions. I suppose it may be true.

I went in and out of town daily, my father being

unwilling to go to Merion.　At times I met James
Wilson, who was steadily urging me to enter the
army.　Wetherill had scarce any other words for me.
But my father, Jack's condition, and my aunt's de-
pending on me, all stood in my way, and I did but
content myself with an hour's daily drill in town
with others, who were thus preparing themselves
for active service.

We were taught, and well too, by an Irish sergeant—I fear a deserter from one of his Majesty's regiments.　As Jack got better, he was eager to have
me put him through his facings, but before he was
fit the summer was nigh over.

It had been a time of great anxiety to all men.
The Virginia colonel was commander-in-chief; a
motley army held Sir William Howe penned up in
Boston, and why he so quietly accepted this sheep-
like fate no man of us could comprehend.　My aunt,
a great letter-writer, had many correspondents, and
one or two in the camp at Cambridge.

"My Virginia fox-hunter," said my aunt, "is having evil days with the New England farmers.　He is
disposed to be despotic, says—well, no matter who.
He likes the whipping-post too well, and thinks all
should, like himself, serve without pay.　A slow man
it is, but intelligent," says my Aunt Gainor; "sure
to get himself right, and patient too.　You will see,
Hugh; he will come slowly to understand these
people."

I smiled at the good lady's confidence, and yet she
was right.　They took him ill at first in that undis-

ciplined camp, and queer things were said of him.
Like the rest, he was learning the business of war,
and was to commit many blunders and get sharp
lessons in this school of the soldier.

These were everywhere uneasy times. Day after
day we heard of this one or that one gone to swell
the ever-changing number of those who beset Sir
William. Gondolas—most unlike gondolas they
were—were being built in haste for our own river
defence. Committees, going from house to house,
collected arms, tent-stuffs, kettles, blankets, and what
not, for our troops. There were noisy elections, arrests
of Tories; and in October the death of Peyton Randolph, ex-president of the Congress, and the news
of the coming of the Hessian hirelings. It was a
season of stir, angry discussion, and stern waiting
for what was to come; but through it all my Jack
prospered mightily in health, so that by September
20 he was fit to leave us.

I still think pleasantly of all the pretty pictures of
pale, fair-haired Jack in the hammock, with Darthea
reading to him, and the Whig ladies with roses from
their gardens, and peaches and what not, all for Jack,
the hero, I being that summer but a small and altogether unimportant personage.

When my Jack went home again, we began at
once to talk over our plans for joining Mr. Washington; I made sure that now there was no greater
obstacle in my way than my father's opinions.
Alas! in November my aunt took what Dr. Rush
called a pernicious ague, and, although bled many

times and fed on Jesuits' bark, she came near to dying. In January she was better, but was become like a child, and depended upon me for everything. If I but spoke of my desire to be in the field, she would fall to tears or declare me ungrateful. She was morally weakened by her disease, and did seem to have changed as to her character. I lamented to Jack that it was my fate to stay, and he must go alone; I would follow when I could.

It was far into April before my aunt was entirely her old self, but as early as the close of January she had decided that she was well, and that to be well you must get rid of doctors. She told the great physician as much, and he left her in vast disgust. Society she would now have had for remedial distraction, but the war had made of it a dismal wreck. The Tories had been warned or sent away; the moderates hardly fared better; and the old gay set was broken up. Nevertheless it was not until far later, in July, '77, that Mr. Chew, Mr. Penn, and other as important neutrals, were ordered to leave the city; until then some remnants of the governor's set kept up more or less of the pleasant life they had once led. But there were no more redcoats in their drawing-rooms, and our antagonists were of the last who had lingered. Even before their departure, any gentleman of the king's service was sure to be told to leave, and meanwhile was apt to find a militiaman at his door.

My aunt would have none of them that winter, and her old Tory friends ceased to be seen at her house, save only Darthea, whilst continental uniforms and gentlemen of the Congress were made warmly welcome; but alas! among these was no match for her at piquet, and she felt that no one had sacrificed more for the country than had she.

In February of '76 a double change took place among us, and to my great discontent. I had seen much of Darthea in the fall and early winter of '75, and had come to know her better. She was fond of riding with my aunt, who had a strong gray stallion full of tricks, but no master of the hardy old lady, whom neither horse nor man ever dismayed. The good spinster was by no means as vigorous as I could have wished, but ride she would on all clear days whether cold or not, and liked well to have Darthea with us. When ill she was a docile patient, but, once afoot, declared all doctors fools, and would have no more of them "and their filthy doses."

We rode of sunlit winter days out to Germantown, or upon the wood roads over Schuylkill, my Aunt Gainor from good nature being pleased to gallop ahead, and leave us to chat and follow, or not, as might suit us.

One fine crisp morning in February we were breasting at a walk the slippery incline of Chestnut Hill, when Darthea, who had been unusually silent, said quite abruptly:

"I am going away, Mr. Wynne."

I was instantly troubled. "Where?" I said.

"Next week, and to New York. My aunt can no longer stand all this mob of rebels. We go to

New York, and for how long I know not. Since, in September, our friend, Dr. John Kearsley, was mobbed and maltreated, my aunt declares you unfit to live among. I must say I thought it brutal, sir. When men of sense and breeding like Mr. Penn, Mr. Chew, and Dr. Kearsley, cannot live unmolested it is time, my aunt thinks, to run."

"No one annoys Mr. Penn or Mr. Chew," said I. "To my mind, they are neutrals, and worse than open foes; but thy doctor is a mad Tory, and a malignant talker. I saw the matter, and I assure thee it was overstated. He lost his temper; 't is a brave gentleman, and I would he were with us. But now that both sides are sure at last that they are really at war, these men who live among us and are ready to welcome every redcoat must have their lesson. It must be Yes or No, in a war like this."

"But I hate that," she returned; "and to be comfortable and snug, and to love ease and Madeira and a quiet horse, and a book and a pipe and a nap of an afternoon, and then to have certain of the baser sort cry, 'Get up and kill somebody!' I think I am with Mr. Ross, and believe that, 'let who will be king, I well know I shall be subject.' Imagine my Aunt Peniston's fat poodle invited to choose between exile and killing rats."

"My dear Darthea, for thee to preach caution and neutrality is delightful."

"Did it sound like that Mr. Congregation?"

"No; to tell the truth, I think it did not."

"Indeed, you are right," says she. "I am a red-

hot Tory, sir. I scare Margaret Chew out of her
sweet wits when I talk blood, blood, sir; and as to
Miss Franks,—she hates to be called Becky,—when I
say I hope to see Mr. Washington hanged, she vows
he is too fine a man, and she would only hang the
ugly ones. So take care, Mr. Stay-at-home, take
care; I am no neutral."

"Thank thee," I said, lifting my hat. "I like open
enemies best."

"Oh, I will say a good word for you, when it comes
to that, and you will need it. Sir Guy will have
Ticonderoga soon, and Mr. Howe New York; so that,
with my loyal cousins and the king in possession,
we shall at least be in civilised society."

"There is a well-worn proverb," said I, "about
counting chickens. Where shalt thou be in New
York?"

"Cousin De Lancey has asked us to stay with them.
When the king's troops return to your rebel town
we shall come back, I suppose."

"I am sorry," I said. "All my friends are flitting
like swallows. Poor Mr. Franks is to go, it seems,
and the gay Miss Rebecca; but she likes the redcoats
best, and another is of the same mind, I fear."

"I am not over-grieved to go myself," said Darthea,
"and we will not quarrel just now about the redcoats.
Have you seen Mr. Warder to-day?"

"I have not."

"Then I am the bearer of ill news. He is to join
your new general in a week or two. He could not
find you this morning. I think he was relieved to

know I should tell you. How much he cares for you!
It is not like a man friendship. It is like the way
we weak girls care for one another. How can he
be such a brave gentleman as he seems—as he must
be? I should have thought it would be you who
would have gone first. Why do you not go? Here
is Miss Wynne's pet girl-boy away to fight, and you
—why do not you go?"

I was puzzled, as well I might be. "Dost thou
want me to go?"

A quick light came into those brown eyes, and a
little flush to the cheeks as she said,—oh, so very
quickly,—"I want all my friends to do what seems
to them right."

"I am glad to answer," I said. "It seems to me
my duty to be with the army; my friends have gone,
and now Graydon, the last to leave, has also gone.
I fancy people smiling to see me still at home—I
who am so positive, so outspoken. But here is my
father, with whom if I go I break for life, and here
is my Aunt Gainor, who bursts into tears if I do but
mention my wish to leave her."

"I see," said Darthea, not looking at me; "now I
understand fully; I did not before. But—will you
think it strange if—if I say—I, a good and loyal
woman—that you should go, and soon?" Then there
was a long pause, and she added, "When will this
cruel war end?"

"God knows," said I. "Thank thee; thou art right,
Darthea."

Another pause as long came after, when she said

abruptly, and in quite another voice, "You do not like Mr. Arthur Wynne; why do you not?"

I was startled. One never knew when she would get under one's guard and put some prickly question.

"Dost thou think I have reason to like him?" I said. "I did like him once, but now I do not; nor does he love me any better. Why dost thou ask me?"

"Oh, for—no matter! I am not going to say why."

"I think thou knowest, Darthea, that he is no friend of mine."

"Let us join your aunt," she said gravely.

"One word more," said I, "and I shall trouble thee no further. Rest sure that, come what may, there is one man who loves thee with a love no man can better."

"I wish you had not said that. There are some, Mr. Wynne, who never know when to take No for an answer."

"I am one," said I.

To this she made no reply, and rode on looking ahead in a dreamy way that fetched back to my memory a prettiness my dear mother had. Presently turning, she said:

"Let it end here; and—and my name is Miss Peniston, please."

There was no pettishness in her voice—only a certain dignity which sits better on little women than on little men, and provokes no smile. She was looking at me with a curious steadiness of gaze as she spoke. It was my last chance for many a day, and I could not let her go with a mere bow of meek submission.

"If I have been rude or discourteous, I am more sorry than I can say. If I called thee Darthea, it was because hope seemed to bring us nearer for one dear moment. Ah! I may call thee Miss Peniston, but for me always thou wilt be Darthea; and I shall love Darthea to the end, even when Miss Peniston has come to be a distant dream and has another name. I am most sorry to have given thee annoyance. Forget that, and pardon me."

"Mr. Wynne, you are a kindly and courteous gentleman. I wish—and you must not misapprehend me—that I loved you. Oh, I do not. Your aunt, who is so good to me, is a fierce wooer. I am afraid of her, and—she must be miles away; let us join her." And with this she shook her bridle, and was off at speed, and my mare and I at her side.

If I have made those who loved Darthea Peniston and me understand this winning soul, I shall be glad; and if not I shall at least have had the pleasure of repeating words and describing actions which live in my remembrance with such exactness as does not apply to much of what, to the outer world, may seem far better entitled to be remembered. She had it in her to hurt you, help you, pity you, mock or amuse you, and back of it all was the honesty and truth of a womanhood capable of courageous conduct, and despising all forms of meanness. That she was variously regarded was natural. Margaret Shippen said she cared only for dress and the men; and the witty Miss Franks, seeing further, but not all, said that Darthea Peniston was an actress of the minute, who believed her every rôle to be real. My wise aunt declared that she was several women, and that she did not always keep some of them in order. It was clear, to me at least, that she was growing older in mind, and was beginning to keep stricter school for those other women with whom my aunt credited this perplexing little lady.

Before I quite leave her for a time, I must let Jack say a word. It will tell more than I then knew or could know, and will save me from saying that which were better said by another.

"At last there is certainty of a long war, and I, being well again, must take my side. It is fortunate when choice is so easy, for I find it often hard in life to know just what is right. Poor Hugh, who has gone further than I from our fathers' faith, will still declare he is of Friends; but he commonly drops our language if he is not excited or greatly interested, and the rest will go too. It is strange that his resoluteness and clear notions of duty have so helped me, and yet that he is so caught and tied fast by Miss Gainor's dependence upon him, and by his scruples as to his father. He cannot do the thing he would. Now that my own father has sold out his business, I at least am left without excuse. I shall go at once, for fear I shall change my mind." A more unlikely thing I cannot imagine to have happened to John Warder.

"I saw Darthea to-day," he goes on to write. "She is going to New York. She talked to me with such frankness as almost broke my heart. She does not know how dear she is to me. I was near to telling her; but if she said No,—and she would,—I might —oh, I could not see her again. I had rather live in doubt. And whether Hugh loves her or not I would I knew. Mistress Wynne does but laugh and say, 'Lord bless us! they all love her!' Hugh is, as to some things, reticent, and of Darthea likes so little to speak that I am led to think it is a serious business for him; and if it be so, what can I but go? for how could I come between him and a woman he loved? Never, surely. Why is life such a tangle? As concerns this thing, it is well I am going. What else is left for me? My duty has long been plain.

"I did venture to ask Darthea of Mr. Arthur Wynne. She said quietly, 'I have had a letter to-day;' and with this she looked at me in a sort of defiant way. I like the man not at all, and wonder that women fancy him so greatly. When I said I was sorry she was going, she replied, 'It is no one's business;' and then added, 'nor Mr. Wynne's neither,' as if Hugh had said a word. In fact, Miss Peniston was almost as cross and abrupt as dear Miss Wynne at her worst. If ever, God willing, I should marry her,—there, I am blushing even to think of such a sweet impossibility,—she would drive me frantic. I should be in small rages or begging her pardon every half-hour of the day.

"What will Hugh say when he hears the Meeting

means to disown us? It troubles me deeply. My father is trembling too, for since a month he is all for resisting oppression, and who has been talking to him I do not know. Miss Wynne called him a decrepit weathercock to me last month, and then was in a fury at herself, and sorry too; but she will talk with him no more. It cannot be because he has sold his Holland cloths so well to the clothier-general. I never can think that.

"When I saw Miss Wynne, and would have seen Hugh had he been in, I told her of my meaning to go away by the packet to Burlington, and thence through New Jersey. She said it was well, but that Hugh should not go yet. He should go soon. Mr. Lee, the new general, had been to see her—a great soldier, she was told. But she had not liked him, because he let her believe he came of the same family as Mr. Richard Henry Lee of Virginia, whereas this is not so. He was lank, sour, and ill dressed, she said, and fetched his two dogs into the house. When he saw Hugh, he said it was time all the young men were out. Miss Wynne disliked this, and it is reported that Mrs. Ferguson and she, meeting after church, had nearly come to blows, because Mrs. Ferguson had said the people who made the war should be in the war, and on this the old lady desired to know if this arrow was meant for her or for her nephew. Mrs. F., not lacking courage, said she might choose.

"So Madam Wynne is pulled this way and that, and I must go alone; and I shall have a lieutenant's

commission, and a pretty fellow am I to order other
men about. I like best the continental line."

I saw Jack the day after my ride with Miss Peniston. I said sadly that he was right, and we talked
it all over that week, running down the river at early
morning after ducks, and through the wide channel
between League Island and the Neck; or else we
were away to Red Bank, or to the Jersey coast, if
the ice permitted, as it often did. It was a wonderful, open winter, as it chanced, and we had more
than our usual share of the ducks, which were very
abundant. As we lay in the gray weeds below the
bluff at Red Bank, we little thought of what it was
to see. Our gallant Mercer, who fell at Princeton,
was to give a name to the fort we built long after;
and there, too, was to die Count Donop, as brave a
man, far from home, sold by his own prince to be
the hireling of a shameful king.

The ducks flew over thick, and between times, as
we waited, we talked at intervals of the war, of
Montgomery's failure to capture Quebec, and of the
lingering siege of Boston; of how the brutal destruction of Norfolk in December had stirred the Virginians, and indeed every true heart in the colonies.
Jack would write when occasion served.

That last day (it was now February, as I have said)
we supped with my aunt, Jack and I. After the meal
was over, she went out of the room, and, coming back,
gave Jack a handsome, serviceable sword, with a
proper sash and tie. Then she must make him take
a hundred pounds in a purse she had netted; and

when he would not she said he was going to school,
and must have a tip, and would hear no more, and
kissed him, at which he got very red. Indeed, she
was deeply moved, as was plain to see from the way
she talked, speaking fast, and saying all manner of
foolish things.

This business of the sword troubled me more than
it ought to have done, and I resolved that nothing
should long keep me out of the field; but alas! it was
many a day before my going became possible. And
so my Jack went away, and Miss Peniston.

The war was dull for a time, as the armies got
ready for a spring at each other's throats. At last,
in March, his Excellency seized Dorchester Heights,
and Boston became no longer tenable. Howe left
it on March 17, and, what was as desirable, some two
hundred cannon and vast stores of ammunition.
Then, on Cambridge Common, our chief threw to the
free winds our flag, with its thirteen stripes, and still
in the corner the blood-red cross of St. George.

Late in this winter of '75-'76, an event took place,
or rather the sequel of an event, which made me feel
deeply the embarrassment in which the condition of
my aunt and father placed me. He who reads may
remember my speaking of a young fellow whom I
saw at the Woodlands, John Macpherson. I took
a great fancy to him later, and we fished and shot
together until he went away, in August of '75, to
join Arnold for his wild march into Canada.

His father, broken and sad, now brought to my
aunt the news of his son's death in the assault on

Quebec, and, speechless with grief, showed her the young fellow's letter, writ the night before he fell. He wrote, with other matter: "I cannot resist the inclination I feel to assure you that I experience no reluctance in this cause to venture a life I consider as only lent, and to be used when my country demands it." He went on to say that, if he died, he could wish his brother. William, an adjutant in the king's army, would not continue in the service of our enemies. I saw, too, General Schuyler's letter of condolence, but this was later.

Nothing had moved me like this. I went away, leaving the father and my aunt. People came to this strong woman, sure of her tenderest help, and I trust she comforted her friend in his loss. This was the first officer of our own set our city lost in war, and the news, I think, affected me more than any. How, indeed, could I dare to stay when the best manhood of the land was facing death in a cause as dear to me as to any?

In June a new calamity fell on me, or I should say on my father; for I felt it but little, or only as in some degree a release from bonds which I hesitated to sever by my own act. On the morning of June 25, my father called me into his counting-room, and, closing the door, sat down, I, as was thought fit, standing until told to be seated. Since he made no sign of any such desire on his part, I knew at once that this was not to be a talk about our affairs, in which, I may say, I had no interest except as to a very moderate salary.

"Thou wilt have to-day a call from Friend Pemberton. The overseers are moved, at last, to call thee to an account. I have lost hope that thou wilt forsake and condemn thy error. I have worked with the overseers to give thee and thy friend, John Warder, time, and this has been with tenderness accorded. No good is yet come of it. If this private admonition be of no effect, thy case will come before overseers again, and thou wilt be dealt with as a disorderly person, recommended to be disowned, when thy misdeeds come to be laid before the Quarterly Meeting for discipline. Already the Yearly Meeting hath found fault with us for lax dealing with such as thou art. Thou hast ceased to obey either thy father or thy God, and now my shame for thee is opened to all men."

Not greatly moved I listened to this summary of what was to happen. "It is too late," I said, "to argue this matter, my dear father. I cannot sin against my conscience. I will receive Mr. Pemberton as thy friend. He is a man whom all men respect and many love, but his ways are no longer my ways. Is that all?" I added. I feared any long talk with my father. We were as sure to fall out at last as were he and my Aunt Gainor.

"Yes," he said; "that is all. And tell Wilson to bring me the invoice of the 'Saucy Sally.'"

This time neither of us had lost temper. He had transacted a piece of business which concerned my soul, and I had listened. It had left me sore, but that was an old and too familiar story. Reflecting

16

on what had passed in the counting-house,—and my
conclusion now shows me how fast I was growing
older,—I put on my hat at once, and set out to find
the overseer deputed to make a private remonstrance
with my father's son. I suppose that my action was
also hastened by a disinclination to lie still, awaiting
an unpleasant and unavoidable business.

Finding James Pemberton in his office, I told him
that my errand was out of respect to relieve him of
the need to call upon a younger man. He seemed
pleased, and opened the matter in a way so gentle
and considerate that I am sure no man could have
bettered the manner of doing it. My attention to
business and quieter life had for a time reassured
the overseers. He would not speak of blood-guiltiness now, for out of kindness to my distressed parent
they had seen fit to wait, and for a time to set it
aside. My father had been in much affliction, and
Friends had taken note of this. Now he had to call
to my mind the testimony of Friends as to war, and
even how many had been reported to the Yearly
Meeting for Sufferings on account of righteous un-
willingness to resist constituted authority, and how
men of my views had oppressed and abused them.
Had I read the letter of the Yearly Meeting of 1774,
warning members not to depart from their peaceful
principles by taking part in any of the political matters then being stirred up, reminding all Friends that
under the king's government they had been favoured
with a peaceful and prosperous enjoyment of their
rights, and the like?

I listened quietly, and said it was too late to discuss these questions, which were many; that my mind was fully made up, and that as soon as possible I meant to enter the army. He had the good sense to see that I was of no inclination to change; and so, after some words of the most tender remonstrance, he bade me to prayerfully consider the business further, since overseers would not meet at once, and even when they did there would be time to manifest to Friends a just sense of my errors.

I thanked him, and went my way, making, however, no sign of grace, so that, on July 4 of this 1776, late in the evening, I received in my aunt's presence a letter from Isaac Freeman, clerk of the Meeting, inclosing a formal minute of the final action of Friends in my case.

"What is that?" said Aunt Gainor, very cheerful over a letter of thanks to her for having sold at cost to the Committee of Safety the cloth of Holland and the blankets she had induced my father to buy for her. She had stored them away for this hour of need, and was now full of satisfaction because of having made my father the means of clothing the continental troops.

"Read it aloud. What is it, sir?" I was smiling over what a few years before would have cost me many a bitter thought.

"Give it me! What is it?" Then she put on a pair of the new spectacles with wire supports to rest on the ears. "Dr. Franklin gave me these new inventions, and a great comfort too. I cannot endure

bridge glasses; they leave dents in one's nose. You
have not seen him lately. He was here to-day. You
should see him, Hugh. He was dressed very fine in
a velvet coat with new, shilling buttons, and bless
me! but he has got manners as fine as his ruffles,
and that is saying a good deal—Mechlin of the best.
You would not know the man."

With this she began to look at my letter. "Hoity-
toity, sir! this is a fine setting down for a naughty
Quaker." And she read it aloud in a strong voice,
her head back, and the great promontory of her nose
twitching at the nostrils now and then with supreme
contempt:

"'To Hugh Wynne: A minute, this Tenth-day of
Sixth-month, 1776, from the monthly Meeting of
Friends held at Philadelphia.

"'Whereas Hugh Wynne hath had his birth and
education among Friends, and, as we believe, hath
been convinced of that divine principle which pre-
serves the followers thereof from a disposition to
contend for the asserting of civil rights in a manner
contrary to our peaceful profession, yet doth not
manifest a disposition to make the Meeting a proper
acknowledgment of his outgoings, and hath further
declared his intention to continue his wrong-doing;

"'Therefore, for the clearing of truth and our
society, we give forth our testimony against such
breaches, and can have no unity with him, the said
Hugh Wynne, as a member of our society until he
become sensible of his deviations, and come to a sense

of his error, and condemn the same to the satisfaction of Friends; which is that we, as Christian men, desire.

"'Signed in, and on behalf of, the Meeting by
"'ISAAC FREEMAN,
"'*Clerk.*'

"What insolent nonsense!" cried Miss Wynne. "I hope your father is satisfied. I assure you I am. You are free at last. Here was James Warder to-day with a like document to the address of my dear Jack. I was assured that it was a terrible disgrace. I bade him take snuff and not be any greater fool than nature had made him. He took my snuff and sneezed for ten minutes. I think it helped him. One can neither grieve nor reason when one is sneezing. It is what Dr. Rush calls a moral alterative. Whenever the man fell to lamenting, I gave him more snuff. I think it helped him. And so the baa-lambs of Meeting have disowned their two black sheep. Well, well! I have better news for you. Mr. Carroll was here just now, with his charming ways. One would think when he is talking that one is the only woman alive. If I thought the priests taught him the trick, I would turn papist. You should observe his bow, Hugh. I thought Mr. Chew's bow not to be surpassed; but Mr. Carroll—oh, where was I?"

"Some good news," I said.

"Yes, yes. He tells me the Congress this evening voted for a Declaration of Independence."

"Indeed!" I cried. "So it has come at last. I,

too, am free, and it is time I went away, Aunt
Gainor."

"We will see," she said. "How can I do without
you? and there is your father too. He is not the
man he was, and I do not see, Hugh, how you can
leave him yet."

It was too true, as my last interview had shown
me. He was no longer the strong, steadily obstinate
John Wynne of a year or two back. He was less
decisive, made occasional errors in his accounts, and
would sometimes commit himself to risky ventures.
Then Thomas Mason, our clerk, or my aunt would
interfere, and he would protest and yield, having now
by habit a great respect for my aunt's sagacity, which
in fact was remarkable.

I went back to my work discontented, and pulled
this way and that, not clearly seeing what I ought
to do; for how could I leave him as he now was?
My aunt was right.

Next day I heard Captain John Nixon read in the
state-house yard the noble words of the declaration. Only a few hundred were there to hear it, and
its vast consequences few men as yet could apprehend.
Miss Norris told me not long after that she climbed
on a barrow and looked over their garden wall at
Fifth street and Chestnut; "and really, Mr. Wynne,
there were not ten decent coats in the crowd." But
this Miss Norris was a hot Tory, and thought us all
an underbred mob, as, I fear, did most of the proprietary set—the men lacking civil courage to fight
on either side, and amazed that Mr. Wilson, and

Mr. Reed, and Mr. Robert Morris, and the Virginia
gentry, should side with demagogues like Adams
and Roger Sherman.

And so time ran on. I fenced, drilled, saw my
companions drift away into war, and knew not how
to escape. I can now look back on my dismissal
from Meeting with more regret than it gave my youth.
I have never seen my way to a return to Friends;
yet I am still apt to be spoken of as one of the small
number who constitute, with Wetherill and Owen
and Clement Biddle, the society of Friends known
as Free Quakers. To discuss why later I did not
claim my place as one of these would lead me to
speaking of spiritual affairs, and this, as I have elsewhere said, I never do willingly, nor with comfort to
myself.

One afternoon in September of this year I was
balancing an account when my father came in and
told me that Mason, our clerk, had just had a fall in
the hold of one of our ships. The day after I saw
him, and although his hurts were painful they hardly
seemed to justify my father in his desire that now
at last he should take a long rest from work.

This threw all the detail of our affairs as largely
into my hands as was possible with a man like my
father. I think he guessed my intention to leave
him for the army, and gladly improved this chance
to load me with needless affairs, and all manner of
small perplexities. My aunt was better—in fact,
well; but here was this new trouble. What could I
do? My father declared that the old clerk would

soon be able to resume his place, and meanwhile,
he should have no one to help him but me. Now
and then, to my surprise, he made some absurd business venture, and was impatient if I said a word of
remonstrance. Twice I was sent to Maryland to see
after our tobacco plantations. I was in despair, and
became depressed and querulous, seeing no present
way, nor any future likelihood, of escape. My father
was well pleased, and even my aunt seemed to me
too well satisfied with the ill turn which fate had
done me. My father was clearly using the poor old
clerk's calamity as an excuse to keep me busy; nor
was it at all like him to employ such subterfuges.
All his life long he had been direct, positive, and
dictatorial; a few years back he would have ordered
me to give up all idea of the army, and would as like
as not have punished resistance with cold-blooded
disinheritance. He was visibly and but too clearly
changing from the resolute, uncompromising man
he had once been. Was he cunning enough to know
that his weakness was for me a bondage far stronger
than his more vigorous rule had ever been?

XV

Y personal difficulties were not made more easy to bear by the course of public events. Howe had taken New York. In November Fort Washington fell. Jack, who was within its walls, got away, but was slightly wounded. Our English general, Lee, had begun already to intrigue against Mr. Washington, writing, as Dr. Rush confided to my aunt, that he, Lee, ought to be made dictator. My aunt received the impression that the doctor, who loved his country well, was becoming discontented with our chief; but neither then nor later did she change her own opinion of the reserved and courteous Virginian.

He soon justified her views of his capacity. On December 1 he broke down the bridges in his rear over the Raritan, and marched through Jersey with a dwindling army. At Princeton he had but three thousand men; destroying every boat, he wisely put the broad Delaware between his army and the enemy.

Lord Cornwallis halted at the river, waiting for it to freeze that he might cross, and until this should happen went back with Howe to New York. About December 15 of '76, General Lee was captured, and,

strange as it may now seem, no calamity yet come
upon us created more consternation. Meanwhile
our own alarmed citizens began to bury their silver
plate. While the feeble were flying, and the doubtful
were ready to renew their oath to the king, the wary
and resolute commander-in-chief saw his chance.

To aid his courageous resolve came Sullivan and
Gates from Lee's late command. " At sunset on
Christmas day we crossed the Delaware," writes Jack.
" My general was in a small boat, with Knox, and
two boatmen. We were ten hours in the ice, and
marched nine miles, after crossing, in a blinding storm
of sleet. By God's grace we took one thousand of
those blackguard Hessians, and, but for Cadwalader's
ill luck with the ice, would have got Donop also. I
had a finger froze, but no worse accident.

" I dare say you know we fell back beyond Assun-
pink Creek, below Trenton. There we fought my
lord marquis again with good fortune. Meanwhile
he weakened his force at Princeton, and, I fancy,
thought we were in a trap; but our general left fires
burning, passed round the enemy's left,. and, as we
came near Princeton at sunrise, fell upon Colonel
Mawhood on his way to join Cornwallis. I was close
to General Mercer when we saw them, and had as
usual a fit of the shakes, hang them ! Luckily there
was small leisure to think.

" In the first onset, which was fierce, our brave
general was mortally wounded; and then, his Excellency coming up, we routed them finely. So away
went Cornwallis, with the trapped hot after the trap-

pers. We have the Jerseys and two thousand prisoners. I do not think even Miss Wynne can imagine what courage it took for our general to turn as he did on an army like that of Cornwallis'. Are you never coming?

"It is sad that the Southern officers look upon us and those of New England as tradesfolk, and this makes constant trouble, especially among the militia, who come and go much as they please. I have had no personal difficulty, but there have been several duels, of which little is said.

"It is to be hoped that Congress will now order all enlistments to be for the war, else we shall soon be in a mortal bad way. Hast heard of Miss Peniston?"

This letter came soon after the smart little winter campaign in Jersey had made us all so happy.

"It will last a good while yet," said James Wilson. "And when are you going, Hugh?" Indeed, I began at last to see a way opened, as we of Friends say; for now, in the spring, our old clerk hobbled back to his desk, and I knew that my father would no longer be left without friendly and familiar help. But before he could assume his full duties August was upon us—August of '77, a year for me most eventful. Darthea's letters to my aunt grew less and less frequent, and, as I thought, had an air of sadness unusual in this gladsome creature. Once she spoke of Captain Wynne as absent, and once that he, like Jack, had had a slight wound in the storm of Fort Washington. Of politics she could say nothing, as her letters had usually to pass our lines.

On July 31 Washington knew that Howe's fleet
was off the Delaware capes.   Meanwhile he had
crossed that river into Pennsylvania, and hurried his
army across country, finally encamping on a Saturday at Nicetown, some five miles from Philadelphia.
I rode out that evening to meet Jack, whose troop
camped even nearer to town, and close to the tents
of the headquarters staff.   The general lay for this
night at Stenton, where our Quaker friends, the
Logans, lived.   He was shown, I was told, the secret
stairway and the underground passage to the stable
and beyond, and was disposed to think it curious.

Jack, now a captain, in a new suit of blue and buff,
looked brown and hardy, and his figure had spread,
but the locks were as yellow and the cheeks as rosy
as ever I knew them.

Dear Aunt Gainor made much of him that evening,
and we talked late into the night of battles and
generals and what had gone with Lord Howe.   I
went to bed discontented, feeling myself to be a very
inconsiderable person, and Jack rode away to camp.
The next day being Sunday, the 24th of August,
his Excellency marched into town by Front street at
the head of the flower of his army, in all about eleven
thousand.   Fine men they were, but many half clad
and ill shod; fairly drilled too, but not as they were
later in the war.   The town was wild with delight,
and every one glad save the Tories and the Quakers,
many of whom remained all day in their houses.

This march being made only to exhibit the army
to friend and foe, the troops moved out High street

and by the middle ferry across the Schuylkill, on
their way toward the Delaware to meet Mr. Howe,
who, having landed at the head of Elk River, was
now on his way toward Philadelphia. His troops
were slow, the roads bad and few, the ague in great
force and severe—or so we heard. I rode sadly with
our people as far as Darby, and then turned homeward a vexed and dispirited man. It was, I think,
on the 4th of August that our general, who had rid-
den on in advance of his army, first met Marquis
Lafayette.

My aunt, who spoke French with remarkable flu-
ency and a calm disregard of accent and inflections,
was well pleased to entertain the French gentleman,
and at her house I had the happiness to make his
acquaintance, greatly, as it proved, to my future advantage. He was glad to find any who spoke his
own tongue well, and discussed our affairs with me,
horrified at the lack of decent uniforms and discipline,
but, like me, pleased with the tall, strong men he saw
in our ranks. Later my acquaintance with French
was of much use to me; so little can a man tell what
value an accomplishment will have for him.

The marquis was very young, and somewhat free
in stating his opinions. At this time he thought
Mr. Howe intended Charleston, and, like others, was
amazed at his folly in not going up the Delaware
Bay to land his troops. His strange strategy left
Burgoyne to the fate in store for him at Saratoga,
where the latter general was to act a first part in a
tragic drama much finer than those he wrote, which

were so greatly praised by the fine ladies in London,
and indeed by some better critics.

A letter of Jack's came to hand during this week.
In it he said my aunt must leave, as he was sure we
had not force enough to keep General Howe out
of Philadelphia. But the old lady said, "Not I, indeed!" and I think no mortal power could have induced her to go away. She even declined to bury
her silver, as many had done. Not so the rest of
the Whigs. Every one fled who knew where to go,
or who feared to be called to account; and none
would hear of defending the town, as should have
been attempted.

Jack's letter went on to say that in Delaware the
general had a narrow escape. "He rode out," says
Jack, "with Marquis Lafayette on a reconnaissance,
attended by but two officers and an orderly. General
Sullivan had an officer follow with a half-troop; but
the general, fearing such numbers might attract
attention, ordered them to wait behind a thicket.
Looking thence, they saw the general ride direct
toward a picket of the enemy, which from their
vantage they could see, but he could not. An English officer, perceiving him, seemed to give an order
to fire; but as the men raised their pieces he struck
them up. As he was about to give the order to fire,
the general, being satisfied, had turned his back to
ride away. It is a curious tale, is it not? and none
can explain it."

Long years after I myself met an English officer,
a General Henderson, in Canada, and on my telling

him the incident, he said at once it was he who was
concerned, and that when the general turned to ride
away he could not make up his mind to shoot down
a man who had turned his back. He was amazed
and pleased to know who it was he thus spared.

On the 11th of September, at evening, came the
disaster of Brandywine, and on the 26th Lord Cornwallis marched into our city, with two batteries and
the Sixteenth Dragoons and Grenadiers. They were
received quietly, and that evening my Cousin Arthur
appeared at our house. My father, who had been
very inert of late, seemed to arouse himself, and expressed quite forcibly his joy and relief at the coming
of the troops. He recounted his griefs, too: how
that, refusing the militia tax, the Committee of Safety
had taken away his great tankard, and later two
tables, which was true enough. Then, to my amazement, my father declared Arthur must stay with us,
which he was nothing loath to do.

I was cool, as you may suppose, but it was difficult
for man or woman to resist Arthur Wynne when
he meant to be pleasant; and so, putting my dislike
aside, I found myself chatting with him about the
war and what not. In fact, he was a guest, and what
else could I do?

My aunt kept herself indoors and would none of
the Galloways and Allens, who had come back in
swarms, nor even the neutrals, like Mr. Penn, whom
she much liked. The day after the town was occupied, Captain Wynne appeared early in the morning,
as we were discussing a matter of business. He

took it for granted, I presume, that my aunt would see him, and went past the turbaned black boy despite his small remonstrances. My aunt rose to the full of her great height, her nose in the air, and letting fall a lapful of papers.

"To what," she said, "have I the honour to owe a visit from Mr. Wynne? Is my house an inn, that any officer of the king may enter whether I will or not?"

Although he must have been surprised, he was perfectly at his ease. Indeed, I envied him his self-possession.

"Madam," he said, "I am charged with a letter from Miss Peniston."

"You may put it on the table," says Mistress Wynne. "My brother may choose his society. I ask the same privilege. It will not consist of gentlemen of your profession."

Mr. Wynne's face grew black under its dark skin. "Madam," he said, "I stay nowhere as an unwelcome guest. I thank you for past kindness, and I humbly take my leave. I could have done you a service as to this business of the quartering of officers, and you shall still have my good offices for the sake of the many pleasant hours I have passed in your house. As my Cousin Hugh says nothing, I am glad to think that he is of a different opinion from that which you have put in words so agreeably." With this he went away, leaving my aunt red in the face, and speechless with wrath.

I thought he had the best of it; but I merely said,

"My dear aunt, you should not have been so hard with him." I did, indeed, think it both unwise and needless.

"Stuff and nonsense!" says Miss Wynne, walking about as my father used to do. "I do not trust him, and he has got that girl in his toils, poor child! I wonder what lies he has told her. How does he hold her? I did think that was past any man's power; and she is unhappy too. When a woman like Darthea begins to find a man out, she can't help showing it, and some are more frank on paper than in talk; that is her way. I am afraid I made mischief once, for I told him long ago that I meant her to marry you; and then I saw he did not like it, and I knew I had been a goose. Whatever is the reason he hates you, Hugh? Oh yes, he does—he does. Is it the woman? I will have no redcoats in my house."

I got a chance to say—what I was sorry to have to say—how little need there was for him to fear poor me, whom Darthea wished to have nothing to do with, I thought.

"Her loves are like her moods, my dear Hugh; who knows how long they will last? Until a woman is married she is not to be despaired of."

I shook my head sadly and went out.

I returned late in the evening, to order my horse to be saddled and sent to me before breakfast next morning; for I kept it at no cost in my aunt's ample stable. To my horror, I found a sentinel at the door, and the hall full of army baggage. In the parlour was a tall Hessian, General von Knyphausen, and

17

Count Donop and others, smoking, much at their ease.
They were fairly civil, but did not concern themselves
greatly if I liked it or not. I found my aunt in bed,
in a fever of vain anger.

She had the bed-curtains drawn, and when I was
bid to enter, put aside the chintz so as to make room
for her head, which appeared in a tall nightcap. I
am unfit, I fear, to describe this gear; but it brought
out all her large features very strongly, and to have
seen her would have terrified a Hessian regiment.

"My house is full of Dutch dogs," she cried. "As
soon as they came they ordered bones." In fact, they
had asked quite civilly if they might have supper.

"I saw them at their feed," says my aunt, "and
the big beast, General Knyphausen, spread my best
butter on his bread with his thumb, sir—his thumb!
Count Donop is better; but Von Heiser! and the
pipes! heavens!" Here she retreated within her
curtains, and I heard her say, "Bessy Ferguson saw
them come in, and must sail across the street and tell
Job—the page with the turban—to congratulate me
for her, and to advise me to get a keg of sauerkraut."

I assured my aunt that fortunately these were gentlemen, but she was inconsolable, declaring herself
ill, and that Dr. Rush must come at once.

"But," I said, "he is gone with all the Congress
to York."

"Then I shall die," moaned my aunt.

At last, knowing her well, I said, "Is it not too
sad?"

"What's that? What?"

"Mr. Howe has taken Mrs. Pemberton's carriage and the pair of sorrels for his own use."

At this my Aunt Gainor's large face reappeared, not as melancholic as before, and I added, "Friend Waln has six to care for, and Thomas Scattergood has the Hessian chaplain and a drunken major. The rest of Friends are no better off."

"Thank the Lord for all His mercies!" said Miss Wynne.

"And Mr. Cadwalader's house on Little Dock street Sir William has."

"A pity that, Hugh. The fine furniture will pay for it, I fear. I think, Hugh, I am better, or I shall be soon."

"They talk of the Meeting over the way for a barrack, Aunt Gainor." Now this was idly rumoured, but how could one resist to feed an occasion so comic?

"I think I should die contented," said Miss Wynne. "Now go away, Hugh. I have had my medicine, and I like it." She was quick at self-analysis, and was laughing low, really happier for the miseries of her Tory acquaintances.

After the bedroom comedy, which much amused me and out of which my aunt got great comfort, she was inclined to be on better terms with the officers so abruptly thrust upon her. For a while, however, she declined to eat her meals with them, and when told that they had had Colonel Montresor to dine, and had drunk the king's health, she sent all the glasses they had used down to the blacks in the kitchen, and bade them never to dare set them on her table again. This much delighted Count Donop, who loved George of Hanover no better than did she, and I learned that she declared the bread-and-butter business was the worst of Von Knyphausen, and was no doubt a court custom. As to Count Donop, she learned to like him. He spoke queer French, and did not smoke. "*Je ne foume pas chamais, madame,*" he said; "*mais le Cheneral, il foume touchours, et Von Heiser le meme,*" which was true. The count knew her London friends, and grieved that he was sent on a service he did not relish, and in which later he was to lose his life.

My aunt fed them well, and won at piquet, and declared they were much to be pitied, although Von Heiser was a horror. When he had knocked down her red-and-gold Delft vase, the gods and the other china were put away, and then the rugs, because of the holes his pipe ashes burned, and still she vowed it was a comfort they were not redcoats. Them she would have poisoned.

Captain André alone was an exception. When, in 1776, he was made a prisoner by Montgomery in Canada, and after that was on parole at Lancaster, I met him; and as he much attracted me, my aunt sent him money, and I was able to ease his captivity by making him known to our friends, Mr. Justice Yeates and the good Cope people, who, being sound Tories, did him such good turns as he never forgot, and kindly credited to us. Indeed, he made for my aunt some pretty sketches of the fall woods, and, as I have said, was welcome where no other redcoat could enter.

My aunt was soon easier in mind, but my own condition was not to be envied. Here was Arthur Wynne at my father's, the Hessians at my aunt's, the Tories happy, seven or eight thousand folks gone away, every inn and house full, and on the street crowds of unmannerly officers. It was not easy to avoid quarrels. Already the Hessian soldiers began to steal all manner of eatables from the farms this side of Schuylkill. More to my own inconvenience, I found that Major von Heiser had taken the privilege of riding my mare Lucy so hard that she was unfit to use for two days. At last my aunt's chicken-coops suffered, and the voice of her pet rooster was no more heard in the land. I did hear that, as this raid of some privates interfered with the Dutch general's diet, one of the offenders got the strappado. But no one could stop these fellows, and they were so bold as to enter houses and steal what they wanted, until severe measures were taken by Mr. Howe. They robbed my father boldly, before his eyes, of two fat Virginia peach-fed hams, and all his special tobacco. He stood by, and said they ought not to do it. This, as they knew no tongue but their own, and as he acted up to his honest belief in the righteousness of non-resistance, and uttered no complaint, only served to bring them again. But this time I was at home, and nearly killed a corporal with the Quaker staff Thomas Scattergood gave my father. The adventure seemed to compensate Miss Wynne for her own losses. The corporal made a lying complaint, and but for Mr. André I should have been put to serious annoyance. Our boys used to say that the Hessian drum-beat said, "Plunder, plunder, plun, plun, plunder." And so for the sad remnant of Whig gentles the town was made in all ways unbearable.

There are times when the life sands seem to run slowly, and others when they flow swiftly, as during this bewildering week. All manner of things happened, mostly perplexing or sad, and none quite agreeable. On the 28th, coming in about nine at night, I saw that there were persons in the great front sitting-room, which overlooked Dock Creek. As I came into the light which fell through the open doorway, I stood unnoticed. The room was full of pipe smoke, and rum and Hollands were on the table, as was common in the days when Friends' Meeting made a minute that Friends be vigilant to see that those who work in the harvest-fields have portions of rum. My father and my cousin sat on one side, opposite a short, stout man almost as swarthy as Arthur, and with very small piercing eyes, so dark as to seem black, which eyes never are.

I heard this gentleman say, "Wynne, I hear that your brother is worse. These elder brothers are unnatural animals, and vastly tenacious of life." On this I noticed my cousin frown at him and slightly shake his head. The officer did not take the hint, if it were one, but added, smiling, "He will live to bury you; unfeeling brutes—these elder brothers. Damn 'em!"

I was shocked to notice how inertly my father listened to the oath, and I recalled, with a sudden sense of distress, what my aunt had said of my father's state of mind. The young are accustomed to take for granted the permanency of health in their elders, and to look upon them as unchanging institutions, until, in some sad way, reminded of the frailty of all living things.

As I went in, Arthur rose, looked sharply at me, and said, "Let me present my cousin, Mr. Hugh Wynne, Colonel Tarleton."

I bowed to the officer, who lacked the politeness to rise, merely saying, "Pleased to see you, Mr. Wynne."

"We were talking," said Arthur, "when you came of the fight at the river with the queer name—Brandywine, is n't it?"

"No," said my father; "thou art mistaken, and I wished to ask thee, Arthur, what was it thou wert saying. We had ceased to speak of the war. Yes; it was of thy brother."

"What of thy brother?" said I, glad of this opening.

"Oh, nothing, except Colonel Tarleton had news he was not so well." He was so shrewd as to think I must have overheard enough to make it useless to lie to me. A lie, he used to say, was a reserve not to be called into service except when all else failed.

"Oh, was that all?" I returned. "I did hear, Cousin Arthur, that the Wyncote estate was growing to be valuable again; some coal or iron had been found."

"So my mother writes me," said Tarleton. "We are old friends of your family."

"You know," I said, "we are the elder branch." I was bent on discovering, if possible, the cause of my cousin's annoyance whenever Wyncote was mentioned.

"I wish it were true about our getting rich," said Arthur, with the relaxed look about the jaw I had come to know so well; it came as he began to speak. "If it were anything but idle gossip, Tarleton, what would it profit a poor devil of a younger son? They did find coal, but it came to nothing; and indeed I learn they lost money in the end."

"I have so heard," said my father, in a dull way. "Who was it told me? I forget. They lost money."

I looked at him amazed. Who could have told him but Arthur, and why? Until a year back his memory had been unfailing.

I saw a queer look, part surprise, part puzzle, go over Tarleton's face, a slight frown above, as slight a smile below. I fancy he meant to twit my cousin, for he said to me:

"And so you are of the elder branch, Mr. Hugh Wynne. How is that, Arthur? How did the elder branch chance to lose that noble old house?"

My cousin sat rapping with his fingers on the table what they used to call the "devil's tattoo," regarding me with steady, half-shut eyes—a too frequent and not well-mannered way he had, and one I much disliked. He said nothing, nor had he a chance, for I instantly answered the colonel: "My father can tell you."

"About what, Hugh?"

"About how we lost our Welsh estate."

My father at this lifted his great bulk upright in the old Penn chair, and seemed more alive.

"It is Colonel Tarleton who asks, not I."

"It is an old story." He spoke quite like himself. "Our cousin must know it well. My father suffered for conscience' sake, and, being a Friend, would pay no tithes. For this he was cast into jail in Shrewsbury Gate House, and lay there a year, suffering much in body, but at peace, it may surely be thought, as to his soul. At last he was set free on condition that he should leave the country."

"And the estate?" asked Tarleton.

"He thought little of that. It was heavily charged with debt made by his father's wild ways. I believe, too, there was some agreement with the officers of the crown that he should make over the property to his next brother, who had none of his scruples. This was in 1670, or thereabouts. A legal transfer was made to my uncle, who, I think, loved my father, and understood that, being set in his ways, he would defy the king's authority to the end. And so — wisely I think — the overruling providence of God brought us to a new land, where we have greatly prospered."

"And that is all?" said the colonel. "What a strange story! And so you are Wynne of Wyncote, and lost it."

"For a greater gain," said my father. "My son has a silly fancy for the old place, but it is lost—lost

—sold; and if we could have it at a word, it would grieve me to see him cast in his lot among a set of drunken, dicing, hard-riding squires—a godless set. It will never be if I can help it. My son has left the creed of his father and of mine, and I am glad that his worldly pride cannot be further tempted. Dost thou hear, Hugh?"

There was a moment of awkward silence. My father had spoken with violence, once or twice strik-- ing the table with his fist until the glasses rang. There was something of his old vehemence in his statement; but as a rule, however abrupt when we were alone, before strangers he was as civil to me as to others. My cousin, I thought, looked relieved as my father went on; and, ceasing to drum on the table, he quietly filled himself a glass of Hollands.

I was puzzled. What interest had Arthur to lie about the value of Wyncote if it was irretrievably lost to us? As my father ended, he glanced at me with more or less of his old keenness of look, smiling a little as he regarded me. The pause which came after was brief, as I have said; for my reflections, such as they were, passed swiftly through my mind, and were as complete as was under the circumstances possible.

"I am sorry for you," said Tarleton. "An old name is much, but one likes to have with it all the memories that go with its ancient home."

"That is true," said I; "and, if my father will pardon me, I like still to say that I would have Wyncote to-day if I could."

"Thou canst not," said my father. "And what we cannot have—what God has willed that we shall not have—it were wise and well to forget. It is my affair, and none of thine. Wilt thou taste some of my newly come Madeira, Friend Tarleton?"

The colonel said "No," and shortly after left us, my cousin going with him.

My father sat still for a while, and then said as I rose, "I trust to hear no more of this nonsense. Thy aunt and thy mother have put it in thy foolish head. I will have no more of it—no more. Dost thou hear?"

I said I would try to satisfy him, and so the thing came to an end.

The day after this singular talk, which so much puzzled me, Arthur said at breakfast that he should be pleased to go with me on the river for white perch. I hesitated; but, my father saying, "Certainly; he shall go with thee. I do not need him," I returned that I would be ready at eleven.

We pulled over toward Petty's Island, and when half-way my cousin, who was steering, and had been very silent for him, said:

"Let her drift a bit; I want to talk to you."

I sat still and listened.

"Why do not you join our army? A commission were easily had."

I replied that he knew my sentiments well, and that his question was absurd.

"No," he said; "I am your friend, although you do not think so. By George! were I you, I would

be on one side or the other. I like my friends to do
what is manly and decisive." "Holloa!" thinks I;
"has Darthea been talking? And why does he, an
officer of the king, want me to go?"

"I shall go some day," I replied, "but when, I know
not yet. It seems to me queer counsel to give a good
rebel. When does Miss Peniston return?" I said.

"What the deuce has that got to do with it? Yes,
she is coming back, of course, and soon; but why do
not you join your army?"

"Let us drop that," I said. "There are many
reasons; I prefer not to discuss the matter."

"Very good," he said; "and, Hugh, you heard a
heap of nonsense last night about Wyncote. Tarleton had too much of your father's rum-punch. Your
people were lucky to lose the old place, and how these
tales of our being rich arose I cannot imagine. Come
and see us some day, and you will no longer envy the
lot of beggared Welsh squires."

All of this only helped the more to make me dis-
believe him; but the key to his lies I had not, and so
I merely said it would be many a day before that
could happen.

"Perhaps," he returned; "but who knows? The
war will soon be over."

"When will Miss Peniston be in town?" said I.

He was not sure; but said I put it in his mind to
say something.

"Well?" said I, on my guard.

He went on: "I am a frank man, Cousin Hugh."
At times he was, and strangely so; then the next

minute he would be indirect or lie to you. The mixture made it hard to understand what he was after.

"I trust," he went on, "that you will pardon me if I say that in England custom does not sanction certain freedoms which in the colonies seem to be regarded as of no moment. I am not of this opinion. Miss Peniston is, I hope, to be my wife. She is young, impulsive, and—well, no matter. Some men take these things coolly; I do not. I am sure you will have the good sense to agree with me. When a woman is pledged to a man, it is fit that she should be most guarded in her relations with other men. I—"

Here I broke in, "What on earth does all this mean?"

"I will tell you. Your aunt writes now and then to Miss Peniston."

"Certainly," said I.

"Yes; she says, too, things concerning you and that lady which are not to my taste."

"Indeed?"

"I have been so honoured as to see some of these famous epistles. I think Darthea is pleased to torment me at times; it is her way, as you may happen to know. Also, and this is more serious, you have yourself written to Darthea."

"I have, and several times. Why not?"

"These letters," he went on, "she has refused to show to me. Now I want to say—and you will pardon me—that I permit no man to write to a woman whom I am to marry unless I do not object."

"Well?" I said, beginning to smile, after my unmanageable habit.

"Here I do object."

"What if I say that, so long as Miss Peniston does not seem displeased, I care not one farthing who objects?"

"By George!" cried he, leaping up in the boat.

"Take care; thou wilt upset the skiff."

"I have half a mind to."

"Nonsense! I can swim like a duck."

"This is no trifle, sir," he returned. "I will allow no man to take the liberty you insist on. It amazes me that you do not see this as I do. I am sorry, but I warn you once for all that I—"

"I am at your service, sir," I broke in.

"Pshaw! nonsense! I am a guest in your father's house. I have thought it my duty, for your sake and my own, to say what I have said. When I know that you have again disobeyed my reasonable and most earnest wish, I shall consider how to deal with the matter. I have been forbearing so far, but I cannot answer for the future."

"Cousin Arthur," I replied, "this seems to me a silly business, in which we have both lost our tempers. I have no hope that Miss Peniston will ever change her mind, and I am free to say to you that I think it useless to persist; but nevertheless—"

"Persist!"

"I said 'persist.' Until Miss Peniston is no longer Miss Peniston, I shall not cease to do all that is in my power to make her change her mind."

"And you call that honourable—the conduct of a gentleman and a kinsman?"

"Yes; I, too, can be frank. I would rather see her marry any other man than yourself. You have sought to injure me, why I shall tell you at my own time. I think you have been deceiving all of us as to certain matters. Oh, wait! I must have my say. If you were—what I do not think you—a straightforward, truthful man, I should think it well, and leave Miss Peniston to what seems to be her choice. You have been frank, and so am I, and now we understand each other, and—no; I heard you to an end, and I must insist that I too be heard. I am not sorry to have had this talk. If I did not care for her who has promised you her hand, I should be careless as to what you are, or whether you have been an enemy in my home while pretending to be a friend. As it is, I love her too well not to do all I can to make her see you as I see you; and this, although for me there is no least hope of ever having a place in her heart. I am her friend, and shall be, and, until she forbids, shall claim every privilege which, with our simpler manners, the name of friend carries with it. I trust I am plain."

"Plain? By heavens! yes. I have borne much, but now I have only to add that I never yet forgave an insult. You would be wiser to have a care. A man who never yet forgave has warned you. What I want I get; and what I get I keep."

"I think," I said, "that we will go ashore."

"With all my heart." And in absolute silence I

pulled back. At the slip he left me without a word, and I secured the boat and walked away, having found ample subject for reflection. Nor was I altogether discontented at my cousin's evident jealousy.

The afternoon of this memorable day I rode out on poor Lucy, whom I had put for safety in our home stables. I went out High to Seventh street, and up to Race street road, where there was better footing, as it had been kept in order for the sport which made us call it Race street, and not Sassafras, which is its real name. I was brought to a stand about Twelfth street, then only an ox-path, by the bayonet of a grenadier, the camps lying about this point. I turned to ride back, when I heard a voice I knew crying:

"Holloa, Mr. Wynne! Are you stopped, and why?"

I said I knew no reason, but would go south. I was out for a ride, and had no special errand.

"Come with me then," he said pleasantly. "I am now the engineer in charge of the defences." This was my Aunt Gainor's old beau, Captain Montresor, now a colonel.

"I am sorry your aunt will see none of us, Mr. Wynne. If agreeable to you, we will ride through the lines."

I asked nothing better, and explaining, awkwardly I fear, that my aunt was a red-hot Whig, we rode south to Spruce street, past the Bettering-house at Spruce and Eleventh streets, where the troops which had entered with Lord Cornwallis were mostly stationed. The main army lay at Germantown, with de-

tachments below the city, on the east and west banks
of the Schuylkill, to watch our forts at Red Bank and
the islands which commanded the Delaware River
and kept the British commander from drawing supplies from the great fleet which lay helpless below.

As we went by, the Grenadiers were drilling on
the open space before the poorhouse. I expressed
my admiration of their pointed caps, red, with silver
front plates, their spotless white leggings and blue-
trimmed scarlet coats.

"Too much finery, Mr. Wynne. These are a king's
puppets, dressed to please the whim of royalty. If
all kings took the field, we should have less of this.
Those miserable devils of Mr. Morgan's fought as
well in their dirty skin shirts, and can kill a man at
murderous distance with their long rifles and little
bullets. It is like gambling with a beggar. He
has all to get, and nothing to lose but a life too
wretched to make it worth keeping."

I made no serious reply, and we rode westward
through the governor's woods to the river. As we
turned into an open space to escape a deep mud-hole,
Mr. Montresor said:

"It was here, I think, you and Mr. Warder made
yourselves agreeable to two of our people." I laughed,
and said it was a silly business and quite needless.

"That, I believe," he cried, laughing, "was their
opinion somewhat late. They were the jest of every
regimental mess for a month, and we were inclined
to think Mr. Washington had better raise a few
regiments of Quakers. Are you all as dangerous?"

18

"Oh, worse, worse," I said. "Jack Warder and I are only half-fledged specimens. You should see the old fellows." Thus jesting, we rode as we were able until we reached the banks of the Schuylkill, picketed on both shores, but on the west side not below the lower ferry, where already my companion was laying a floating bridge which greatly interested me.

"We have a post on the far hill," he said, "I am afraid to Mr. Hamilton's annoyance. Let us follow the river."

I was able to guide him along an ox-road, and past garden patches across High street, to the upper ferry at Callowhill street. Here he pointed out to me the advantage of a line of nine forts which he was already building. There was to be one on the hill we call Fairmount to command the upper ferry. Others were to be set along to the north of Callowhill street road at intervals to Cohocsink Creek and the Delaware.

The great trees I loved were falling fast under the axes of the pioneers, whom I thought very awkward at the business. Farm-houses were being torn down, and orchards and hedges levelled, while the unhappy owners looked on in mute despair, aiding one another to remove their furniture. The object was to leave a broad space to north of the forts, that an attacking force might find no shelter. About an hundred feet from the blockhouses was to be an abatis of sharpened logs, and a mass of brush and trees, through which to move would be difficult.

I took it all in, and greedily. The colonel no doubt thought me an intelligent young fellow, and was kind enough to answer all my questions. He may later have repented his freedom of speech. And now I saw the reason for all this piteous ruin. Compensation was promised and given, I heard, but it seemed to me hard to be thus in a day thrust out of homes no doubt dear to these simple folk. We went past gardens and fields, over broken fences, all in the way of destruction. Tape-lines pegged to the earth guided the engineers, and hundreds of negroes were here at work. Near to Cohocsink Creek we met the second Miss Chew, riding with her father. He was handsome in dark velvet, his hair clubbed and powdered beneath a flat beaver with three rolls, and at his back a queue tied with a red ribbon. He had remained quietly inactive and prudent, and, being liked, had been let alone by our own party. It is to be feared that neither he nor the ribbon was quite as neutral as they had been. Miss Margaret looked her best. I much dislike "Peggy," by which name she was known almost to the loss of that fine, full "Margaret," which suited better her handsome, uptilted head and well-bred look.

On the right side rode that other Margaret, Miss Shippen, of whom awhile back I spoke, but then only as in pretty bud, at the Woodlands. It was a fair young rose I now saw bowing in the saddle, a woman with both charm and beauty. Long after, in London, and in less merry days, she was described by Colonel Tarleton as past question the handsomest

woman in all England. I fear, too, she was the
saddest.

"And where have you kept yourself, Mr. Wynne?"
she asked. "You are a favourite of my father's,
you know. I had half a mind not to speak to you."

I bowed, and made some gay answer. I could
not well explain that the officers who filled their
houses were not to my taste.

"Let me present you to Mr. André," said Mr.
Shippen, who brought up the rear.

"I have the honour to know Mr. Wynne," said the
officer. "We met at Lancaster when I was a prisoner in '76; in March, was it not? Mr. Wynne did
me a most kind service, Montresor. I owe it to him
that I came to know that loyal gentleman, Mr. Cope,
and the Yeates people, who at least were loyal to me.
I have not forgotten it, nor ever shall."

I said it was a very small service, and he was kind
to remember it.

"You may well afford to forget it, sir; I shall not,"
he returned. He was in full uniform; not a tall man,
but finely proportioned, with remarkably regular
features and a clear complexion which was set off
to advantage by powdered hair drawn back and tied
in the usual ribboned queue.

We rode along in company, happy enough, and
chatting as we went, Mr. André, as always, the life
of the party. He had the gracious frankness of a
well-mannered lad, and, as I recall him, seemed far
younger than his years. He spoke very feelingly
aside to me of young Macpherson, who fell at Quebec.

He himself had had the ill luck not to be present when that gallant assault was made. He spoke of us always as colonials, and not as rebels; and why was I not in the service of the king, or perhaps that was a needless question?

I told him frankly that I hoped before long to be in quite other service. At this he cried, "So, so! I would not say it elsewhere. Is that so? 'T is a pity, Mr. Wynne; a hopeless cause," adding, with a laugh, that I should not find it very easy to get out of the city, which was far too true. I said there were many ways to go, but how I meant to leave I did not yet know. After I got out I would tell him. We had fallen back a little as we talked, the road just here not allowing three to ride abreast.

"I shall ask the colonel for a pass to join our army," I said merrily.

"I would," said he, as gay as I; "but I fear you and Mistress Wynne will have no favours. Pray tell her to be careful. The Tories are talking."

"Thanks," said I, as we drew aside to let pass a splendid brigade of Hessians, fat and well fed, with shining helmets.

"We are drawing in a lot of men from Germantown," said André, "but for what I do not know. Ah, here comes the artillery!"

I watched them as we all sat in saddle, while regiment after regiment passed, the women admiring their precision and soldierly bearing. For my part, I kept thinking of the half-clad, ill-armed men I had seen go down these same streets a little while before.

"I will go," I said to myself; and in a moment I had made one of those decisive resolutions which, once made, seem to control me, and to permit no future change of plan.

By this time we were come to the bridge over Cohocsink Creek, I having become self-absorbed and silent. The colonel called my attention to his having dammed the creek, and thus flooded the low meadows for more complete defence. I said, "Yes, yes!" being no longer interested.

Mr. Shippen said, "We will cross over to the 'Rose of Bath' and have a little milk-punch before we ride back." This was an inn where, in the garden, was a mineral water much prescribed by Dr. Kearsley. I excused myself, however, and, pleading an engagement, rode slowly away.

I put up my mare in my aunt's stable, and went at once into her parlour, full of my purpose.

I sat down and told her both the talk of two days before with Tarleton and my cousin, and also that I had had in my boat.

She thought I had been foolishly frank, and said, "You have reason to be careful, Hugh. That man is dangerous. He would not fight you, because that would put an end to his relations with your father. Clerk Mason tells me he has already borrowed two hundred pounds of my brother. So far I can see," she went on; "the rest is dark—that about Wyncote, I mean. Darthea, when once she is away, begins to criticise him. In a word, Hugh, I think he has reason to be jealous."

"O Aunt Gainor!"

"Yes. She does not answer your letters, nor should she, but she answers them to me, the minx! a good sign, sir."

"That is not all, aunt. I can stand it no longer. I must go; I am going."

"The army, Hugh?"

"Yes; my mind is made up. My two homes are hardly mine any longer. Every day is a reproach. For my father I can do little. His affairs are almost entirely wound up. He does not need me. The old clerk is better."

"Will it be hard to leave me, my son?"

"You know it will," said I. She had risen, tall and large, her eyes soft with tears.

"You must go," she said, "and may God protect and keep you. I shall be very lonely, Hugh. But you must go. I have long seen it."

Upon this, I begged she would see my father often, and give me news of him and of Darthea whenever occasion served. Then she told me Darthea was to return to the city in two days, and she herself would keep in mind all I had wished her to do. After this I told her of the difficulties I should meet with, and we talked them over. Presently she said, "Wait;" then left the room, and, coming back, gave me a sword the counterpart of Jack's.

"I have had it a year, sir. Let me see," she cried, and would have me put it on, and the sash, and the buff-and-blue sword-knot. After this she put a great hand on each shoulder just as she had done with

Jack, and, kissing me, said, "War is a sad thing, but there are worse things. Be true to the old name, my son." Nor could she bide it a moment longer, but hurried out with her lace handkerchief to her eyes, saying as she went, "How shall I bear it! How shall I bear it!"

She also had for me a pair of silver-mounted pistols, and an enamelled locket with my mother's ever dear face within, done for her when my mother was in England by the famous painter of miniatures, Mr. Malbone.

And now I set about seeing how I was to get away. Our own forces lay at Pennypacker's Mills, or near by; but this I did not know until later, and neither the British nor I were very sure as to their precise situation. It was clear that I must go afoot. As I walked down Second street with this on my mind, I met Colonel Montresor with a group of officers. He stopped me, and, after civilly presenting me, said:

"Harcourt and Johnston"—this latter was he who later married the saucy Miss Franks and her fortune — "want to know if you have duck-shooting here on the Schuylkill."

Suddenly, as I stood, I saw my chance and how to leave the town. I said, "It is rather early, but there are a few ducks in the river. If I had a boat I would try it to-morrow, and then perhaps, if I find any sport, one of you would join me the day after."

"Very good," said they, as well pleased as I.

"And the boat?" I said.

The colonel had one, a rather light skiff, he told me. He used it to go up and down to look at the bridges he was now busily laying. When I asked for its use the next day, he said Yes, if I would send him some ducks; adding that I should need a pass. He would send it that evening by a sergeant, and an order for the skiff, which lay on this side at the lower ferry. I thanked him, and went away happy in the success of my scheme.

I came upon André just after. "Not gone yet?" he said.

I replied, "Not yet; but I shall get away."

He rejoined that he would not like to bet on that, and then went on to say that if my aunt had any trouble as to the officers quartered on her, would she kindly say so. The Hessians were rough people, and an exchange might be arranged. Gentlemen of his own acquaintance could be substituted. He himself was in Dr. Franklin's house. It was full of books, and good ones too.

I thanked him, but said I fancied she was Whig enough to like the Hessians better.

On Second street I bought a smock shirt, rough shoes, and coarse knit stockings, as well as a good snapsack, and, rolling them up securely, left them at home in the hay-loft. My sword and other finery I must needs leave behind me. I had no friends to say good-bye to, and quite late in the evening I merely ran in and kissed my aunt, and received eight hun-

dred pounds in English notes, her offering to the
cause, which I was to deliver to the general. Her
gift to me was one hundred pounds in gold, just
what she gave to my Jack. The larger sum she had
put aside by degrees. It embarrassed me, but to
refuse it would have hurt her.

I carefully packed my snapsack, putting the gold
in bags at the bottom, and covering it with the flan-
nel shirts and extra shoes which made up my outfit.
I could not resist taking my pistols, as I knew that
to provide myself as well in camp would not be possible. The bank-bills I concealed in my long stockings, and would gladly have been without them had
I not seen how greatly this would disappoint my aunt.
She counted, and wisely, on their insuring me a more
than favourable reception. Lastly, I got me a small
compass and some tobacco for Jack.

It must be hard for you, in this happier day, when
it is easy to get with speed anywhere on swift and
well-horsed coaches, to imagine what even a small
journey of a day or two meant for us. Men who
rode carried horseshoes and nails. Those who drove
had in the carriage ropes and a box of tools for re-
pairs. I was perhaps better off than some who drove
or rode in those days, for afoot one cannot be stalled,
nor easily lose a shoe, although between Philadelphia
and Darby I have known it to happen.

I knew the country I was to travel, and up to a
point knew it well; beyond that I must trust to good
fortune. Early in the evening came a sergeant with
the promised order for the boat, and a pass signed

by Sir William Howe's adjutant. At ten I bade my
father good-night and went upstairs, where I wrote
to him, and inclosed the note in one for my aunt.
This I gave to Tom, our coachman, with strict orders
to deliver it late the next day. I had no wish that
by any accident it should too early betray my true
purpose. My gun I ostentatiously cleaned in the late
afternoon, and set in the hall.

No one but my aunt had the least suspicion of
what I was in act to do. At last I sat down and
carefully considered my plan, and my best and most
rapid way of reaching the army. To go through
Germantown and Chestnut Hill would have been the
direct route, for to a surety our army lay somewhere
nigh to Worcester, which was in the county of Philadelphia, although of late years I believe in Montgomery. To go this plain road would have taken me
through the pickets, and where lay on guard the chief
of the British army. This would, of course, be full of
needless risks. It remained to consider the longer road.
This led me down the river to a point where I must
leave it, shoulder my snapsack, and trudge down the
Darby road, or between it and the river. Somewhere
I must cross the highway and strike across-country
as I could to the Schuylkill below Conshohocken, and
there find means to get over at one of the fords.
Once well away from the main road to Darby and
Wilmington, I should be, I thought, safe. After
crossing the Schuylkill I hoped to get news which
would guide me. I hardly thought it likely that the
English who lay at Germantown and Mount Airy

would picket beyond the banks of the Wissahickon. I might have to look out for foraging English west of the Schuylkill, but this I must chance.

I was about to leave home, perhaps forever, but I never in my life went to bed with a more satisfied heart than I bore that night.

XVI

T break of day I woke, and, stealing down-stairs, took gun, powder-horn, and shot, and in the stable loft put the ammunition in the top of my snapsack; then, quickly changing my clothes, concealed those I had put off under the hay, and so set out.

The town was all asleep, and I saw no one until I passed the Bettering-house, and the Grenadiers clean-ing their guns, and powdering their queues and hair, and thence pushed on to the river. The lower ferry, known also as Gray's, lay just a little south of where the Woodlands, Mr. James Hamilton's house, stood among trees high above the quiet river.

A few tents and a squad of sleepy men were at the ferry. I handed my order and pass to the sergeant, who looked me over as if he thought it odd that a man of my class should be so equipped to shoot ducks. However, he read my pass and the order for the boat, pushed the skiff into the water, and proposed, as he lifted my snapsack, to let one of his men row me. I said No; I must drift or paddle on to the ducks, and would go alone. Thanking him, I pushed out into the stream. He wished me good luck, and pocketed my shilling.

It was now just sunrise. I paddled swiftly down-
stream. Not a hundred yards from the ferry I saw
ducks on the east shore, and, having loaded, paddled
over to Rambo's Rock, and was lucky enough to get
two ducks at a shot. Recrossing, I killed two more
in succession, and then pushed on, keeping among
the reeds of the west bank. As I passed Bartram's
famous garden, I saw his son near the river, busy,
as usual, with his innocent flowers.

A half-mile below I perceived, far back of the
shore, a few redcoats. Annoyed no little,—for here
I meant to land,—I turned the boat, still hidden by
the tall reeds, and soon drew up the skiff at Bartram's,
where, taking gun and snapsack, I went up the slope.
I found Mr. William Bartram standing under a fine
cypress his father had fetched as a slip from Florida
in 1731. He was used to see me on the river, but
looked at my odd costume with as much curiosity as
the sergeant had done. He told me his father had
died but ten days before, for which I felt sorry, since,
except by Friends, who had disowned the good botan-
ist, he was held in general esteem. I hastily but
frankly told Mr. Bartram my errand. He said:

"Come to the house. A company or two has just
now passed to relieve the lower fort."

After I had a glass of milk, and good store of
bread and butter, I asked him to accept my gun, and
that he would do me the kindness to return the skiff,
and with it to forward a note, for the writing of
which Mrs. Bartram gave me quill and paper.

I wrote:

"Mr. Hugh Wynne presents his compliments to Mr. Montresor, and returns his skiff. He desires Mr. Montresor to accept two brace of ducks, and begs to express his sincere thanks for the pass, which enabled Mr. Wynne to make with comfort his way to the army. Mr. Wynne trusts at some time to be able to show his gratitude for this favour, and meanwhile he remains Mr. Montresor's obedient, humble servant.

"October 1, 1777.

"Mr. Wynne's most particular compliments to Mr. André. It proved easier to escape than Mr. André thought."

I could not help smiling to think of the good colonel's face when he should read this letter. I glanced at the arms over the fireplace, thanked the good people warmly, and, as I went out, looked back at the familiar words old John Bartram set over the door in 1770:

> 'T is God alone, Almighty Lord,
> The Holy One by me adored.

It seemed the last of home and its associations. I turned away, passed through the grounds, which extended up to the Darby road, and, after a careful look about me, moved rapidly southward. Here and there were farm-houses between spurs of the broken forest which, with its many farms, stretched far to westward. I met no one.

I knew there was a picket at the Blue Bell Inn, and so, before nearing it, I struck into a woodland, and, avoiding the farms, kept to the northwest until

I came on to a road which I saw at once to be Gray's
Lane. Unused to guiding myself by compass, I had
again gotten dangerously near to the river. I pushed
up the lane to the west, and after half an hour came
upon a small hamlet, where I saw an open forge and
a sturdy smith at work. In a moment I recognised
my old master, Lowry, the farrier. I asked the way
across-country to the Schuylkill. He stood a little,
resting on his hammer, not in the least remembering
me. He said it was difficult. I must take certain
country lanes until I got into the Lancaster road,
and so on.

I did not wish to get into the main highway, where
foragers or outlying parties might see fit to be too
curious. I said at last, "Dost not thou know thy old
prentice, Hugh Wynne?"

I felt sure of my man, as he had been one of the
Sons of Liberty, and had fallen out with Friends in
consequence, so that I did not hesitate to relate my
whole story. He was pleased to see me, and bade me
enter and see his wife. As we stood consulting, a
man cried out at the door:

"Here are more Hessians." And as he spoke we
heard the notes of a bugle.

"Put me somewhere," I said, "and quick."

"No," he cried. "Here, set your snapsack back
of this forge. Put on this leather apron. Smudge
your face and hands."

It took me but a minute, and here I was, grimy
and black, a smith again, with my sack hid under a
lot of old iron and a broken bellows.

As they rode up—some two dozen yagers—I let fall the bellows handle, at which my master had set me to work, and went out to the doorway. There, not at all to my satisfaction, I saw the small Hessian, Captain von Heiser, our third and least pleasant boarder, the aide of General Knyphausen. Worse still, he was on Lucy. It was long before I knew how this came to pass. They had two waggons, and, amidst the lamentations of the hamlet, took chickens, pigs, and grain, leaving orders on the paymaster, which, I am told, were scrupulously honoured.

Two horses needed shoeing at once, and then I was told Lucy had a loose shoe, and my master called me a lazy dog, and bid me quit staring or I would get a strapping, and to see to the gentleman's mare, and that in a hurry. It was clear the dear thing knew me; for she put her nose down to my side to get the apples I liked to keep for her in my side pockets. I really thought she would betray me, so clearly did she seem to me to understand that here was a friend she knew. A wild thought came over me to mount her and ride for my life. No horse there of the heavy Brandenburgers could have kept near her. It would have been madness, of course, and so I took my six-pence with a touch of my felt hat, and saw my dear Lucy disappear in a cloud of dust, riding toward the town.

"That was a big risk for thee," said the smith, wiping the sweat from his forehead with his sleeve. "I will mount and ride with thee across-country through the Welsh Barony. There thou wilt not be far from the river. It is a good ten-mile business."

19

After a little, when I had had some milk and rum, the horses were saddled, and we crossed by an ox-road through the forest past the settlement of Cardington, and then forded Cobb's Creek. A cross-road carried us into the Haverford road, and so on by wood-ways to the old Welsh farms beyond Merion.

We met no one on the way save a farmer or two, and here, being near to the Schuylkill, my old master farrier took leave of me at the farm of Edward Masters, which lay in our way, and commended me to the care of this good Free Quaker.

There I was well fed, and told I need to look out only on this side the river for Tories. They were worse than Hessianers, he said, and robbed like highwaymen. In fact, already the Tories who came confidently back with the British army had become a terror to all peaceful folk between Sweedsboro and our own city. Their bands acted under royal commissions, some as honest soldiers, but some as the enemies of any who owned a cow or a barrel of flour, or from whom, under torture, could be wrested a guinea. All who were thus organised came at length to be dreaded, and this whether they were bad or better. Friend Masters had suffered within the week, but, once over the Schuylkill, he assured me, there need be no fear, as our own partisans and foragers were so active to the north of the stream as to make it perilous for Tories.

With this caution, my Quaker friend went with me a mile, and set me on a wood path. I must be put over at Hagy's Ford, he feared, as the river was in flood and too high for a horse to wade; nor was it much better at Young's Ford above. Finally he said, "The ferryman is Peter Skinner, and as bad as the Jersey Tories of that name. If thou dost perceive him to talk Friends' language in reply to thy own talk, thou wilt do well to doubt what he may tell thee. He is not of our society. He cannot even so speak as that it will deceive. Hereabouts it is thought he is in league with Fitz." I asked who was Fitz. He was one, I was told, who had received some lashes when a private in our army, and had deserted. The British, discovering his capacity, now used him as a forager; but he did not stop at hen-roosts.

With this added warning, I went on, keeping north until I came to the Rock road, by no means mis-named, and so through Merion Square to Hagy's Ford Lane and the descent to the river. I saw few people on the way. The stream was in a freshet, and not to be waded. My ferryman was caulking a dory. I said:

"Wilt thou set me across, friend, and at what charge?"

To this he replied, "Where is thee bound?"

I said, "To White Marsh."

"Thee is not of these parts."

"No."

He was speaking the vile tongue which now all but educated Friends speak, and even some of these; but at that time it was spoken only by the vulgar.

"It will cost thee two shillings."

"Too much," said I; "but thou hast me caught. I must over, and that soon."

He was long about getting ready, and now and then looked steadily across the stream; but as to this I was not troubled, as I knew that, once beyond it, I was out of danger.

I paid my fare, and left him looking after me up the deep cut which led to the more level uplands. Whistling gaily, and without suspicion, I won the hilltop by what I think they called Ship Lane.

Glad to be over Schuylkill and out of the way of risks, I sat down by the roadside at the top of the ascent. The forest was dense with underbrush on either side, and the hickories, and below them the sumachs, were already rich with the red and gold of autumn. Being rather tired, I remained at rest at least for a half-hour in much comfort of body and mind. I had been strongly urged by my love for Darthea to await her coming; but decisions are and were with me despotic, and, once I was of a mind to go, not even Darthea could keep me. Yet to leave her to my cousin and his wiles I hated. The mo. I discussed him in the council of my own thoughts, the more I was at a loss. His evident jealousy of one so much younger did seem to me, as it did to my aunt, singular. And why should he wish me to be away, as clearly he did? and why also malign me to my father? I smiled to think I was where his malice could do me no harm, and, rising, pulled my snapsack straps up on my shoulders, and set my face to the east.

Of a sudden I heard to left, "Halt, there!" I saw a long rifle covering me, and above the brush a man's face. Then stepped out to right, as I obeyed the order, a fellow in buckskin shirt and leggings, with a pistol. I cried out, "I surrender;" for what else could I do? Instantly a dozen men, all armed, were in the road, and an ill-looking lot they were. The leader, a coarse fellow, was short and red of face, and much pimpled. He had hair half a foot long, and a beard such as none wore in those days.

I had but time to say meekly, "Why dost thou stop me, friend?" when he jerked off my sack and, plunging a hand inside, pulled out a pistol.

"A pretty Quaker! Here," and he put back the pistol, crying, as the men laughed, "sergeant, strap this on your back. Quick! fetch out the horses; we will look him over later. Up with him behind Joe! Quick—a girth! We have no time to waste. A darned rebel spy! No doubt Sir William may like to have him."

In truth, no time was lost nor any ceremony used, and here was I strapped to the waist of a sturdy trooper, behind whom I was set on a big-boned roan horse, and on my way home again.

"Which way, Captain Fitz?" said the sergeant. "The ford is high." In a moment we were away, in all, as I noted, about a score.

The famous Tory chief—he was no better than a bold thief—made no reply, but rode northwest with his following for the ford below Conshohocken, as I fancied. He went at speed through the open pine forest, I, my hands being free, holding on to my man as well as I could, and, as you may suppose, not very

20

happy. A mile away we came out on a broad road.
Here the captain hesitated, and of a sudden turned
to left toward the river, crying loudly, with an oath,
"Follow me!" The cause was plain.

Some twenty troopers came out into the road not
a hundred yards distant, and instantly rode down on
us at a run. Before we could get as swift a pace,
they were close upon us; and then it was a wild and
perilous race downhill for the river, with yells, curses,
and pistol-balls flying, I as helpless, meanwhile, as
a child. The big roan kept well up to the front
near the captain. Looking back, through dust and
smoke, I saw our pursuers were better horsed and
were gaining. A man near me dropped, and a horse
went down. With my left hand I caught hold of the
strap which fastened me to the rascal in the saddle.
He was riding for life, and too scared to take note of
the act. I gave the buckle a quick jerk, and it came
loose, and the strap fell. I clutched the man by the
throat with my right hand, and squeezed his gullet
with a death-grip. He made with his right hand for a
holster pistol, losing his stirrups, and kicking as
if in a fit. I only tightened my grip, and fetched
him a crack under the left ear with my unengaged
hand. He was reeling in the saddle when, at this
instant, I was aware of a horseman on my right. I
saw a sabre gleam in air above us, and, letting go
my scamp's throat, I ducked quickly below his left
shoulder as I swung him to left, meaning to chance
a fall. He had, I fancy, some notion of his peril, for
he put up his hand and bent forward. I saw the

flash of a blade, and, my captor's head falling forward, a great spout of blood shot back into my face, as the pair of us tumbled together headlong from his horse. I was dimly conscious of yells, oaths, a horse leaping over me, and for a few seconds knew no more. Then I sat up, wiped the blood away, and saw what had happened.

The trooper lay across me dead, his head nearly severed from the trunk, and spouting great jets of blood. A half-dozen dead or wounded were scattered along the road. Not a rod away was the sergeant who had my sack pinned under his horse, and far ahead, in a cloud of dust, that terrible swordsman riding hard after the bandit. Fitz, well mounted, got off, I may add, and, with three or four, swam the river, living to be hanged, as he well deserved.

By the time I was up and staggering forward, bent on recovering my sack, the leader, who had given up the chase, rode toward me. I must have been a queer and horrid figure. I was literally covered with blood and mud. The blood was everywhere,—in my hair, over my face, and down my neck,—but I wanted my precious sack.

"Halt!" he cried out. "Here, corporal, tie this fellow."

"Pardon me," said I, now quite myself. "I was the prisoner of these rascals."

"Indeed? Your name?"

"Hugh Wynne."

"Where from?"

"From the city."

"Where to?"

"To join the army."

"Your business? What are you?"

"Gentleman."

"Good heavens! you are a queer one! We shall see. Are you hurt? No? Great Cæsar! you are an awful sight!"

"I was tied to that fellow you disposed of, and with your permission I will get my snapsack yonder."

"Good; get it. Go with him, corporal, and keep an eye on him."

In a half-hour the dead were stripped and pitched aside, the wounded cared for in haste, and the horses caught.

"Can you ride?" said my captor. "By George, you must!"

"Yes, I can ride."

"Then up with you. Give him a leg."

I wanted none, and was up in a moment on the bare back of a big farm mare; their errand had been, I learned, the purchase of horses. The captain bade me ride with him, and, turning north, we rode away, while the big brute under me jolted my sore bones.

"And now," said the captain, "let me hear, Mr. Wynne, what you have to say. Take a pull at my flask."

I did so, and went on to relate my adventures briefly—the duck-shooting, which much amused him, the escape at the forge, and what else seemed to be needed to set myself right. He looked me over again keenly.

"You had a close thing of it."

"Yes," said I; "you are a terrible swordsman, and a good one, if you will pardon me."

"I meant to cut him on the head, but he put his neck where his head should have been. There is one rascal the less; but I missed the leader. Hang him!"

"He will take care of that," said I.

Then my companion said I must join his troop, and would I excuse his rough dealing with me?

I declared myself well content, and explained as to his offer that I was much obliged, and would think it over; but that I desired first to see the army, and to find my friend, Captain Warder, of the Pennsylvania line.

"Yes; a stout man and dark?"

"No; slight, well built, a blond."

"Good; I know him. I was testing your tale, Mr. Wynne. One has need to be careful in these times." For a few moments he was silent, and then asked sharply, "Where did you cross?"

I told him.

"And are there any outlying pickets above the upper ferry on the west bank?"

I thought not, and went on to tell of the bridging of the river, of the lines of forts, and of the positions held in the city by the Grenadiers and the Highlanders. A large part of the army, I said, was being withdrawn from Germantown, I supposed with a view to attack the forts below the city.

"What you say is valuable, Mr. Wynne." And he

quickened the pace with an order, and pushed on at speed.

It seemed to me time to know into whose company I had fallen, and who was the hardy and decisive rider at my side.

"May I take the liberty to ask with what command I am ?"

"Certainly. I am Allan McLane, at your service. I will talk to you later; now I want to think over what you have told me. I tried to get into the city last week, dressed as an old woman; they took my eggs—Lord, they were aged !—but I got no farther than the middle ferry. Are you sure that troops are being withdrawn from Germantown ?"

I said I was, and in large numbers. After this we rode on in silence through the twilight. I glanced now and then at my companion, the boldest of our partisan leaders, and already a sharp thorn in the side of General Howe's extended line. He was slight, well made, and dark, with some resemblance to Arthur Wynne, but with no weak lines about a mouth which, if less handsome than my cousin's, was far more resolute.

I was ready to drop from my rough steed when we began, about nine at night, to see the camp-fires of our army on either side of Skippack Creek. A halt at the pickets, and we rode on around the right flank among rude huts, rare tents, rows of spancelled horses,—we call it "hobbled" nowadays,—and so at last to a group of tents, the headquarters of the small cavalry division.

"Halt!" I heard; and I literally almost tumbled off my horse, pleased to see the last of him.

"This way, sir," said McLane. "Here is my tent. There is a flask under the pine-needles. I have no feather-bed to offer. Get an hour's rest; it is all you can have just now. When I find out the headquarters, you must ride again." And he was gone.

I found a jug of water and a towel; but my attempts to get the blood and mud out of my hair and neck were quite vain. I gave it up at last. Then I nearly emptied the flask which McLane had left me, set my sack under my head, pulled up a blanket, and in a minute was out of the world of war and sound asleep.

I do not know how long my slumber lasted on my fragrant bed of pine. I heard a voice say, "Are you dead, man?" And shaken roughly, I sat up, confused, and for a moment wondering where I was.

"Come," said McLane. "Oh, leave your sack."

"No," I said, not caring to explain why.

In a moment I was in the saddle, as fresh as need be, the cool October night-wind in my face.

"Where are we bound?" I asked.

"Headquarters. I want you to tell your own news. Hang the man!" We had knocked down a lurching drunkard, but McLane stayed to ask no questions, and in a half-hour we pulled up in the glare of a huge fire, around which lay aides, some asleep and others smoking. A few yards away was a row of tents.

McLane looked about him. "Holloa, Hamilton!" he cried to a slight young man lying at the fire.

"Tell his Excellency I am here. I have news of importance."

A moment after, the gentleman, who was to become so well known and to die so needlessly, came back, and we followed him to the larger of the tents. As he lifted the fly he said, "Captain McLane to see your Excellency."

On a plain farm-house table were four candles, dimly lighting piles of neatly folded papers, a simple camp-bed, two or three wooden stools, and a camp-chest. The officer who sat bareheaded at the table pushed aside a map and looked up. I was once more in the presence of Washington. Both McLane and I stood waiting—I a little behind.

"Whom have you here, sir?"

"Mr. Wynne, a gentleman who has escaped in disguise to join the army. He has news which may interest your Excellency." As he spoke I came forward.

"Are you wounded, sir?"

"No," said I; "it is another man's blood, not mine." He showed no further curiosity, nor any sign of the amazement I had seen in the faces of his aides-de-camp on my appearance at the camp-fire.

"Pray be seated, gentlemen. Do me the favour, Captain McLane, to ask Colonel Hamilton to return. Mr. Wynne, you said?"

"Yes, your Excellency."

Then, to set myself right, I told him that I had had the honour to have met him at the house of my aunt, Mistress Wynne. "With permission, sir," I added,

"I am charged to deliver to your Excellency eight hundred pounds which Mistress Wynne humbly trusts may be of use to the cause of liberty." So saying, I pulled the English notes out of my long stockings and laid them before him.

"I could desire many recruits like you," he said. "Mr. Hamilton, I beg to present Mr. Wynne. Have the kindness to make memoranda of what he may tell us." He spoke with deliberation, as one who had learned to weigh his words, not omitting any of the usual courteous forms, more common at that time than in our less formal day. General Knox came in as we sat down.

He was a sturdy man with a slight stoop, and had left his book-shop in Boston to become the trusted friend and artillery officer of the great Virginian, who chose his men with slight regard to the tongues of the Southern officers, for whom they were too often "shopkeepers" or "mere traders."

"Report of court martial on Daniel Plympton, deserter," said Knox. The general took the papers, and for ten minutes at least was intently concerned with what he read. Then he took a pen and wrote a line and his name, and, looking up, said, "Approved, of course. Parade his regiment at daybreak for execution. Your pardon, gentlemen." And at once he began to put to me a series of questions rather slowly. The absence of hurry surprised me, young as I was, and not yet apt to take in all I might see. Every minute some one appeared. There were papers to sign, aides coming and going, impatient sounds without, a man's death decreed; but with no sign of haste he went on to finish.

At last he rose to his feet, we also standing, of course. "Are you sure that Sir William has recalled any large force from Germantown?—any large force?"

I knew that the Grenadiers and many Hessians had come in, and a considerable part of the artillery, but to what extent or precisely in what numbers I could not be sure. He seemed to me to be intensely considering what I told him.

At last he said, "You must be tired. You have brought much needed help, and also good news." Why good I did not then understand. "And now what do you desire? How can I serve you, Mr. Wynne?"

I said I wished to be in the ranks for a time, until I learned a little more of the duty.

He made no comment, but turning to McLane, said, "Captain McLane, you will care for this gentleman. I trust occasion may serve, Mr. Wynne, to enable me to offer Mistress Wynne my thanks. When you desire a commission, Mr. Hamilton will kindly remind me of the service you have done your country to-day. You have acted with your usual discretion, Captain McLane. Good-night, gentlemen." We bowed and went out.

On our way back we rode a footpace, while the captain, now ready enough to talk, answered my many questions. "Yes; the general was a reserved, tranquil man, with a chained-up devil inside of him;

could lay a whip over a black fellow's back if a horse were ill groomed, or call a man—and he a general —a d—— drunkard; but that would be in the heat of a fight. An archbishop would learn to swear in the army, and the general had no more piety than was good for men who were here to commit murder."

The next day I set out afoot, as I preferred, to look for Jack, and a nice business I found it. The army was moving down the Skippack road to Worcester township, and the whole march seemed, to me at least, one great bewildering confusion of dust, artillery, or waggons stalled, profane aides going hither and thither, broken fences, women standing at farm-house doors, white and crying, as the long line of our foot passed; and over all rang sharp the clink and rattle of flanking cavalry as the horse streamed by, trampling the ruddy buckwheat-fields, and through ravaged orchards and broken gardens. Overhead, in a great cloud high in air, the fine dust was blown down the line by the east wind. It was thick and oppressive, choking man and horse with an exacting thirst, mocked by empty wells and defiled brooks. No one knew where any one else was, and in all my life, save on one memorable evening, I never heard as great a variety of abominable language.

I had done my best, by some change of underclothes and the industrious use of soap and water, to make my appearance less noticeable; but it was still bad enough, because I had no outer garments except those I was wearing. Had I been better dressed, I had fared better; for in those days clothes were con-

sidered, and you might easily tell by his costume if a
man were a mechanic, a farmer, a small trader, or a
gentleman.

I fell at last upon an officer who was endeavouring
to get his horse a share of wayside ditch water. I
said to him, seeing my chance, that his horse had
picked up a stone; if 'he would wait a moment I
would knock it out. On this, and upon his thanking me, I asked where I might find Wayne's brigade,
for in it, as I knew, was my captain of the Third
Pennsylvania Continental foot. He told me it was
a mile ahead. Comforted by this news, I walked on,
keeping chiefly in the fields, for there alone was it
possible to get past the marching columns.

About eleven there was a halt. I passed a lot of
loose women in carts, many canvas-covered commissary waggons, footsore men fallen out, and some
asleep in the fields,—all the scum and refuse of an
army,—with always dust, dust, so that man, beast,
waggons, and every green thing were of one dull
yellow. Then there was shouting on the road; the
stragglers fled left and right, a waggon of swearing
women turned over into a great ditch, and with
laughter, curses, and crack of whip, two well-horsed
cannon and caissons bounded over the field, crashing
through a remnant of snake fence, and so down the
road at speed. I ran behind them, glad of the gap
they left. About a mile farther they pulled up, and
going by I saw with joy the red and buff of the
Pennsylvania line. Behind them there was an
interval, and thus the last files were less dusty. But

for this I should have gone past them. A soldier told me that this was the regiment I sought, and, searching the ranks eagerly as they stood at ease, I walked swiftly along.

"Holloa!" I shouted. I saw Jack look about him. "Jack!" I cried. He ran to me as I spoke. I think I should have kissed him but for the staring soldiers. In all my life I never was so glad. There was brief time allowed for greetings. "Fall in! fall in!" I heard. "March!"

"Come along," he said. And walking beside him, I poured out news of home, of my Aunt Gainor, and of myself.

A mile beyond we halted close to the road near to Methacton Hill, where, I may add, we lay that night of October 2. Having no tents, Jack and I slept on the ground rolled up in Holland blankets, and sheltered in part by a wicky-up, which the men contrived cleverly enough.

I saw on our arrival how—automatically, as it seemed to me—the regiments found camping-grounds, and how well the ragged men arranged for shelters of boughs, or made tents with two rails and a blanket. The confusion disappeared. Sentries and pickets were posted, fires were lit, and food cooked. The order of it seemed to me as mysterious as the seeming disorder of the march.

After some talk with Jack, I concluded to serve as a volunteer, at least for a few weeks, and learn the business better before I should decide to accept the general's kindness. Accordingly I took my place

in the ranks of Jack's company, and, confiding most
of my gold to his care, kept in a belt under my
clothes not more than six guineas, as I remember.
No uniform was to be had at any price; but I was
hardly worse off than half of the men who made up
our company. A musket, and what else was wanted,
I obtained without trouble, and as to the drill, I knew
it well enough, thanks to the Irish sergeant who had
trained us at home.

Our duties, of course, kept us much apart—that is,
Jack and myself; but as he made use, or pretended
to make use, of me as an orderly, I was able to see
more of him that day than otherwise would have
been possible. My pistols I asked him to use until I
could reclaim them, and I made him happy with the
tobacco I brought, and which I soon saw him divid-
ing among other officers; for what was Jack's was
always everybody's. And, indeed, because of this
generosity he has been much imposed upon by the
selfish.

HUGH WYNNE
Vol. II.

HUGH AND DARTHEA.

HUGH WYNNE

I

O N this night of the 2d of October, Jack
told me we should move next morning
or the day after. He had seen General
Wayne on an errand for our colonel.
"A strong talker, the general; but as
ready to fight as to talk." In fact, ammunition was
issued, and before dawn on the 4th the myriad noises
of an army breaking camp aroused me. It was a
gray morning over-head, and cool. When we fell
into line to march, Jack called me out of the ranks.

"There will be a fight, Hugh. Mr. Howe has sent
troops into Jersey, and weakened his hold on the
village, or so it is thought. In fact, you know that,
for it was you that fetched the news. If—I should
get killed—you will tell your aunt—not to forget me
—and Darthea too. And my father—my father,
Hugh—I have written to him and to Miss Wynne—
in case of accident." The day before a fight Jack
was always going to be killed. I do not think I ever
thought I should be hit. I had, later in the war, a
constant impression that, if I were, it would be in the
stomach, and this idea I much disliked. I fell to
thinking of Darthea and Jack, wondering a little,

until the drum and fife struck up, and at the word
we stepped out.

I have no intention to describe more of the fight
at Germantown than I saw, and that was but little.
It seemed to me confusion worse confounded, and
I did not wonder that Graydon had once written
me from the North that we were in a "scuffle for
liberty." The old village was then a long, broken
line of small, gray stone houses, set in gardens on
each side of the highway, with here and there a
larger mansion, like the Chew House, Cliveden, and
that of the Wisters.

The ascent from the city is gradual. At Mount
Airy it is more abrupt, and yet more steep at Chestnut Hill, where my aunt's house, on the right, looks
down on broken forests, through which the centre
marched by the Perkiomen road. The fight on our
right wing I knew nothing of for many a day.

As we tramped on our march of many miles, the
fog which the east wind brought us grew thicker,
but there was less dust. Soon after dusk of morning we came out of the woods, and moved up the
ascent of Chestnut Hill, where I wondered to find
no defences. There were scarce any houses hereabouts, and between the hill and the descent to Mount
Airy our own regiment diverged to the left, off the
road. There were hardly any fences to trouble us,
and where the lines were broken by gardens or
hedges, we went by and remade the line, which was
extended more to left as we moved away from the
highway.

At last we were halted. I was thinking of the glad days I had spent hereabouts when we heard to right the rattle of muskets. McLane had driven in the advanced picket of the enemy. Then the right of our own force fell on some British light infantry, and, swinging the left on the right as a pivot, our own flanking regiment faced their guns, so that we were in part back on the main road. The sun came out for a little, but the fog thickened, and it was lost. I saw Jack look at me, and noticed how flushed he was, and that his face was twitching. So heavy was the fog that, as we saw the guns, we were almost on them. To see fifty feet ahead was impossible. I saw two red flashes as the muskets rang out. There were wild cries, quick orders: " Fire! fire! " And with a great shout we ran forward, I hearing Jack cry, " The bayonet! the bayonet! " I saw in the smoke and fog men fall to right and left, and in a moment was after Jack, who stood between the guns, fencing with two big grenadiers. I clubbed one of them with my butt, and Jack disposed of the second.

Meanwhile the English line had broken, and men who had fallen hurt or were standing were crying for quarter. I saw none given. It was horrible. Our men were paying a sad debt, contracted on the 20th of September, when Gray surprised Wayne at Paoli, and there were no wounded left and few prisoners.

It was a frightful scene, and when the officers succeeded to stop the slaughter, the account had been mercilessly settled, and there was scarce a living enemy in sight. Hastily reforming, we went on again, more to left of the main road, through tents, scattered baggage, dying horses, and misty red splotches where the scarlet uniforms lay thick on the wet grass. As we pushed on, the fog broke a little, and a confused mass of redcoats was seen, some running, and some following tumultuously their colo-nel, Musgrave, into the solid stone house of Clive-den, while the larger number fled down the road and over the fields.

Meanwhile Sullivan's people came up. Two cannon set across the road—they were but four-pounders—opened with small effect on the stone house. The fire from the windows was fierce and fatal. Men dropped here and there, until Jack called to us to lie down. We were at this time behind the mansion. As we lay, I saw Jack walking to and fro, and at last coolly lighting a pipe. Our company lay to the left a little, and away from the rest of the regiment. I called to Jack:

"Let us rush it, Jack, and batter down the back door."

Jack, as I rose, called out to me, with a fierce oath, to keep still and obey orders. I dropped, and as I did so saw an officer with a white flag shot down as he went forward to ask a surrender.

Then we were ordered to march, leaving a regiment to continue the siege; a half-hour had been lost. We went at a run quite two miles down the slope, now on, now off the main street, with red gleams now and then seen through this strangeness of fog. The Brit-ish were flying, broken and scattered, over the fields.

I heard "Halt!" as we swung parallel with the road at the market-place, where the Grenadiers made a gallant stand, as was known by the more orderly platoon firing. Then we, too, broke out in great blaze, and after, what with fog and smoke, a fight in a cellar were as good.

The next minute our people came down the highway, and, between the two fires, the English again gave way. I heard, "Forward! We have 'em!" Some near me hesitated, and I saw Jack run by me crying, "The bayonet, men! After me!" I saw no more of Jack for many a day. We were in the wide market-place—a mob of furious men, blind with fog and smoke, stabbing, clubbing, striking, as chance served. My great personal strength helped me well. Twice I cleared a space, until my musket broke. I fell twice, once with a hard crack on the head from the butt of a musket. As some English went over me, I stabbed at them madly, and got a bayonet thrust in my left arm. I was up in a moment, and for a little while, quite unarmed, was in the middle of a confused mass of men raging and swearing like maniacs. Suddenly there was no one to be seen near me; the noise of muskets, the roar of cannonry, red flashes in the fog in front—that was all, as I stood panting and dazed. Next I heard wild cries back of me, and the crash of musketry. Stephens's division, coming up behind us, began to fire, mistaking us, in the infernal darkness, for an enemy. Our people broke under it, and, passing me, ran, beaten; for the panic spread in the very moment of victory.

I turned, not understanding, stumbled over a dead man, and suddenly felt as if a stone had struck my left leg above the knee. I fell instantly, and for a time—I do not know how long—lost consciousness. It could have been but a few moments.

When I came to myself, I got up, confused and giddy, and began to walk, but with painful difficulty, stumbling over dead or wounded men. Our people were gone, and I saw no one for a little, till I heard the quick tramp of feet and saw through the fog the red line of a marching regiment almost upon me. I made an effort to fall to one side of the street, but dropped again, and once more knew nothing. I think they went over me. When evening came, I found myself lying with others on the sidewalk in front of the Wister house. How I was taken thither I know as little as any. I was stiff, sore, and bloody, but soon able to look about me. I found a bandage around my leg, and felt in no great pain unless I tried to move. Men in red coats came and went, but none heeded my cry for water, until an old servant-woman, who during the fight had refused to leave the house, brought me a drink. I knew her well. I tried to tell her who I was, but my parched tongue failed me, and a rough corporal bade her begone. My watch, a good silver one, was stolen, but my money-belt was safe.

Beside me were many other wounded, one man hideous with his jaw broken; he seemed to me dying. By and by soldiers fetched others. Then a detachment of Virginians went past, in their fringed skin shirts, prisoners, black with smoke, dirty and sullen. Surgeons' aids came and went in and out, and soon the sidewalk was crowded with the wounded. At last they carried a dying general into the house. I asked his name, but no one answered me. It was the brigadier Agnew, now lying at rest in the lower burial-ground by Fisher's Lane.

An officer came and counted us like sheep. About nine a row of carts stopped,—country waggons seized for the purpose,—and, with small tenderness, we were told to get in, or at need lifted in. I was put, with eight others, in a great Conestoga wain without a cover. Soon a detachment of horse arrived, and thus guarded, we were carted away like logs.

The road was never good, but now it was full of holes and cut up by the wheels of artillery. I shall never forget the misery of that ride. I set my teeth and resolved to utter no groan. Before us and behind us were many loads of wounded men, chiefly such as seemed fit to travel. There were nine of us. One was dead before we reached town. As we jolted on, and the great wain rocked, I heard the crack of the drivers' whips, and far and near, in the darkness or near beside me, curses, prayers, mad screams of pain, or men imploring water.

When near to Nicetown, came on a cold, heavy rain which chilled us to shivering. I let my handkerchief get soaked, and sucked it. Then I wet it again—the rain a torrent—and gave it into the hand of him who was next me. He could not use his arm, nor could I turn to aid him, nor did he answer me.

At times we waited on the way, so that it was one
in the morning when we found ourselves in Chestnut
street in front of the State-House.   It was still dismally raining.   We were told to get out, and with
help I did so, a line of soldiers standing on each side;
but no one else near, and it was too dark to see if
any whom I knew were to be seen.   When they pulled
out the man next to me, his head fell, and it was
clear that he was dead.   He was laid on the sidewalk,
and we were helped or made to crawl upstairs to the
long room in the second story.

Here some surgeons' mates came and saw to us
quite patiently.   Soldiers fetched bread and water.
I asked a pleasant kind of youth, a surgeon's aid,
to let my aunt know of my condition.   He said he
would, and, without the least doubt that he would
keep his word, I managed to get into a position of
partial ease, and, sure of early relief, lay awaiting
the sleep which came at last when I was weary with
listening to the groans of less patient men.   The
young surgeon never troubled himself with the de-
livery of my message.   May the Lord reward him!

II

HE mad screams of a man in an agony
of pain awoke me on this Sunday, October 5, at daybreak. The room was a
sorry sight. Some had died in the night,
and were soon carried out for burial. I
lay still, in no great pain, and reflected on the swift
succession of events of the past week. I had had
bad luck, but soon, of course, my aunt or father
would know of my misfortune. As I waited for what
might come, I tried to recall the events of the battle.
I found it almost impossible to gather them into
consecutive clearness, and often since I have wondered to hear men profess to deliver a lucid history
of what went on in some desperate struggle of war.
I do not believe it to be possible.

Being always of a sanguine turn of mind, I
waited, full of comforting hope. About five, after
some scant diet, we were told to get up and go downstairs. It was still dark because of the continuous
rain and overcast skies. I refused to walk, and was
lifted by two men and put in a waggon. A few early
idlers were around the door to see us come out. I
looked eagerly for a face I knew, but saw none. Our
ride was short. We went down Sixth street, and

drew up at the Walnut street front of the prison, called, while the British held the town, the Provost. It was unfinished, a part being temporarily roofed over with boards. At the back was a large yard with high walls. Some, but not all, of the windows in the upper story had transverse slats to keep those within from seeing out. On the Sixth street side were none of these guards, and here the windows overlooked the potter's field, which now we call Washington Square.

As I managed, with some rough help, to get up the steps, a few early risen people paused to look on. Others came from the tumble-down houses on the north side of Walnut street, but again I was unfortunate, and saw none I knew.

My heart fell within me as I looked up at the gray stone walls and grated windows. The door soon closed behind a hundred of us, not a few being of the less severely wounded. Often in passing I had thought, with a boy's horror, of this gloomy place, and tried to imagine how I should feel in such a cage. I was to learn full well.

With fifteen others, I was shut up in a room about twenty-two feet square, on the Sixth street side and in the second story. I was, but for a Virginia captain, the only wounded man among these, the rest being stout country fellows, ruddy and strong, except one lean little man, a clerk, as I learned later, and of the commissary department.

As I had again refused to walk upstairs, I was carried, and not rudely laid down by two soldiers in

a corner of the bare room, now to be for many a
day our prison. The rest sat down here and there
in dull silence, now and then looking at the door
as if there hope was to be expected to enter. I
called the Virginia captain, after an hour had gone
by, and asked him to lift and ease my hurt leg.
He was quick to help, and tender. In a few minutes we came to know each other, and thus began
a friendly relation which has endured to this present
time.

For a day or two soldiers were employed as turnkeys, but then a lot of rough fellows took their
places, and we began to feel the change. I may say
the like of our diet. For a week it was better than
our pot-luck in camp. We had rye bread, tea without sugar, and horribly tough beef; but within two
weeks the diet fell to bread and water, with now
and then salt or fresh beef, and potatoes or beans,
but neither rum nor tea. A surgeon dressed my
wounds for a month, and then I saw him no more.
He was a surly fellow, and would do for me nothing
else, and was usually half intoxicated. The arm was
soon well, but the leg wound got full of maggots
when it was no longer cared for, and only when, in
January, I pulled out a bit of bone did it heal.

Once a day, sometimes in the morning, more often
in the afternoon, we were let out in the yard for an
hour, watched by sentries, and these also we heard
outside under our windows. Observing how quickly
the big country louts lost flesh and colour, I set myself to seeing how I could keep my health. I talked

with my unlucky fellow-prisoners, ate the food even
when it was as vile as it soon became, and when in
the yard walked up and down making acquaintances
as soon as I was able, while most of the rest sat
about moping. I felt sure that before long some one
would hear of me and bring relief. None came.

The scoundrel in charge was a Captain Cunningham. He had risen from the ranks. A great, florid,
burly, drunken brute, not less than sixty years old.
This fellow no doubt sold our rations, for in December we once passed three days on rye bread and
water, and of the former not much; one day we had
no food.

He kicked and beat his victims at times when
drunk, and when I proposed to him to make ten
pounds by letting my aunt know where I was, he
struck me with a heavy iron key he carried, and cut
open my head, as a great scar testifies to this day.

In late December the cold became intense, and we
were given a blanket apiece to cover us as we lay
on the straw. We suffered the more from weather
because it chanced that, in October, the frigate
"Augusta" blew up in the harbour, and broke half
the panes of glass. In December the snow came in
on us, and was at times thick on the floor. Once or
twice a week we had a little fire-wood, and contrived
then to cook the beans, which were rarely brought
us more than half boiled.

We did our best, the captain and I, to encourage our
more unhappy companions, who, I think, felt more
than we the horrors of this prisoned life. We told

stories, got up games, and I induced the men to go
a-fishing, as we called it; that is, to let down their
ragged hats through the broken window-panes by
cords torn from the edges of our blankets. Now and
then the poor folks near by filled these nets with stale
bread or potatoes; but one day, after long ill luck,
a hat was of a sudden felt to be heavy, and was
declared a mighty catch, and hauled up with care.
When it was found to be full of stones, a strange
misery appeared on the faces of these eager, half-
starved wretches. The little clerk said, "We asked
bread, and they gave us a stone," and of a sudden,
broke out into hideous exuberance of blasphemy,
like one in a minute distraught. It was believed
Cunningham had been he who was guilty of this
cruel jest; but as to this I have no assurance. Our
efforts to cultivate patience, and even gay endurance,
by degrees gave way, as we became feeble in body,
and the men too hungry to be comforted by a joke.
At last the men ceased to laugh or smile, or even
to talk, and sat in corners close to one another for
the saving of body warmth, silent and inert.

A stout butcher, of the Maryland line, went mad,
and swore roundly he was George the king. It was
hard, indeed, to resist the sense of despair which
seemed at last to possess all alike; for to starvation
and cold were added such filth and vileness as men
of decent habits felt more than those accustomed
to be careless as to cleanliness.

The Virginian, one Richard Delaney, soon got over
a slight hurt he had, and but for him I should not

be alive to-day. The place swarmed with rats, and
he and I set to work capturing them, filling their
holes as they came out at evening, and chasing them
until we caught them. They kept well in the intense
cold, and when we were given fire-wood, we cooked
and ate them greedily.

Meanwhile death was busy among the starving
hundreds thus huddled together. We saw every day
hasty burials in the potter's field. I wrote twice,
with charred wood, on the half of a handkerchief, and threw it out of the window, but no good
came of this; I suppose the sentries were too vigilant.

A turnkey took one of my guineas, promising to
let my aunt hear of me. I saw him no more. As
to Cunningham, he was either too drunk to care, or
expected to make more out of our rations than by a
bribe, and probably did not credit the wild promises
of a ragged prisoner. At all events, no good came
of our many efforts and devices, which were more
numerous than I have patience to relate. From the
beginning my mind was full of schemes for escaping,
and these I confided to Delaney. They served, at
least, to keep hope fat, as he said.

Early in December I began to have dysentery, and
could eat no more, or rarely; but for Delaney I should
have died. He told me, about this time, that the men
meant to kill Cunningham and make a mad effort to
overcome the guard and escape. It seemed to me the
wildest folly, but they were grown quite desperate
and resolute for something—all but the butcher, who

sang obscene songs or doleful hymns, and sat dejected in a corner.

The day after I saw the little commissary clerk talking in the yard to Cunningham, and that evening this rascal appeared with two soldiers and carried off four of the dozen left in our room; for within a week several had died of the typhus, which now raged among us. The next morning the clerk was found dead, strangled, as I believe, in the night, but by whom we never knew.

I got over the dysentery more speedily than was common, but it was quickly followed by a burning fever. For how long I know not I lay on the floor in the straw, miserably rolling from side to side. The last impression I recall was of my swearing wildly at Delaney because he would insist on putting under me his own blanket. Then I lost consciousness of my pain and unrest, and knew no more for many days. I came to a knowledge of myself to find Delaney again caring for me, and was of a sudden aware how delicious was the milk he was pouring down my throat. What else Delaney did for me I know not, except that he found and cared for my money, and bribed the turnkey with part of it to bring me milk daily for some two weeks. But that we had hid the guineas for a while in the ashes of the fireplace, I should have lost this chance and have died; for one day Cunningham made us all strip, and searched us thoroughly.

About the end of January, Delaney, seeing me bettered and able to sit up a little, told me this strange story. While I was ill and unconscious, an

officer had come to inspect the prison. Cunningham
was very obsequious to this gentleman, and on Delaney's seizing the chance to complain, said it was a
pack of lies, and how could he help the dysentery
and typhus? All jails had them, even in England,
which was too true.

"I went on," said Delaney, "to say that it was an
outrage to confine officers and men together, and
that Mr. Wynne and myself should be put on parole.
The inspector seemed startled at this, and said, 'Who?'
I had no mind to let a lie stand in your way, and I
repeated, 'Captain Wynne,' pointing to you, who
were raving and wild enough. He came over and
stood just here, looking down on you for so long that
I thought he must be sorry for us. Then he said, in
a queer way, and very deliberately, 'Will he get
well? He ought to be better looked after.' Cunningham said it was useless, because the surgeon had
said you would be over yonder (pointing to the potter's field) in a day or two." Which, in fact, was his
cheerful prediction. It was safe to say it of any who
fell ill in the jail.

"This officer appeared puzzled or undecided. He
went out and came back alone, and leaned over you,
asking me to pull the blanket from your face. I
did so, as he seemed afraid to touch it. You, my
dear Wynne, were saying 'Dorothea' over and over;
but who is Dorothea the Lord knows, or you. The
officer at last, after standing awhile, said, 'it was a
pity, but it was of no use; you would die.' As for
me, I told him that we were officers starving, and

were entitled to better treatment. He said he would see to it; and that is all. He went away, and we are still here; but if ever—"

I broke in on Delaney's threat with, "Who was the man?"

"Cunningham consigned me to a more comfortable climate than this when I asked him, and the turnkey did not know."

"What did he look like?" said I.

"He was tall, very dark, and had a scar over the left eye."

"Indeed? Did he have a way of standing with half-shut eyes, and his mouth a little open?"

"Certainly. Why, Wynne, you must know the man."

"I do—I do. He is my cousin."

"I congratulate you." And so saying, he went away to the door to receive our rations, of which now every one except ourselves stole whatever he could lay hands on.

It did seem to me, as I lay still, in much distress of body, and thought over that which I now heard for the first time, that no man could be so cruel as Arthur had shown himself. Time had gone by, and he had done nothing. If, as appeared likely, he was sure I was almost in the act of death, it seemed yet worse; for how could I, a dying man, hurt any one? If for any cause he feared me, here was an end of it. It seemed to me both stupid and villainous. He had warned me that I had everything to dread from his enmity if I persisted in writing to Darthea. As-

II.—2

suredly he had been as good as his word. He was
unwilling to risk any worldly advantages by giving
me a gentleman's satisfaction, and could coldly let
me die far from the love of those dear to me, in not
much better state than a pig perishing in a sty. Nay;
the pig were better off, having known no better
things.

I thought much as I lay there, having been near
to death, and therefore seriously inclined, how impossible it must ever be for me to hate a man enough
to do as Arthur had done. As the days went on, the
hope which each week brought but hatched a new
despair; and still I mended day by day; and for this
there was a singular cause. I kept thinking of the
hour when my cousin and I should meet; and as I
fed this animal appetite I won fresh desire to live,
the motive serving as a means toward health of body.

Concerning what had caused Arthur to lift no
finger of help, I tried to think no more. If it were
because of Darthea, why should he so fear me? I
wished he had more reason. He must have learned
later that I was still alive, and that I was, when he
saw me, in no state to recognise him. It looked worse
and worse as I thought about it, until at last Delaney,
hearing me talk of nothing else, told me I would go
mad like the butcher if I let myself dwell longer
upon it. Thus wisely counselled, I set it aside.

It was now the beginning of February; I was
greatly improved, and fast gaining strength, but had
lost, as I guessed, nearly three stone. There were but
six of us left, the butcher dying last on his rotten

straw in awful anguish of terror and despair.
Delaney and I consoled each other all this dreary
winter, and we did all men could do for the more
unfortunate ones, whose sicknesses and deaths made
this hell of distress almost unbearable.

The diet was at times better, and then again, as a
drunkard's caprice willed, there might be no food for
a day. If we were ourselves wretched and starved,
we were at least a source of comfort and food to
those minor beings to whom we furnished both board
and bed.

I do not mean to tell over the often-heard story
of a prison; what we did to while away the hours;
how we taxed our memories until the reading, long
forgotten, came back in morsels, and could be put
together for new pleasure of it.

There was one little man who had been a broken-
down clergyman, and had entered the army. His
chief trouble was that he could get no rum, and of
this he talked whenever we would listen. He had,
like several sots I have known, a remarkable memory,
and was thus a great resource to us, as he could repeat whole plays, and a wonderful amount of the
Bible. As it was hard to arouse him, and get him
to use his power to recall what he had read, in an evil
hour we bribed him with some choice bits of our
noble diet. After this the price would rise at times,
and he became greedy. His mind gave way by degrees, but he still kept his memory, being also more
and more eager to be paid for his power to interest
or amuse us.

When at last he grew melancholy and sleepless, and walked about all night, it was a real addition to our many evils. He declared that he must soon die, and I heard him one night earnestly beseeching God, in language of great force and eloquence, to forgive him. In the morning he was dead, having strangled himself resolutely with a strip of blanket and a broken rung of a stool, with which he had twisted the cord. It must have taken such obstinate courage as no one could have believed him to possess. He had no capacity to attach men, and I do not think we grieved for him as much as for the loss of what was truly a library, and not to be replaced.

On the 3d of February I awakened with a fresh and happy thought in my mind. My good friend the late lamented Dr. Franklin, used to say that in sleep the mind creates thoughts for the day to hatch. I am rather of opinion that sleep so feeds and rests the brain that when first we awaken our power to think is at its best. At all events, on that day I suddenly saw a way to let the sweet outside world know I was alive.

At first I used to think of a chaplain as a resource, but I never saw one. The surgeon came no more when I grew better. Being now able to move about a little, I had noticed in the yard at times, but only of late, a fat Romanist priest, who was allowed to bring soup or other diet to certain prisoners. I soon learned that, because Cunningham was of the Church of Rome, those who were of his own faith were favoured. Indeed, now and then a part of my lessening guineas obtained from these men a share of the supplies which the priest, and, I may add, certain gray-clad sisters, also brought; but this was rare.

That day in the yard I drew near to the priest, but saw Cunningham looking on, and so I waited with the patience of a prisoned man. It was quite two weeks before my chance came. The yard being small, was literally full of half-clad, whole-starved men, who shivered and huddled together where the sunlight fell. Many reeled with weakness; most were thin past belief, their drawn skin the colour of a decayed lemon. From this sad crowd came a strange odour, like to cheese, and yet not like that. Even to remember it is most horrible. Passing near to a stout old Sister of Charity, I said quietly:

"I have friends who would help me. For God's love, see Miss Wynne in Arch street, across from the Meeting."

"I will do your errand," she said.

"Others have said so, sister, and have lied to me."

"I will do it," she said. "And if she is away?"

I thought of my father. He seemed my natural resource, but my cousin would be there. A final hope there was. I was foolish enough to say, "If she is not in town, then Miss Darthea Peniston, near by. If you fail me, I shall curse you while I live."

"I will not fail you. Why should you poor prisoners be so ill used? Trust me."

I turned away satisfied, remembering that when I left Darthea was about to return. If she came to know, that would be enough. I had faith in her friendship and in her; and—if ever I saw her again —should I tell her what now I knew of Arthur Wynne? I learned many lessons in this awful place, and among them caution. I would wait and see.

Both Delaney and I strongly desired an exchange, and not merely a parole. We imagined exchanges to be frequent. My own dilemma, Delaney pointed out, was that I was not in the army, although I had been of it. And so we speculated of things not yet come about, and what we would do when they did come.

The next day went by, and the morning after, it being now February 19, we were all in the yard. A turnkey came and bade me follow him. I went, as you may imagine, with an eager heart, on the way, as I hoped, out of this death in life. As I questioned the man, he said there was an order for a lady to see me.

Now at this time my hair was a foot long, and no way to shear it. We had taken the blankets of the dead, and made us coats by tearing holes through which to thrust our arms. Then, as we lacked for buttons, or string for points, we could do no more than wrap these strange gowns about us so as to cover our rags.

My costume troubled me little. I went to the foul-smelling room, now empty, and waited until the man came back. As he opened the door, I saw the good Sister of Charity in the hall, and then—who but Dar-thea? She was in a long cloak and great muff, and held in her hand a winter mask.

Seeing me in this blue blanket, all unshorn, and with what beard I had covering my face, when all men but Hessians shaved clean, I wonder not, I say, that, seeing this gaunt scarecrow, she fell back, saying there was some mistake.

I cried out, "Darthea! Darthea! Do not leave me. It is I! It is I, Hugh Wynne."

"My God!" she cried, "it is Hugh! It is! it is!" At this she caught my lean yellow hand, and went on to say, "Why were we never told? Your Aunt Wynne is away. Since we thought you dead, she has ordered mourning, and is gone to her farm, and leaves the servants to feed those quartered on her. But you are not dead, thank God! thank God! I was but a day come from New York, and was at home when the dear old sister came and told me. I made her sit down while I called my aunt. Then Arthur came, and I told him. He was greatly shocked to hear it. He reminded me that some while before he had told me that he had seen a man who looked like you in the jail, and was about to die; and now could it—could it have been you? He is for duty at the forts to-day, but to-morrow he will get you a parole. He supposed a day made no matter; at all events, he must delay that long. I never saw him so troubled."

"Well he might be," thought I. I merely said, "Indeed?" But I must have looked my doubt, for she added quickly:

"Who could know you, Mr. Wynne?"

I stood all this while clutching at my blanket to cover my filth and rags, and she, young and tender,

now all tears, now flashing a smile in between, like
the pretty lightning of this storm of gentle pity.

"And what fetched you here to this awful place?"
I said. "God knows how welcome you are, but—"

"Oh," she cried, "when Arthur went, I said I
would wait, but I could not. My aunt was in a rage,
but I would go with the dear sister; and then I found
Sir William, and Mr. Montresor was there; and you
will be helped, and an end put to this wickedness.
But the parole Arthur will ask for—that is better."

"Darthea," I said hoarsely, my voice breaking, "I
have been here since early in October. I have been
starved, frozen, maltreated a hundred ways, but I can
never take a parole. My friend Delaney and I are
agreed on this. As to exchanges, I have no rank,
and I may be a year inactive. I will take my chance
here." I think death had been preferable to a parole
obtained for me by Arthur Wynne. No; I was not
made of my father-rock to do this and then to want
to kill the man. I could not do that. I put it on
the parole. Delaney and I had agreed, and on this
I stood firm.

She implored me to change my mind. "How obstinate you are!" she cried. "Do you never change?
Oh, you are dreadfully changed! Do not die; you
must not." She was strange in her excitement.

Then I thought to ask to have Delaney in, and
to bid him tell that vile and wicked story; but it
seemed no place nor time to hurt her who had so
helped me, daring to do what few young women had
ever dared even to think of. As I hesitated, I was

struck with a thought which was like a physical pain.
It put myself and the other wretched business quite
out of my head.

"O Darthea!" I cried, "you should never have
come here. Go at once. Do not stay a minute. This
is a house poisoned. Seven died of fever in this room.
Write me what else is to say, but go; and let me have
some plain clothes from home, and linen and a razor
and scissors and, above all," and I smiled, "soap.
But go! go! Why were you let to come?"

"I will go when I have done. Why did I come?
Because I am your friend, and this is the way I read
friendship. Oh, I shall hear of it too. But let him
take care; I would do it again. And as to the parole,
he shall get it for you to-morrow, if you like it or not.
I will write to you, and the rest you shall have; and
now good-by. I am to be at home for Mr. Montresor in a half-hour. This is but a bit of payment for
the ugly little girl, who is very honest, sir, I do assure you."

"Do go," I cried. "And, oh, Darthea, if this is
your friendship, what would be your love!"

"Fie! fie! Hush!" she said, and was gone.

In two hours came a note, and I learned, for I had
asked to hear of the war, that Washington was not
dead. We had been told that he was. I heard, too,
of Burgoyne's surrender, news now near to five
months old, of Count Donop's defeat and death, of
the fall of our forts on the Delaware, of Lord Cornwallis gone to England, of failures to effect exchanges.
Then she went on to write: "Your father was, strange

to say, roused out of a sort of lethargy by the news of your death. Jack managed to get a letter to your aunt to say you were missing, and Arthur had search made for you; but many nameless ones were buried in haste, and he could not find your name on the lists of prisoners." None had been made to my knowledge. "We all thought you dead. Your aunt is in mourning, but only of late, thinking it could not be that you were lost to her. It is well, as you do not like your cousin, that you should know how kind he has been, and what a comfort to your father. Indeed,— and now it will amuse you,—he told Arthur, you being dead, he had still a son, and would consider Arthur as his heir. All this ought to make you think better of Arthur, whom, I do believe, you have no reason to dislike. I beg of you to think otherwise of him; my friends must be his. And have I not proved I am a friend? I fear I cannot at once get news of you to Mistress Wynne, who has gone to live at the Hill Farm." And so, with other kind words, she ended, and I, putting the note in a safe place, sat on my straw, and laughed to think of Arthur's filial care and present disappointment.

In a few hours came the turnkey, quite captured by Darthea, and no doubt the richer for a good fee He fetched a portmantle just come, and an order to put me in a room alone. I left Delaney with sorrow, but hoped for some way to help him. In an hour I was clean for the first time in five months, neatly shaven, my hair somehow cut, and I in sweet linen and a good, plain gray suit, and a beaver to match.

Then I sat down to think, the mere hope of escape making me weak, and what came of it you shall hear.

The next day I was ordered forth with a few others, and, luckily, late in the afternoon. I covered my fine clothes with the blanket and went out. In the yard, just before our time was up, I saw the sister, to my delight, and perceived too, with joy, that the prisoners did not recognise me, decently shaven as I was. Only one thing held me back or made me doubt that I was now close to liberty : I was so feeble that at times I staggered in walking. I knew, however, that when my new clothes became familiar in the jail my chance of escape would be over. I must take the present opportunity, and trust to luck.

My scheme I had clearly thought out. I meant, when in the yard, to drop the blanket cover, and coolly follow the sister, trusting to my being taken, in my new garments, for a visitor. It was simple, and like enough to succeed if my strength held out. It was now dusk, and a dark, overclouded day. A bell was rung, this being the signal for the gang of prisoners to go to their rooms. Falling back a little, I cast aside the blanket, and then following the rest, was at once in the hall, dimly lit with lanterns. It was some eighty feet long. Here I kept behind the group, and went boldly after the stout sister. No one seemed disposed to suspect the well-dressed gentleman in gray. I went by the turnkey, keeping my face the other way. I was now some fifteen feet from the great barred outer door. The two sentries stepped back to let the sister go by. Meanwhile the gate-keeper, with his back to me, was busy with his keys. He unlocked the door and pulled it open. A greater lantern hung over it. I was aghast to see the wretch, Cunningham, just about to enter. He was sure to detect me. I hesitated, but the lookout into space and liberty was enough for me. The beast fell back to let the sister pass out. I dashed by the guards, upset the good woman, and, just outside of the doorway, struck Cunningham in the face—a blow that had in it all the gathered hate of five months of brutal treatment. He fell back, stumbling on the broad upper step. I caught him a second full in the neck, as I followed. With an oath, he rolled back down the high steps, as I, leaping over him, ran across Walnut street. One of the outside guards fired wildly, but might as well have killed some passer-by as me.

Opposite were the low houses afterward removed to enlarge Independence Square. I darted through the open door of a cobbler's shop, and out at the back into a small yard, and over palings into the open space. It was quite dark, as the day was overcast. I ran behind the houses to Fifth street. Here I jumped down the raised bank and turned northward.

Beside me was a mechanic going home with his lantern, which, by military law, all had to carry after fall of night. He looked at me as if in doubt, and I took my chance, saying, "Take no notice. I am a prisoner run away from the jail."

"I'm your man," he said. "Take the lantern, and walk with me. I hear those devils." And indeed there was a great noise on Walnut street and in the square. Men were dimly seen running to and fro, and seizing any who had no lanterns.

We went on to Chestnut street, and down to Second. I asked him here to go to Dock Creek with me.

At my own home I offered him my last guinea, but he said No. I then told him my name, and desired he would some day, in better times, seek me out. And so the honest fellow left me. Many a year after he did come to me in debt and trouble, and, you may be sure, was set at ease for the rest of his life.

Looking up, I saw light in the window, and within I could see Arthur and three other officers. The liquors and decanters were on a table, with bread and cheese, plain to be seen by hungry eyes. My father's bulky form was in his big Penn arm-chair, his head fallen forward. He was sound asleep. Colonel Tarleton had his feet on a low stool my mother used for her basket of sewing material and the stockings she was so constantly darning. Harcourt and Colonel O'Hara were matching pennies, and my cousin was standing by the fire, speaking now and then, a glass in his hand.

The dog asleep in the stable was no more considered than was my poor father by these insolent guests. An almost overmastering rage possessed me as I gazed through the panes; for no one had closed the shutters as was usually done at nightfall. I was hungry, cold, and weak, and these—! I turned away, and went down the bank of Dock Creek to the boat-house. It was locked, and this made it likely my boat had escaped the strict search made by the British. No one being in sight, I went around the house to the stable at the farther end of the garden. As I came near I smelt the smoke of our old Tom's pipe, and then seeing him, I called softly, "Tom! Tom!"

. He jumped up, crying, "Save us, Master Hugh!" and started to run. In a moment I had him by the arm, and quickly made him understand that I was alive, and needed food and help. As soon as he was recovered from his fright, he fetched me milk, bread, and a bottle of Hollands. After a greedy meal, he carried to the boat, at my order, the rest of the pint of spirits, oars, paddle, and boat-key. On the way it occurred to me to ask for Lucy. She had been seized by the Hessian, Von Heiser, and was in my aunt's stable. I had not asked about the mare without a purpose; I was in a state of intense mental clearness, with all my wits in order. In the few minutes that followed I told Tom not to let any one know of my coming, and then, pushing off, I dropped quietly down the creek.

It was cold and very dark, and there was some ice afloat in small masses, amidst which my boat, turning with no guidance, moved on the full of the ebb tide toward the great river. For about two hundred yards I drifted, lying flat on my back. At the outlet of the creek was a sudden turn where the current almost fetched me ashore on the south bank. There from the slip nearly overhead, as the boat whirled around, I heard a sentinel call out, "Stop there, or I fire!" I remained motionless, feeling sure that he would not risk an alarm by reason of a skiff gone adrift. As he called again the boat slewed around, and shot, stern first, far out into the great flood of the Delaware. Never had it seemed to me a dearer friend. I was free. Cautiously using the paddle without rising, I was soon in mid-river. Then I sat up, and, taking a great drink of the gin, I rowed upstream in the darkness, finding less ice than I had thought probable.

My plan now was to pull up to Burlington or Bristol; but I soon found the ice in greater masses, and I began to be puzzled. I turned toward Jersey, and hither and thither, and in a few minutes came upon fields of moving ice. It was clear that I must land in the city, and take my chance of getting past the line of sentries. I pulled cautiously in at Arch street, and saw a sloop lying at a slip. Lying down, I used the paddle until at her side. Hearing no sound, I climbed up over her low rail, and made fast the boat. I could see that no one was on deck. A lighted lantern hung from a rope near the bow. I took it down, and boldly stepped on the slip. A sentry, seeing me come, said, "A cold night, captain." "Very," I rejoined, and went on up the slope. Chance had favoured me. In a few minutes I saw my aunt's house, shut up, but with a light over the transom of the hall door. I passed on, went up to Third street, around to the back of the premises, and over the palings into the long garden behind the dwelling.

As I stood reflecting I heard Lucy neigh, and no
voice of friend could have been sweeter. I smiled
to think that I was a man in the position of a thief,
but with a right to take whatsoever I might need.
I began to suspect, too, that no one was in the house.
Moving toward it with care, I found all the back
doors open, or at least not fastened. A fire burned
on the kitchen hearth, and, first making sure of the
absence of the servants, I shot the bolt of the hall door,
fastened the pin-bolts of the windows which looked
on the front street, and went back to the kitchen with
one overruling desire to be well warmed. I had been
cold for four months. Making a roaring fire, I
roasted myself for half an hour, turning like a duck
on a spit. Heat and good bread and coffee I craved
most. I found here enough of all, but no liquors;
the gin I had finished, a good pint, and never felt it.
Still feeling my weakness, and aware that I needed
all my strength, I stayed yet a minute, deep in
thought, and reluctant to leave the comfort of the
hearth. At last I took a lantern and went upstairs.
The china gods and beasts were all put away, the
silver tankards and plate removed, the rugs gone.
My good Whig aunt had done her best to make her
despotic boarders no more comfortable than she
could help. All was neglect, dust, and dirt; pipes
and empty bottles lay about, and a smell of stale tobacco smoke was in the air. Poor Aunt Gainor!

Upstairs the general had moved into the room
sacred to her spinster slumbers. The servants had
taken holiday, it seemed, and the officers appeared

to have been indifferent, or absent all day; for this
room was in a vile condition, with even the bed not
yet made up, and the curtains torn. In this and the
front chamber, used commonly as my aunt's own
sitting-room, was a strange litter of maps, papers,
and equipments, two swords, a brace of inlaid pistols,
brass-plated, two Hessian hats, the trappings of a
Brunswick chasseur, and a long military cloak with
a gold-braided regimental number under a large
crown on each shoulder. A sense of amusement stole
over me, although I was so tired I could have fallen
with fatigue. I was feeling my weakness, and suffering from what even to a man in health would have been
great exertion. A full flask of rum lay on the table;
I put it in my pocket, leaving the silver cover. Next
I put on the long cloak, a tall Anhalter helmet, and
a straight, gold-mounted sword. The pistols I took
also, loading and priming them, and leaving only
the box where they had lain.

It was now almost ten, and I could not hope to
be long left in easy possession. Then I turned
to the table. Much of the confused mass of papers
was in German. I put in my pocket a beautifully drawn map of our own lines at Valley Forge.
I gave it to Alexander Hamilton soon after the
war.

A small pipe—I think the Germans call meer-
schaum—I could not despise, nor a great bundle of
tobacco, which I thrust into the inside pouch of the
cloak.

Last I saw a sealed letter to Lieutenant-Colonel
II.—3

Ernst Ludwig Wilhelm von Specht, also one to Colonel Montresor. These were much to my purpose. Finally, as I heard the great clock on the stairway strike ten, I scribbled on a sheet of paper under Von Knyphausen's arms, "Captain Allan McLane presents his compliments to General von Knyphausen, and hopes he will do Captain McLane the honour to return his visit.—February 20, 1778, 10 P. M."

I laughed as I went downstairs, in that mood of merriment which was my one sign of excitement at the near approach of peril. A pause at the grateful fire, and a moment later I was saddling Lucy, looking well to girth and bit, and last buckling on the spurs of a Hessian officer.

In a few minutes I was trotting up Fifth street. I knew only that the too extended lines had been drawn in close to the city, after the sharp lesson at Germantown; but I did not know how complete were the forts and abatis crossing from the Delaware to the Schuylkill, to the north of Callowhill street. I meant to pass the lines somewhere, trusting to the legs of Lucy, who well understood the change of riders, and seemed in excellent condition.

I turned off into the fields to the westward at Vine street, riding carefully; and soon, as I moved to north, saw that fences, fruit-trees, and the scattered remnant of the wood were gone. Stumbling through mud and over stumps, I began to see before me one of Montresor's blockhouses, and presently, for now the night was far too clear, the forms of sentries on top. Dismounting, I moved aside a hundred yards, so that I passed unseen between two of these forts. But a good piece to the north of them I came on a strong stockade, and saw beyond it a hazy mass of what I took to be a monster tangle of dead trees, well fitted to delay a storming-party. Then I remembered my ride with Montresor. I was caught. I stood still in the night, wondering what to do: behind me the hum and glow of the city, before me freedom and darkness.

A man thinks quickly in an hour like that. I mounted, feeling the lift of my weak body an exertion, and rode back into Vine, and so to Front street. A hundred yards before me was a great camp-fire, to left of where the road to Germantown diverges. I saw figures about it passing to and fro. I felt for my pistols in the holsters of the saddle, and cocked the one on my right, loosened the long straight Hessian blade, and took the two letters in my bridle-hand.

As I rode up I saw, for the fire was brightly blazing, that there were tents, pickets to left and right, men afoot, and horses not saddled. A sergeant came out into the road. "Halt!" he cried. In broken English, I said I had a letter for Colonel Montresor, to be given in the morning when he would be out to inspect the lines, and one for Lieutenant-Colonel von Specht. The man took the letters. I meant to turn back, wheel, and go by at speed; but by evil luck a wind from the north blew open my cloak, and in the brilliant firelight he saw my gray clothes.

"Holloa!" he cried. "What's the word? You

are not in uniform. Get off!" So saying, he caught
the rein he had dropped, a man or two running toward us as he spoke.

If I could, I would have spared the man: but it
was his life or mine; I knew that. I fired square at
his chest, the mare reared, the man fell with a cry.
I let Lucy have both spurs. She leaped as a deer
leaps, catching a fellow in the chest with her shoulder,
and was off like a crazy thing. I looked ahead; the
way was clear. A glance back showed me the road
full of men. I heard shouts, orders, shot after shot.
I was soon far beyond danger, and going at racing
speed through the night; but I had scared up a pleasant hornets' nest. The last picket was a quarter of
a mile ahead, perhaps. I pulled up, and with difficulty made the mare walk. There were fires on both
sides, and a lot of alert soldiers out in the road. I
turned off into the fields behind a farm-house, glad
of the absence of fences. The next moment I felt
the mare gather herself with the half-pause every
horseman knows so well. She had taken a ditch,
and prettily too.

Keeping off the highway, but in line with it, I
went on slowly, leaning over in the saddle. After
a mile, and much stumbling about, I ceased to hear
noises back of me, and turned, approaching the road
I had left. No one was in sight. Why I was not
followed by the horse I know not. I wrapped my
cloak about me, and rode on up the deserted highway. I was free, and on neutral ground. All I had
to fear was an encounter with one of the foraging

parties which kept the country around in constant
terror. I met no one. The sole unpleasant thought
which haunted my cold night ride was the face of
the poor devil I had shot. I put it aside. Prison
life had at least taught me the habit of dismissing
the torment of vain reflection on an irreparable past

I went by the old burying-ground of Germantown,
and the rare houses, going slowly on account of the
road, which was full of deep holes, and so through
the market-place where we made our last charge.

At last I breasted the slippery rise of Chestnut
Hill, and throwing my cloak over the mare, that I
had taught to stand, went up to the door of my Aunt
Gainor's house.

I knocked long before I was heard. A window
was opened above me, and a voice I loved called out
to know what I wanted. I replied, "It is I, Hugh.
Be quick!" A moment later I was in her dear old
arms, the servants were called up, and my faithful
Lucy was cared for. Then I fell on a settle, at the
limit of my strength. I was put to bed, and glad I
was to stay there for two days, and not even talk.
Indeed, what with good diet and milk and spirits and
clean sheets, I slept as I had not done for many a
night.

As soon as I was up and fit to converse, I was
made to tell my story over and over. Meanwhile
my aunt was desperately afraid lest we should be
visited, as was not rare, by foragers or Tory partisans. I must go, and at once. Even war was to
be preferred to this anxiety. But before I went she

must tell me what she thought of this strange business of my cousin. I had been wise not to tell Darthea. A rascal like Arthur would trip himself up soon or late. Then she fell to thinking, and, bidding me cease for a little, sat with her head in her large hands, having her elbows on the table.

"Hugh," she said at last, "he must have more cause to be jealous than we know. He has still more now. Is it only the woman? Can it be anything about the estate in Wales? It must be; you remember how he lied to us about it; but what is it?"

"He thinks I regret the loss of Wyncote, and that I would like to have it. I am afraid I found it pleasant to say so, seeing that it annoyed him."

"I wish he may have some such cause to hate you, and no other. But why? Your grandfather made a legal conveyance of an unentailed property, got some ready money,—how much I never knew,—and came away. How can you interfere with Arthur? The Wynnes, I have heard, have Welsh memories for an insult. You struck him once."

"The blow!" and I smiled. "Yes; the woman! Pray God it be that. The estate—he is welcome to it. I hardly think a Welsh home would bribe me to leave my own country. But I do not see, aunt, why you so often talk as if Wyncote were ours, and stolen from us. I do not want it, and why should I?"

"Is not that unreasonable, Hugh?" she returned, with more quietness in the way of reply than was usual when she was arguing. "You are young now. The anger between England and ourselves makes all things in Great Britain seem hateful to you, to me, to all honest colonials; but this will not last. Peace will come one day or another, and when it does, to be Wynne of Wyncote—"

"Good gracious, Aunt Gainor! let us set this aside. Arthur Wynne's lies have stirred us all to think there must be some reason for such a keen desire to mislead me, you, and my father—above all, my father. But it is my father's business, not mine; nor, if I may be excused, is it yours."

"That is true, or would be if your father were well or interested. He is neither—neither; and there is something in the matter. I shall ask my brother."

"You have done that before."

"I have, but I got nothing. Now he is in such a state that he may be more free of speech. I think he could be got to tell me what neither he nor my own father liked to speak of."

Upon this, I told my aunt that I did trust she would not take advantage of my father's weak mind to get that which, when of wholesome wits, he had seen fit to conceal. I did not like it.

"Nonsense!" she cried, "nonsense! if you could have the old home—"

"But how can I? It is like promising fairy gold, and I don't want it. I should like to go there once and see it and my cousins, and come home to this country."

I was, in fact, weary of the thing, and my aunt would have talked it over all day. She could not see why I was so set in my mind. She kept urging

that something would turn up about it, and we should
have to act; then I would change my mind. I hardly
knew why that which once had been a delightful and
mysterious bait now lured me not at all. What with
the great war, and my own maturity, and Darthea,
Wyncote had shrunken out of the world of my desires. It was too dreamy a bribe for one of my turn
of mind. I would have given half Wales for an hour
alone with Arthur Wynne.

Then through my meditations I heard, "Well, mark
my word, Master Absolute; there is some flaw in
their title, and—and soon or late—"

"Oh, please, aunt—"

"Well, do not make up your mind. I am afraid
of you when you make up your mind. You are as
set in your ways as your father. Do you remember
what Nicholas Waln said of him: 'When John
Wynne puts down his foot, thou hast got to dig it
up to move him'?"

She was right; nor did I defend myself. I laughed,
but was sad too, thinking of my poor old father,
whom I could not see, and of how far he was now
from being what his friend had described.

I said as much. My aunt replied, "Yes, it is too
true; but I think he is less unhappy, and so thinks
Dr. Rush."

After this our talk drifted away, and my aunt
would once more hear of my note in McLane's name
left for the Hessian general. "I hope yet to ask him
of it," she cried, "and that dear Mr. André—I can
see his face. It is the French blood makes him so

gentle. Catch him for me in the war. I should like
to have him on parole for a sixmonth." And at this
she laughed, and heartily, as she did most things.

When this talk occurred we were in a great front
room in the second story. There was a deep bow-
window to westward, and here my aunt liked to be
at set of sun, and to look over what seemed to be a
boundless forest; for the many scattered farms were
hid away in their woodland shelters, so that from
this vantage of height it looked as though the country beyond might be one great solitude. Nearer
were well-tilled farms, on which the snow still lay in
melting drifts.

As we sat, I was smoking the first tobacco I had
had since I left the jail. This habit I learned long
before, and after once falling a captive to that con-
soler and counsellor, the pipe, I never gave it up. It
is like others of the good gifts of God : when abused
it loses its use, which seems a silly phrase, but does
really mean more than it says. Jack hath somewhere
writ that words have souls, and are always more than
they look or say. I could wish mine to be so taken.
And as to tobacco and good rum, Jack said—but I
forget what it was—something neat and pretty and
honest, that took a good grip of you. The tricks an
old fellow's memory plays him are queer enough. I
often recall the time and place of something clever
a friend hath said long ago, but when I try to get it
back, I have but a sense of its pleasantness, as of a
flavour left in the mouth, while all the wise words
of his saying are quite forgot. Dr. Rush thinks that

we are often happy or morose without apparent cause,
when the mind is but recalling the influence of some
former joy or grief, but not that which created either.
The great doctor had many hard sayings, and this
was one.

As I sat reflecting, I felt a sudden consciousness
of the pleasure my tobacco gave, and then of how
delightful it was to be, as it were, growing younger
day by day, and of how, with return of strength,
came a certain keenness of the senses as to odours,
and as to what I ate or drank. It seemed to me a
kind of reward for suffering endured with patience.

My Aunt Gainor sat watching me with the pleasure
good women have over one too weak to resist being
coddled. When I had come to this happy condition
of wanting a pipe, as I had jolted out of my pouch
the tobacco I stole, she went off and brought the good
weed out of the barn, where she had saved her last
crop under what scant hay the Hessian foragers
left her. I must smoke in her own library, a thing
unheard of before; she loved to smell a good tobacco.

"O Aunt Gainor!"

"But Jack!" she said. She did not like to see
Jack with a pipe. He looked too like a nice girl, with
his fair skin and his yellow hair.

I smoked on in mighty peace of mind, and soon
she began again, being rarely long silent, "I hope
you and your cousin will never meet, Hugh."

The suddenness of this overcame me, and I felt
myself flush.

"Ah!" she said, "I knew it. There is little love lost between you."

"There are things a man cannot forgive."

"Then may the good God keep you apart, my son."

"I trust not," said I. "I can forgive an insult, even if I am Welsh and a Wynne; but oh, Aunt Gainor, those added weeks of misery, foulness, filth, and pain I owe to this man! I will kill him as I would kill any other vermin." Then I was ashamed, for to say such things before women was not my way.

"I could kill him myself," said my aunt, savagely. "And now do have some more of this nice, good gruel," which set me to laughing.

"Let him go," said I, "and the gruel too."

"And that is what you must do, sir. You must go. I am all day in terror."

And still I stayed on, pretty easy in mind; for my aunt had set a fellow on watch at Mount Airy, to let us know if any parties appeared, and we kept Lucy saddled. I sorely needed this rest and to be fed; for I was a mere shadow of my big self when I alighted at her door on that memorable 20th of February.

The day before I left this delightful haven between jail and camp, came one of my aunt's women slaves with a letter she had brought from the city, and this was what it said:

"DEAR MISTRESS WYNNE: At last I am honoured with the permission to write and tell you that Mr. Hugh Wynne is alive. It was cruel that the general would not earlier grant me so small a favour as to pass an open letter; but Arthur found much difficulty, by reason, I fear, of your well-known opinions. He was on the way to the jail when he heard of Mr. Hugh Wynne's having escaped, after dreadfully injuring the poor man who took such good care of him all winter. How it came that he lay five months in this vile abode neither Arthur nor I can imagine, nor yet how he got out of the town.

"Arthur tells me that insolent rebel, Allan McLane, broke into your house and stole the beautiful sword the Elector of Hesse gave to General von Knyphausen, and what more he took the Lord knows. Also he left an impudent letter. The general will hang him whenever he catches him; but there is a proverb: perhaps it is sometimes the fish that is the better fisherman.

"I have a queer suspicion as to this matter, and as to the mare Lucy being stolen. I am so glad it is I that have the joy to tell you of Mr. Hugh Wynne's safety; and until he returns my visit, and forever after, I am, madam,

　　　　　　"Your devoted, humble servant,
　　　　　　　　　　　　　　"DARTHEA.
　"To Mad^m Wynne,
　　"At the Hill Farm,
　　　"Chestnut Hill."

My aunt said it was sweet and thoughtful of Darthea, and we had a fine laugh over the burglary of that bad man, McLane. The woman went back with two notes stitched into the lining of her gown; one was from my aunt, and one I wrote; and to this day Darthea alone knows what it said. God bless her!

It was March 20 of '78 before I felt myself fully able to set out for camp. I had run no great risk. The country had been ravaged till it was hard to find a pig or a cow. Farmers were on small rations, and the foragers had quit looking for what did not exist. One dull morning I had the mare saddled, and got ready to leave. It was of a Friday I went away; my aunt as unwilling to have me set out as she had been eager to have me go the day before. My Quaker training left me clear of all such nonsense, and, kissing the dear lady, I left her in tears by the roadside.

III

T is a good eighteen-mile ride to Valley Forge over the crooked Perkiomen road, which was none the better for the breaking up of the frost. I rode along with a light heart, but I was watchful, being so used to disastrous adventures. Happily, I met with no difficulties.

A few miles from the bridge General Washington had built, I fell in with a party of horse. The officer in command seemed at first suspicious, but at last sent me on with two troopers. On the last Sunday of the month Friends were persistently in the habit of flocking into the city to General Meeting. They were not unwelcome, for they were apt to carry news of us, and neither we nor the enemy regarded them as neutrals. Our commander-in-chief, in an order of this day, declared "that the plans settled at these meetings are of the most pernicious tendency," and on this account directed General Lacy "that the parties of light horse be so disposed as to fall in with these people."

It was one of these parties of horse I had encountered. The officer sent me on with a guard, and thus, in the company of two troopers, I rode through a

46

fairly wooded country to the much-worn road leading
down to the river. Here my guards left me with the
picket at the bridge. It was a half-hour before the
officer here stationed was satisfied, and meanwhile I
stared across the Schuylkill at the precipitous bluffs,
and wondered where lay the army which had passed
the winter back of them. A few men along the far
shore, and on the hill beyond a little redoubt, were
all the signs of life or of war and its precautions.
The bridge, over which presently I rode, was of army
waggons weighted with stone, and on top rails with
rude scantling. On the high posts driven into the
river-bed for stay of the bridge were burned the
names of the favourite generals. Once over, I walked
Lucy up a cleft in the shore cliff, and came out on
the huts of General Varnum's brigade. The little
world of an army came in view. I was on the first
rise from the stream, a mile and a half to the south
of the Valley Creek. To westward the land fell a little, and then rose to the higher slope of Mount Joy.
To north the land again dropped, and rose beyond to
the deep gulch of the Valley Creek. On its farther
side the fires of a picket on Mount Misery were seen.
Everywhere were regular rows of log huts, and on
the first decline of every hill slope intrenchments,
ditches, redoubts, and artillery. Far beyond, this
group of hills fell gradually to the rolling plain. A
mile away were the long outlying lines of Wayne,
and the good fellows with whom I had charged at
Germantown.

Everywhere the forests were gone. Innumerable

camp-fires and a city of log huts told for what uses
they had fallen. On the uplands about me ragged
men were drilling; far away I heard the cavalry
bugles. A certain sense of elation and gaiety came
over me. It lasted no long time, as I rode Lucy over
the limestone hillocks and down to the lesser valley,
which far away fell into the greater vale of Chester.

The worst of the winter's trials were over, and yet
I was horror-struck at the misery and rags of these
poor fellows. No wonder men deserted, and officers
were resigning in scores, desperate under the appeals
of helpless wife and family in far-away homes. It
was no better on the upland beyond. Everywhere
were rude huts in rows, woeful-looking men at drill,
dejected sentries, gaunt, hungry, ill clothed, with
here and there a better-dressed officer to make the
rest look all the worse.

I thought of the grenadier British troops, fat and
strong, in the city I had fled from, and marvelled to
think of what kept them from sweeping this squalid
mob away, as a housewife switches out the summer
flies. Full of thought, I rode a mile through the
melting drifts of snow, and came on Wayne's brigade,
which held the lines looking in this direction.

I was long about it; but at last a man pointed out
a hut, and I went in. "Holloa, Jack!" I cried.

"Hugh! Hugh! Where on earth are you from?"
And he flushed as he used to do, and gave me a great
bear-hug, saying, "And you are not dead! not dead!
Thank God! thank God!"

Thus again we met, to my unspeakable joy. He

was about as lean as I had been, but on the whole, thanks to his florid skin, looked well or better than the best of that half-fed army. How we talked, how we poured out our news that cold March afternoon, I shall not take space to tell; nor his great wonder at seeing me after all had believed me dead.

After supper came a half-dozen officers, and I heard all the camp gossip, and was made heartily welcome. Everything was on the mend, they said. Steuben was drilling the men; Greene was the new and efficient quartermaster-general. Supplies were pouring in. Mrs. Washington and Lady Stirling had come. The French were sure to make a treaty with us. As they talked of their privations I learned, for the first time, of the full horrors of the winter camp at the forge in the valley. There was still enough wretchedness to show how far worse must have been the pitiable condition of the army during that winter of '77–'78. I passed the next day at rest with Jack. I had had enough of the volunteer business, and determined, to Jack's regret, to take service with the horse. I was still unfit to march, and it seemed to me wise for this reason to stick to Lucy's good legs, at least until my own were in better order.

I think Jack felt that he was under some necessity to take care of me, or from that affection he has ever shown desired to keep me near him. He only hoped I would not incline to join McLane's troop, and when I asked why, declaring that to be my utmost desire, he said it was a service of needless peril.

II.—4

Upon this I laughed so that the hut shook, and
poor Jack became quite disconcerted, and fell to
making a variety of excuses. It is of this he says:
"Hugh is come from death, and there is more to
live for. For me, that am often unready and weak,
here is again his ever just helpfulness. He is but
a shadow of himself, and I cannot wonder that he is
so bitter against the enemy, or that he desires, less
on account of his bodily feebleness than from a wish
to revenge his cruel treatment, to serve with the
horse. They are never more quiet than gadflies. It
is dangerous duty, and should it cost this dear life,
how shall I ever face Mistress Wynne?"

I myself had but one thought in my own mind
this Sunday in March, as I rode through the east
wind. It is my way, and always was, to have but a
single idea in mind, and to go straight to my object
the nearest way. He was right in his belief that it
was my burning wish to pay the debts of my poor
abused body. I knew not when we should move,
and the dislike of tiresome drills under Steuben, with
a restless, perhaps a wholesome, instinct to lead a
more active life, conspired to make my hatred seem
reasonable.

I could see, as I rode along through the canton-
ment and the long lines of huts, how well chosen was
the valley camp. The Schuylkill flowing from the
Blue Hills turned here to eastward, the current was
deep, the banks were high and precipitous. To the
west, in a deep gorge, the Valley Creek protected the
camp. Running down from Mount Joy, a broad

spur turned northward to the Schuylkill. Between
this ridge and the river lay an angular table-land,
falling to the valley beyond. Along this ridge, and
high on Mount Joy, were the intrenchments laid out
by Du Portail, and within them were the camps of
rare tents and the rows of wooden huts.

Riding north amid the stumps and the lessening
drifts of snow, past the dark huts, and the files of
ragged men in line for morning service, I came down
to the angle between the Valley Creek and the Schuylkill. The river was full, and ran a gray-brown flood.
Where the trampled slope rose from the creek I
came upon a small but solid house, built of gray
and ruddy sandstones, a quaint, shell-curved penthouse above the open doorway. Here were horses
held by orderlies, the blue and white of French uniforms, buff-and-blue officers, and the guard of fifty
light horse on a side road in the saddle, facing the
house. I knew I had found the headquarters. Looking about, I saw, to my joy, Mr. Hamilton talking
with some of our allies. I rode up, and as they
turned, I said, "I am Mr. Hugh Wynne, Colonel
Hamilton."

"Good heavens, sir! You are not dead then, after
all!"

"No," I said, laughing; "I am alive, thank you.
I have been in prison for months, and I am come
now to ask for that commission in the light horse
about which I must beg you to remind his Excellency."

"No wonder," said he, "I did not recognise you.

We are now going to morning service. I will see
to it at once. We thought you dead. Indeed, his
Excellency wrote to Mistress Wynne of you. The
general has full powers at last, and you are sure of
your commission. Now I must leave you."

A few more needed words were said, and I drew
aside to see the staff ride away. In a few minutes
the young aide came back.

"You may join McLane at once. You will have
an acting commission until a more formal one reaches
you. I suppose you have no news?"

"None," I said, "except of how a British jail looks."

"His Excellency desires your company at dinner
to-day at six."

I said I had no uniform.

"Look at mine," he cried, laughing. "I have only
one suit, and the rest are hardly better off."

I drew back and waited. In a few minutes the
general came out, and mounting, sat still until all of
the staff were in the saddle.

He had changed greatly from the fresh, clear-
skinned country gentleman I saw first in Philadelphia. His face was more grave, his very ruddy skin
less clear and more bronzed. I observed that his
eyes were deep set, light blue in colour, and of unusual size; his nose was rather heavy and large; the
mouth resolute and firm, with full lips. His general
expression was sedate and tranquil. In full, neat
buff and blue, his hair powdered, the queue carefully
tied, he sat very erect in the saddle, and looked to
be a good horseman.

This is all I remember at that time of this high-minded gentleman. I heard much of him then and later; and as what I heard or saw varies a good deal from the idea now held of him, I shall not refrain from saying how he seemed to us, who saw him in camp and field, or in the hour of rare leisure. But I shall do better, perhaps, just now to let my friend say what he seemed to be to his more observant and reflective mind. It was writ long after.

"Abler pens than mine," says Jack, "have put on record the sorrowful glory of that dreadful camp-ground by Valley Forge. It is strongly charactered in those beseeching letters and despatches of the almost heartbroken man, who poured out his grief in language which even to-day no man can read unmoved. To us he showed only a gravely tranquil face, which had in it something which reassured those starving and naked ones. Most wonderful is it, as I read what he wrote to inefficient, blundering men, to see how calmly he states our pitiful case, how entirely he controls a nature violent and passionate beyond that of most men. He was scarcely in the saddle as commander before the body which set him there was filled with. dissatisfaction.

"I think it well that we know so little of what went on within the walls of Congress. The silence of history has been friendly to many reputations. There need be no silence as to this man, nor any concealment, and there has been much. I would have men see him as we saw him in his anger, when no language was too strong; in his hour of serene kindliness, when Hamilton, the aide of twenty, was 'my boy'; in this starving camp, with naked men shivering all night in their blankets by the fires, when 'he pitied those miseries he could neither relieve nor prevent.' Am I displeased to think that although he laughed rarely he liked Colonel Scammel's strong stories, and would be amused by a song such as no woman should hear?

"This serene, inflexible, decisive man, biding his hour, could be then the venturesome soldier, willing to put every fortune on a chance, risking himself with a courage that alarmed men for his life. Does any but a fool think that he could have been all these things and not have had in him the wild blood of passion? He had a love for fine clothes and show. He was, I fear, at times extravagant, and, as I have heard, could not pay his doctor's bill, and would postpone that, and send him a horse and a little money to educate his godson, the good doctor's son. As to some of his letters, they contained jests not gross, but not quite fit for grave seigniors not *virginibus puerisque.* There is one to Lafayette I have been shown by the marquis. It is most amusing, but— oh, fie! Was he religious? I do not know. Men say so. He might have been, and yet have had his hours of ungoverned rage, or of other forms of human weakness. Like a friend of mine, he was not given to speech concerning his creed."

My Jack was right. Our general's worst foes were men who loved their country, but who knew not to comprehend this man. I well remember how I used to stop at the camp-fires and hear the men talk of him. Here was no lack of sturdy sense. The notion of Adams and Rush of appointing new major-generals every year much amused them, and the sharp logic of cold and empty bellies did not move them from the belief that their chief was the right man. How was it they could judge so well and these others so ill?

He had no tricks of the demagogue. He coveted no popularity. He knew not to seek favour by going freely among the men. The democratic feeling in our army was intense, and yet this reserved aristocrat had to the end the love and confidence of every soldier in the ranks.

IV

SHALL pass lightly over the next two
months. I saw Jack rarely, and McLane
kept us busy with foraging parties and
incessant skirmishes. Twice we rode disguised as British troopers into the very
heart of the city, and at night as far down as Second
street bridge, captured a Captain Sandford and carried him off in a mad ride through the pickets. The
life suited maid Lucy and myself admirably. I grew
well and strong, and, I may say, paid one of my debts
when we stole in and caught a rascal named Varnum,
one of our most cruel turnkeys. This hulking coward
went out at a run through the lines, strapped behind
a trooper, near to whom I rode pistol in hand. We
got well peppered and lost a man. I heard Varnum
cry out as we passed the outer picket, and supposed
he was alarmed, as he had fair need to be.

We pulled up a mile away, McLane, as usual, laughing like a boy just out of a plundered apple-orchard.
To my horror Varnum was dead, with a ball through
his brain. His arms, which were around the trooper's
waist, were stiffened, so that it was hard to unclasp
them. This rigidness of some men killed in battle
I have often seen.

56

On Saturday, the 16th of May, Marquis Lafayette came to our huts and asked me to walk apart with him. We spoke French at his request, as he did not wish to be overheard, and talked English but ill. He said his Excellency desired to have fuller knowledge of the forts on the Neck and at the lower ferry, as well as some intelligence as to the upper lines north of the town. Mr. Hamilton thought me very fit for the affair, but the general-in-chief had said, in his kind way, that I had suffered too much to put my neck in a noose, and that I was too well known in the town, although it seemed to him a good choice.

When the marquis had said his say I remained silent, until at last he added that I was free to refuse, and none would think the worse of me; it was not an order.

I replied that I was only thinking how I should do it.

He laughed, and declared he had won a guinea of Mr. Hamilton. "I did bet on your face, Monsieur Vynne. I make you my compliments, and shall I say it is 'Yes'?"

"Yes; and I shall go to-morrow, Sunday." And with this he went away.

When I told McLane he said it was a pity, because the redcoats were to have a grand fandango on the 18th, and he meant to amuse himself that evening, which he did to some purpose, as you shall hear.

I spent the day in buying from a farmer a full Quaker dress, and stained my face that night a fine brownish tint with stale pokeberry juice. It was all the ink we had.

Very early on the 17th I rode at dawn with a
trooper to my aunt's house, and in the woods back
of it changed my clothes for the Quaker rig and
broad-brimmed hat.   To my delight, my aunt did not
know me when I said I wanted to buy her remaining
cow.   She was angry enough, until I began to laugh
and told her to look at me.   Of course she entreated
me not to go, but seeing me resolved, bade me take
the beast and be off.   She would do without milk;
as for me, I should be the cause of her death.

I set out about six with poor Sukey, and was so
bothered by the horrible road and by her desire to
get back to her stall that it was near eleven in the
morning before we got to town.   As usual, food was
welcome, and a trooper was sent with me to the
commissary at the Bettering-house, where I was paid
three pounds six after much sharp bargaining in
good Quaker talk.   A pass to return was given me,
and with this in my pocket I walked away.

I went through the woods and the Sunday quiet of
the camps without trouble, saying I had lost my way,
and innocently showing my pass to everybody.   Back
and to south of the works on Callowhill were the Hessians and the Fourth foot.   The Seventh and Four-
teenth British Grenadiers lay from Delaware
Seventh to westward; the Yagers at Schuylkill Third
street, or where that would be on Mr. Penn's plan;
and so to Cohocsink Creek dragoons and foot.   North
of them were Colonel Montresor's nine blockhouses,
connected by a heavy stockade and abatis, and in
front of this chevaux-de-frise and the tangled mass
of dead trees which had so beaten me when I escaped.

The stockade and the brush and the tumbled fruit-trees were dry from long exposure, and were, I thought, well fitted to defy attack.

I turned west again, and went out to the Schuyl-kill River, where at the upper ferry was now a bridge with another fort. Then I walked southward along the stream. The guards on the river-bank twice turned me back; but at last, taking to the woods, I got into the open farm country beyond South Street, and before dark climbed a dead pine and was able to see the fort near to Mr. James Hamilton's seat of the Woodlands, set high above the lower ferry, which was now well bridged.

Pretty tired, I lay down awhile, and then strolled off into town to get a lodging. When past Walnut street I found the streets unusually full. I had of purpose chosen First-day for my errand, expecting to find our usual Sunday quiet, but the licence of an army had changed the ways of this decorous town. Every one had a lantern, which gave an odd look of festivity, and, to comply with the military rule, I bought me a lantern. Men were crying tickets for the play of the "Mock Doctor" on Tuesday, and for Saturday, "The Deuce is in Him!" Others sold places for the race on Wednesday, and also hawked almanacs and Tory broadsides. The stores on Second street were open and well lighted, and the coffee-house was full of redcoats carousing, while loose women tapped on the windows and gathered at the doors. All seemed merry and prosperous. Here and there a staid Quaker in drab walked up the busy street on his homeward way, undistracted by the merriment and noise of the thronged thoroughfare. A dozen red-coats went by to change the guards set at the doors of general officers. A negro paused on the sidewalk, crying, "Pepper-pot, smoking hot!" Another offered me the pleasant calamus-root, which in those days people liked to chew. A man in a red coat walked in the roadway ringing a bell and crying, "Lost child!" Sedan-chairs or chaises set down officers. The quiet, sedate city of Penn had lost its air of demure respectability, and I felt like one in a strange place. This sense of alien surroundings may have helped to put me off my guard; for, because of being a moment careless, I ran a needless risk. Over the way I saw two blacks holding lanterns so as to show a great bill pasted on a wall. I crossed to look at it. Above was a Latin motto, which I cannot now recall, but the body of it I remember well:

"All Intrepid, able-bodied Heroes who are willing to serve against the Arbitrary Usurpations of a Tyranickal Congress can now, by enlisting, acquire the polite Accomplishments of a Soldier.

"Such spirited Fellows will, besides their Pay, be rewarded at the End of the War with

Fifty Acres
of Land,

To which every Heroe may retire and Enjoy His Lass and His Bottle."

This so much amused me that I stood still to gaze; for below it was seen the name of an old schoolmate,

William Allen, now a lieutenant-colonel, in want of Tory recruits.

I felt suddenly a rousing whack on the back, and turning in a rage, saw two drunken grenadiers.

"Join the harmy, friend; make a cussed fine Quaker bombardier."

I instantly cooled, for people began to stop, pleased at the fun of baiting a Quaker. The others cried, "Give us a drink, old Thee-and-Thou!" Some soldiers paused, hoping for a ring and a fight. I was pushed about and hustled. I saw that at any moment it might end ill. I had a mighty mind toward anything but non-resistance, but still, fearing to hit the fellows, I cried out meekly, "Thou art wrong, friends, to oppress a poor man." Just then I heard William Allen's voice back of me, crying, "Let that Quaker alone!" As he quickly exercised the authority of an officer, the gathering crowd dispersed, and the grenadiers staggered away. I was prompt enough to slip down High street, glad to be so well out of it.

At the inn of the "Bag of Nails," on Front street, I found a number of Friends, quiet over their Hollands. I sat down in a dark corner, and would have had a well-earned bowl; but I was no sooner seated than in came a man with a small bell, and, walking among the guests, rang it, saying, "It is half after ten, and there will be no more liquor served. No more! no more!"

I knew that it would be impossible to break this decree, and therefore contented myself with cold

beef and cole-slaw. I went to bed, and thought
over the oddity of my being helped by William Allen,
and of how easily I might have been caught.

In washing next morning I was off my guard, and
got rid of the most of my pokeberry juice. I saw
my folly too late, but there was no help for it. I
resolved to keep my wide brim well down over my
face, seeing in a mirror how too much like my own
self I had become.

I settled my score and went out, passing down the
river-front. Here I counted and took careful note of
the war-ships anchored all the way along the Delaware. At noon I bought an " Observer," and learned
that Mr. Howe had lost a spaniel dog, and that
there was to be a great festival that night in honour of Sir William Howe's departure for England.
Would Darthea be there? I put aside the temptation to see that face again, and set about learning what forts were on the neck of land to south,
where the two rivers, coming together at an angle,
make what we call the Neck. It was a wide lowland
then, but partly diked and crossed by many ditches ; a
marshy country much like a bit of Holland, with here
and there windmills to complete the resemblance.

It was so open that, what with the caution required
in approaching the block forts and the windabout
ways the ditches made needful, it was late before I
got the information I needed. About nine on this
18th of May, and long after dusk, I came upon the
lower fort, as to which the general was desirous of

more complete knowledge. I walked around it, and was at last ordered off by the guards.

My errand was now nearly done. My way north took me close to Walnut Grove, the old country-seat of my father's friend, Joseph Wharton, whom, on account of his haughty ways, the world's people wickedly called the Quaker duke. The noise of people come to see, and the faint strains of distant music, had for an hour reminded me, as I came nearer the gardens of Walnut Grove, that what McLane had called the great fandango in honour of Sir William Howe was in full activity. Here in the tall box alleys as a child I had many times played, and every foot of the ground was pleasingly familiar.

The noise increased as I approached through the growing darkness; for near where the lane reached the Delaware was a small earthwork, the last of those I needed to visit. I tried after viewing it to cross the double rows of grenadiers which guarded this road, but was rudely repulsed, and thus had need to go back of their line and around the rear of the mansion. When opposite to the outhouses used for servants I paused in the great crowd of townsfolk who were applauding or sullenly listening to the music heard through the open windows. I had no great desire to linger, but as it was dark I feared no recognition, and stayed to listen to the fine band of the Hessians and the wild clash of their cymbals, which, before these Germans came, no one had heard in the colonies. My work was over. I had but to go far back of the house and make my way to camp by any one of the ferries. Unluckily the music so attracted me that I stayed on, and, step by step, quite at my ease, drew nearer to the mansion.

The silly extravagance of the festival, with its afternoon display of draped galleys and saluting ships gay with flags, and its absurd mock show of a tournament in ridiculous costumes, I have no temptation to describe, nor did I see this part of it. It was meant to honour Sir William Howe, a man more liked than respected, and as a soldier beneath contempt. I had no right to have lingered, and my idle curiosity came near to have cost me dear. The house was precisely like Mount Pleasant, later General Arnold's home on the Schuylkill. In the centre of a large lawn stood a double mansion of stone, and a little to each side were seen outhouses for servants and kitchen use. The open space toward the water was extensive enough to admit of the farcical tilting of the afternoon. A great variety of evergreen trees and shrubs gave the house a more shaded look than the season would otherwise have afforded. Among these were countless lanterns illuminating the grounds, and from the windows on all sides a blaze of light was visible. Back of the house two roads ran off, one to west and one to north, and along these were waggons coming and going, servants, orderlies, and people with supplies.

At this locality there was much confusion, and, picking up a pair of lanterns, I went unquestioned past the guard on the south side of Walnut Lane.

Indeed, the sentries here and most of the orderlies were by this time well in liquor. Once within the grounds, which I knew well, I was perfectly at home. No one of the guests was without at the side or front. Now and then a servant passed through the alleys of clipped box to see to the lanterns. I was quite alone. In the shelter of a row of low hemlocks and box I stood on a garden-seat at the south side of the house, fifteen feet from a large bow-window, and, parting the branches, I commanded a full view of the dancing-room. I had no business here, and I knew it; I meant but to look and be gone. The May night was warm and even sultry, so that the sashes were all raised and the curtains drawn aside. I saw with ease a charming scene.

The walls were covered with mirrors lent for the occasion, and the room I commanded was beautifully draped with flags and hangings. Young blacks stood at the doors, or came and went with refreshments. These servants were clad in blue and white, with red turbans and metal collars and bracelets. The six Knights of the Blended Roses, or some like silliness, had cast their queer raiments and were in uniform. Their six chosen ladies were still in party-coloured costumes, which were not to my taste. Most of the women—there were but some threescore, almost all Tories or Moderates—were in the gorgeous brocades and the wide hooped skirts of the day. The extravagance of the costumes struck me. The head-dresses, a foot above the head with aigrets and feathers and an excess of powder, seemed to me quite astonishing.

II.—5

I stood motionless, caught by the beauty of the moving picture before me. I have ever loved colour, and here was a feast of it hard to equal. There were red coats and gold epaulets, sashes and ribboned orders, the green and red of the chasseurs of Brunswick, blue navy uniforms, the gold lace and glitter of staff-officers, and in and out among them the clouds of floating muslin, gorgeous brocades, flashing silk petticoats, jewels, and streaming ribbons. The air was full of powder shaken from wig, queue, and head-dress; spurs clinked, stiff gown skirts rustled. The moving mass of colour, lovely faces, and manly forms bent and swayed in ordered movement as the music of the grenadier band seemed to move at will these puppets of its harmony.

They were walking a minuet, and its tempered grace, which I have never ceased to admire, seemed to suit well the splendour of embroidered gowns and the brilliant glow of the scarlet coats. I began to note the faces and to see them plainly, being, as I have said, not fifteen feet away from the window. Sir William Howe was dancing with Miss Redman. I was struck, as others have been, with his likeness to Washington, but his face wanted the undisturbed serenity of our great chief's. I dare say he knew better than to accept as his honest right the fulsome homage of this parting festival. I thought indeed that he looked discontented. I caught glimpses of Colonel Tarleton bowing to Miss Bond. Then I saw Miss Franks sweeping a deep curtsey to Lord Cathcart as he bowed. There were the fair Shippen

women, the Chews, the provost's blonde daughter
with Sir John Wrottesley, Mrs. Ferguson, my aunt's
"Tory cat," in gay chat with Sir Charles Calder, Galloways, Allens—a pretty show of loyal dames, with
—save the officers—few young men I knew.

I started as Darthea moved across the window-
space on the arm of André, while following them
were Montresor and my cousin. I felt the blood go
to my face as I saw them, and drew back, letting the
parted branches come together. With this storm of
love and hate came again the sudden reflection that
I had no right to be here, and that I was off the track
of duty. I stood a moment; the night was dark;
lights gleamed far out on the river from the battle-
ships. The strains of their bands fell and rose,
faintly heard in the distance.

I saw as it were before me with distinctness the
camp on the windy hill, the half-starved, ragged men,
the face of the great chief they loved. Once again
I looked back on this contrasting scene of foolish
luxury, and turned to go from where I felt I never
should have been. Poor old Joseph Wharton! I
smiled to think that, could he have known to what
worldly use his quiet Quaker home had come, he
would have rolled uneasy in his unnamed grave in
the ground of the Arch Street Meeting.

Turning, I gave a few moments of thought to my
plans. Suddenly the music ceased, and, with laughter
and pretty cries of expectation, gay gown and fan
and hoop and the many-coloured uniforms trooped
out from the doors, as I learned later, to see the

fireworks, over which were to be set off for final flattery in fiery letters, " *Tes Lauriers Sont Immortels.*" I hope he liked them, those unfading laurels! The shrubbery was at once alive with joyous women and laughing men.

I had not counted on this, and despite my disguise I felt that any moment might put me in deadly peril. The speedy fate of a spy I knew too well.

They were all around me in a minute, moving to and fro, merry and chatting. I heard André say to Darthea, " It must please the general; a great success. I shall write it all to London. Ah, Miss Peniston! how to describe the ladies! "

"And their gowns! " cried Darthea, ",their gowns! "

"I am reduced to desperation," said André. "I must ask the women to describe one another; hey, Wynne? " They were now standing apart from the rest, and I, hid by the bushes, was not five feet away.

"A dangerous resource," returned Wynne. "The list of wounded vanities would be large. How like a brown fairy is Miss Franks! Who shall describe her? No woman will dare."

"You might ask Mr. Oliver de Lancey," said Miss Darthea. "She would be secure of a pretty picture."

"And you," said Wynne—"who is to be your painter? "

"I shall beg for the place," cried André.

"I think I shall take some rebel officer," said Darthea, saucily. "Think how fresh we should look to those love-starved gentlemen whom Sir William has brought to such abject submission."

André laughed, but not very heartily. As to Wynne, he was silent. The captain went on to say how sad it was that just as the general was ready to sweep those colonials out of existence—

"Why not say rebels, André?" Wynne broke in.

"Better not! better not! I never do. It only makes more bitter what is bad enough. But where are the fireworks?"

Meanwhile I was in dire perplexity, afraid to stir, hoping that they would move away.

"There is a seat hereabouts," said my cousin. "You must be tired, Miss Peniston."

"A little."

"I will look," said Wynne. "This way."

As I was in possession of the seat, I got down at once, but in two steps Arthur was beside me, and for an instant the full blaze from the window caught me square in the face. He was nearest, but Darthea was just behind him, and none other but André close at hand.

"By heavens!" I heard, and my cousin had me by the collar. "Here, André! A spy! a spy! Quick!"

I heard a cry from Darthea, and saw her reel against my cousin's shoulder.

"Help! help! I am—ill."

Arthur turned, exclaiming, "Darthea! My God!" and thus distracted between her and me, let slack his hold. I tore away and ran around the house, upsetting an old officer, and so through the shrubbery and the servants, whom I hustled one way and another. I heard shouts of "Spy!" "Stop thief!"

and the rattle of arms all around me. Several waggons blocked the roadway. I felt that I must be
caught, and darted under a waggon body. I was
close to the lines as I rose from beneath the waggon.

At this instant cannonry thundered out to north,
and a rocket rose in air. The grenadiers looked up
in surprise. Seeing the momentary disorder of these
men, who were standing at intervals of some six feet
apart, I darted through them and into the crowd
of spectators. I still heard shouts and orders, but
pushed in among the people outside of the guard,
hither and thither, using my legs and elbows to good
purpose. Increasing rattle of musketry was heard
in the distance, the ships beating to quarters, the
cries and noises back of me louder and louder. I
was now moving slowly in the crowd, and at last got
clean away from it.

What had happened I knew not, but it was most
fortunate for me. When a few yards from the people
I began to run, stumbling over the fields, into and
through ditches, and because of this alarm was at
last, I concluded, reasonably safe.

I had run nearly a mile before I sat down to get
my breath and cool off. Away to north a great flare
of red fire lit up the sky. What it was I knew not,
but sat awhile and gave myself leave to think. My
cousin had instantly known me, but he had hesitated
a moment. I knew the signs of indecision in his
face too well to be misled. I had felt, as he seized
me, that I was lost. I could not blame him; it was
clearly his duty. But I do not think I should have

willingly recognised him under like circumstances.
My very hatred would have made me more than hesitate. Still, who can say what he would do in the
haste of such a brief moral conflict? I could recall,
as I sat still and reflected, the really savage joy in
his face as he collared me. How deeply he must
love her! He seemed, as it were, to go to pieces at
her cry. Was she ill? Did her quick-coming sense
of my danger make her faint? I had seen her
unaccountably thus affected once before, as he who
reads these pages may remember. Or was it a ready-
witted ruse? Ah, my sweet Darthea! I wanted to
think it that.

The blaze to northward was still growing brighter,
and being now far out on the marshes south of the
town, I made up my mind to use my pass at the
nearer ferry, which we call Gray's, and this, too, as
soon as possible, for fear that orders to stop a Quaker spy might cause me to regret delay.

When I came to Montresor's bridge my thought
went back to my former escape, and, avoiding all
appearance of haste, I stayed to ask the sergeant in
charge of the guard what the blaze meant. He said
it was an alert.

A few days after, McLane related to me with glee
how with Clowe's dragoons and a hundred foot he
had stolen up to the lines, every man having a pot
of tar; how they had smeared the dry abatis and
brush, and at a signal fired the whole mass of dried
wood. He was followed into the fastnesses of the
Wissahickon, and lost his ensign and a man or two

near Barren Hill. The infantry scattered and hid
in the woods, but McLane swam his horse across the
Schuylkill, got the help of Morgan's rifles, and, returning, drove his pursuers up to their own intrenchments. He said it was the best fun he had ever had,
and he hoped the Tory ladies liked his fireworks.
At all events, it saved my neck.

As I walked through Gray's Lane I fell to reflecting upon André's behaviour, of which I have said
nothing. I came to the conclusion that he could
hardly have recognised me. This seemed likely
enough, because we had not met often, and I too,
apart from my disguise, had changed very greatly.
And yet why had he not responded to an obvious
call to duty? He certainly was not very quick to
act on Arthur's cry for help. But Darthea was on
his arm, and only let it go when she fell heavily
against my cousin.

I had a fine story for Jack, and so, thinking with
wonder of the whirl of adventure into which I had
fallen ever since I left home, I hurried along. It is
a singular fact, but true, that certain men never have
unusual adventures. I am not one of these. Even
in the most quiet times of peace I meet with odd
incidents, and this has always been my lot. With
this and other matters in my mind, resolving that
never again would I permit any motive to lead me
off the track of the hour's duty, I walked along. I
had had a lesson.

I sought my old master's house, and reached it in
an hour. Here I found food and ready help, and

before evening next day, May 19, was at the camp.
I spent an hour in carefully writing out my report,
and Jack, under my directions, being clever with the
pencil, made plans of the forts and the enemy's defences, which I took to headquarters, and a copy of
which I have inserted in these memoirs. I had every
reason to believe that my report was satisfactory.
I then went back to discourse with Jack over my
adventures. You may see hanging framed in my
library, and below General von Knyphausen's sword,
a letter which an orderly brought to me the next
day:

"SIR: It would be an impropriety to mention in
general orders a service such as you have rendered.
To do so might subject you to greater peril, or to ill
treatment were you to fall into the hands of the enemy. I needed no fresh proof of your merit to bear
it in remembrance. No one can feel more sensibly
the value of your gallant conduct, or more rejoice
for your escape.

"I have the honour to be

"Your obed^t Hum^e Servt,

"G^e WASHINGTON.

"To Lieut. Hugh Wynne, etc."

This was writ in his own hand, as were many of
his letters, even such as were of great length. The
handwriting betrays no mark of haste, and seems
penned with such exactness as all his correspondence
shows. It may be that he composed slowly, and thus

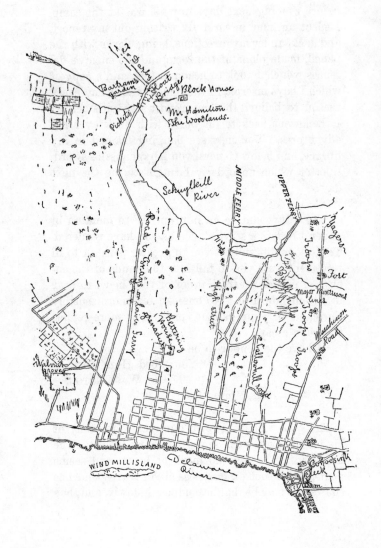

of need wrote with no greater speed than his thought permitted. I at least found it hard to explain how, in the midst of affairs, worried, interrupted, distracted, he does at no time show in his penmanship any sign of haste.

When I handed this letter to Jack I could not speak for a moment, and yet I was never much the victim of emotion. My dear Jack said it was not enough. For my own part, a captain's commission would not have pleased me as well. I ran no risk which I did not bring upon myself by that which was outside of my duty; and as to this part of my adventure, I told no one but Jack, being much ashamed of the weakness which came so near to costing me not only my life, but—what would have been worse—the success of my errand.

V

HE warm spring weather, and General Greene's good management as quartermaster, brought us warmth and better diet. The Conestoga wains rolled in with grain and good rum. Droves of cattle appeared, and as the men were fed the drills prospered. Soldiers and officers began to amuse themselves. A theatre was arranged in one of the bigger barns, and we—not I, but others—played "The Fair Penitent." Colonel Grange had a part, and made a fine die of it; but the next day, being taken with a pleurisy, came near to making a more real exit from life. I think it was he who invited Jack Warder to play *Calista*. Lady Kitty Stirling had said he would look the part well, with his fair locks and big innocent blue eyes, and she would lend him her best silk flowered gown and a fine lot of lace. Jack was in a rage, but the colonel, much amused, apologised, and so it blew over. His Excellency and Lady Washington were to see the play, and the Ladies Stirling and Madam Greene were all much delighted.

"The Recruiting Officer" we should have had later, but about the latter part of May we got news of the British as about to move out of my dear home city. After this was bruited about, no one cared to do anything but get ready to leave the winter huts and be after Sir Henry. In fact, long before this got out there was an air of hopeful expectation in the army, and the men began, like the officers, to amuse themselves. The camp-fires were gay, jokes seemed to revive in the warm air, and once more men laughed. It was pleasant, too, to see the soldiers at fives, or the wickets up and the cricket-balls of tightly rolled rag ribbons flying, or fellows at leap-frog, all much encouraged by reason of having better diet, and no need now to shrink their stomachs with green persimmons or to live without rum. As to McLane and our restless Wayne, they were about as quiet as disturbed wasps. The latter liked nothing better this spring than to get up an alert by running cannon down to the hills on the west of the Schuylkill, pitching shot at the bridges, and then to be off and away before the slow grenadiers could cross in force. Thus it was that never a week went by without adventures. Captain McLane let neither man nor horse live long at ease; but whatever he did was planned with the extreme of care and carried out with equal audacity.

The army was most eager for the summer campaign. We had begun, as I have said, to suspect that Sir Henry Clinton, who had succeeded Howe, was about to move; but whither he meant to march, or his true object, our camp-fire councils could not guess as yet.

Very early in the evening of June 17, I met Colonel Hamilton riding in haste. " Come," he said; " I

am to see Wayne and the marquis. Clinton is on
the wing, as we have long expected. He will very
likely have already crossed into the Jerseys. Will
you have a place in the foot if his Excellency can get
you a captaincy?"

I said "Yes" instantly.

"You seem to know your own mind, Mr. Wynne.
There will be more hard knocks and more glory."

I thought so too, but I was now again in the full
vigour of health, and an appointment in the foot
would, as I hoped, bring me nearer to Jack.

And now joy and excitement reigned throughout
the camps. The news was true. On the 18th of June
Sir Henry Clinton, having gotten ready by sending
on in advance his guns and baggage, cleverly slipped
across the Delaware, followed by every Tory who
feared to remain; some three thousand, it was said.

Long before dawn we of McLane's light horse
were in the saddle. As we passed Chestnut Hill I
fell out to tell my aunt the good news. I was scarce
gone by before she began to make ready to follow
us. As we pushed at speed through Germantown,
it became sure that the evacuation had been fully
accomplished. We raced down Front street at a rate
which seemed reckless to me. McLane gave no orders, but galloped on ahead in his usual mad way.
The townsfolk were wild with joy. Women stood
in tears as we went by; men cheered us and the boys
hurrahed. At Arch and Front streets, as we pulled up,
I saw a poor little cornet come out of a house half
bewildered and buttoning his red jacket. I pushed

Lucy on to the sidewalk and caught him by the collar. He made a great fuss and had clearly overslept himself. I was hurriedly explaining, amid much laughter, when McLane called out, "A nice doll-baby! Up with him!" And away he went, behind a trooper. At Third street bridge were two other officers who must have been tipsy overnight and have slept too late. At last, with our horses half dead, we walked them back to Front and High streets, and got off for a rest and a mug of beer at the coffee-house. Soon came a brigade of Virginians, and we marched away to camp on the common called Centre Square.

The streets were full of huzzaing crowds. Our flags, long hid, were flying. Scared tradesmen were pulling down the king's arms they had set over their signs. The better Tory houses were closed, and few of this class were to be seen in the streets.

Major-General Arnold followed after us. Unable, because of his wound, to accept a command in the field, he took up his abode as commandant of the city in Mr. Morris's great house at the northeast corner of Front and High streets. I saw this gallant soldier in May, at the time he joined the camp at the Forge, when he was handsomely cheered by the men. He was a man dark and yet ruddy, soldierly looking, with a large nose, and not unlike his Excellency as to the upper part of his face. He was still on crutches, being thin and worn from the effects of the hurt he received at Saratoga.

As soon as possible I left the troop and rode away

on Lucy down High street to Second and over the
bridges to my home.

I was no longer the mere lad I had left it. Command of others, the leisure for thought in the camp,
the sense that I had done my duty well, had made
of me a resolute and decisive man. As I went
around to the stables in the rear of the house it
seemed to me as if I must in a minute see those blue
eyes, and hear the pretty French phrases of tender
love which in times of excitement used to rise to my
mother's lips. It is thus as to some we love. We
never come to feel concerning them that certainty
of death which sets apart from us forever others who
are gone. To this day a thought of her brings back
that smiling face, and she lives for me the life of
eternal remembrance.

No one was in the stable when I unsaddled the
tired mare. At the kitchen door the servants ran
out with cries of joy. With a word I passed them,
smelling my father's pipe in the hall, for it was evening, and supper was over.

He rose, letting his pipe drop, as I ran to fall on
his great chest, and pray him to pardon, once for all,
what I had felt that it was my duty to do. I was
stayed a moment as I saw him. He had lost flesh
continually, and his massive build and unusual height
showed now a gaunt and sombre man, with clothes
too loose about him. I thought that his eyes were
filling, but the habits of a life controlled him.

He held to a chair with his left hand, and coldly
put out the right to meet my eager grasp. I stood

still, my instinct of tenderness checked. I could only repeat, "Father, father, I have come home."

"Yes," he said, "thou hast come home. Sit down."

I obeyed. Then he stooped to pick up his pipe, and raising his strong gray head, looked me over in perfect silence.

"Am I not welcome," I cried, "in my mother's home? Are we always to be kept apart? I have done what, under God, seemed to me His will. Cannot you, who go your way so steadily, see that it is the right of your son to do the same? You have made it hard for me to do my duty. Think as seems best to you of what I do or shall do, but have for me the charity Christ teaches. I shall go again, father, and you may never see me more on earth. Let there be peace between us now. For my mother's sake, let us have peace. If I have cost you dear, believe me, I owe to you such sad hours as need never have been. My mother—she—"

During this outburst he heard me with motionless attention, but at my last word he raised his hand. "I like not thy naming of thy mother. It has been to me ever a reproach that I saw not how far her indulgence was leading thee out of the ways of Friends. There are who by birthright are with us, but not of us—not of us."

This strange speech startled me into fuller self-command. I remembered his strange dislike to hear her mentioned. As he spoke his fingers opened and shut on the arms of the chair in which he sat, and

II.—6

here and there on his large-featured face the muscles twitched.

"I will not hear her named again," he added. "As for thee, my son, this is thy home. I will not drive thee out of it."

"Drive me out!" I exclaimed. I was horror-struck.

"And why not? Since thou wert a boy I have borne all things: drunkenness, debauchery, blood-guiltiness, rebellion against those whom God has set over us, and at last war, the murder of thy fellows."

I was silent. What could I say? The words which came from my heart had failed to touch him. He had buried even the memory of my mother. I remembered Aunt Gainor's warnings as to his health, and set myself at once to hear and reply with gentleness.

He went on as if he knew my thought: "I am no longer the man I was. I am deserted by my son when I am in greatest need of him. Had it not pleased God to send me for my stay, in this my loneliness, thy Cousin Arthur, I should have been glad to rest from the labours of earth."

"Arthur! My cousin!"

"I said so. He has become to me as a son. It is not easy for one brought up among dissolute men to turn away and seek righteousness, but he hath heard as thou didst never hear, nor wouldst. He hath given up dice and cards, and hath asked of me books such as Besse's 'Sufferings' and George Fox's 'Testimony.'"

This was said so simply and in such honest faith that I could not resist to smile.

"I did not ask thee to believe me," said my father, sharply; "and if because a man is spiritually reminded and hath stayed to consider his sin, it is for thee but cause of vain mirth, I will say no more. I have lost a son, and found one. I would it had been he whom I lost that is now found."

I answered gravely, "Father, the man is a hypocrite. He saw me dying a prisoner in jail, starved and in rags. He left me to die."

"I have heard of this. He saw some one about to die. He thought he was like thee."

"But he heard my name."

"That cannot be. He said it was not thee. He said it!"

"He lied; and why should he have ever mentioned the matter to thee—as indeed he did to others—except for precaution's sake, that if, as seemed unlike enough, I got well, he might have some excuse? It seems to me a weak and foolish action, but none the less wicked."

My father listened, but at times with a look of being puzzled. "I do not think I follow thy argument, Hugh," he said, "neither does thy judgment of the business seem favoured by that which I know of thy cousin."

"Father, that man is my enemy. He hates me because—because Darthea is my friend, and but for her I should have rotted in the jail, with none to help me."

"Thy grandfather lay in Shrewsbury Gate House a year for a better cause, and as for thy deliverance,

I heard of it later. It did seem to Arthur that the young woman had done more modestly to have asked his help than to have been so forward."

My father spoke with increase of the deliberateness at all times one of his peculiarities, which seemed to go well with the bigness of his build. This slowness in talk seemed now to be due in part to a slight trouble in finding the word he required. It gave me time to observe how involved was the action of his mind. The impression of his being indirect and less simple than of old was more marked as our talk went on than I can here convey by any possible record of what he said. I only succeeded in making him more obstinate in his belief, as was always the case when any opposed him. Yet I could not resist adding: "If, as you seem to think, Arthur is my friend, I would you could have seen his face when at that silly Mischianza he caught me in disguise."

"Did he not do his duty after thy creed and his?"

"It was not that, father. Some men might have hesitated even as to the duty. Mr. André did not help him, and his debt to us was small. Had I been taken I should have swung as a spy on the gallows in Centre Square."

"And yet," said my father, with emphatic slowness, "he would have done his duty as he saw it."

"And profited by it also," said I, savagely.

"There is neither charity nor yet common sense in thy words, Hugh. If thou art to abide here, see that thy ways conform to the sobriety and decency of Friends. I will have no cards nor hard drinking."

"But good heavens! father, when have I ever done these things here, or indeed anywhere, for years?"

His fingers were again playing on the arms of Mr. Penn's great chair, and I made haste to put an end to this bewildering talk.

"I will try," I said, "to live in such a way as shall not offend. Lucy is in the stable, and I will take my old room. My Aunt Gainor is to be in town to-morrow."

"I shall be pleased to see her."

"And how is the business, father?" I said. "There are no ships at sea, I hope. The privateers are busy, and if any goods be found that may have been for use of the king's people, we might have to regret a loss."

"*I* might," he returned sharply. "I am still able to conduct my own ventures."

"Of course, sir," I said hastily, wondering where I could find any subject which was free from power to annoy him. Then I rose, saying, "There is an early drill. I shall have to be on hand to receive General Arnold. I shall not be back to breakfast. Good-night."

"Farewell," he said. And I went upstairs with more food for thought than was to my liking. I had hoped for a brief season of rest and peace, and here was whatever small place I held in my father's heart filled by my cousin.

When, not long after, for mere comfort, I had occasion to speak to the great Dr. Rush of my father, he said that when the brain became enfeebled men were apt to assign to one man acts done by another, and that this did explain the latter part of my father's talk about cards and drinking. Also he said that with defect of memory came more or less incapacity to reason, since for that a man must be able to assemble past events and review them in his memory. Indeed, he added, certain failures of remembrance might even permit a good man to do apparent wrong, which seemed to me less clear. The good doctor helped me much, for I was confused and hurt, seeing no remedy in anything I could do or say.

I lit the candles in my old room and looked about me. My cousin had, it appeared, taken up his abode in my own chamber, and this put me out singularly; I could hardly have said why. The room was in the utmost confusion. Only that morning Arthur Wynne had left it. Many of the lazier officers had overslept themselves, as I have said, and came near to being quite left behind. Lord Cosmo Gordon, in fact, made his escape in a skiff just before we entered.

The bed was still not made up, which showed me how careless our slaves must have become. The floor was littered with torn paper, and in a drawer, forgot in Arthur's hurry, were many bills, paid and unpaid, some of which were odd enough; also many notes, tickets for the Mischianza, theatre-bills, portions of plays,—my cousin was an admirable actor in light parts,—and a note or two in Darthea's neat writing. I had no hesitation in putting them all on the hearth. There was nothing in me to make me take advantage of what I found. I kept the Mischianza tickets, and that was all. I have them yet. On the table were Fox's "Apology," "A Sweet Discourse to Friends," by William Penn, and the famous "Book of Sufferings." In the latter was thrust a small, thin betting-tablet, such as many gentlemen then carried. Here were some queer records of bets more curious than reputable. I recall but two: "Mr. Harcourt bets Mr. Wynne five pounds that Miss A. will wear red stockings at the play on May 12th. Won, A. Wynne. They were blue, and so was the lady." "A. W. bets Mr. von Speiser ten pounds that he will drink four quarts of Madeira before Mr. von S. can drink two; Major de Lancey to measure the wine. Lost, A. W. The Dutch pig was too much for me."

Wondering what Darthea or my father would think of these follies, I tossed the books and the betting-tablet on the pile of bills on the hearth. I have since then been shown in London by General Burgoyne the betting-book at Brooks's Club. There are to be seen the records of still more singular bets, some quite abominable; but such were the manners of the day. My cousin, as to this, was like the rest.

In a closet were cast-off garments and riding-boots. I sent for Tom, and bade him do with these as he liked; then I set fire to the papers on the hearth, ordered the room put in order, and after a pipe in the orchard went to bed.

VI

Y father was out when, the next day at noon, I found in the counting-house our old clerk, Thomas Mason. He, like myself, had seen with distress my father's condition; but he told me, to my surprise, that he was still acute and competent in most matters of business.

"Look at this, Mr. Hugh," he said, showing me careful entries in the day-book, in my father's hand, of nearly one thousand pounds lent to my Cousin Arthur. My father had spoken to Mason of an intention to alter his will. He never did alter it, but, believing me dead, tore it up and made no new one. None of our ships were at sea. Most of them had been sold as transports to the British quartermaster. My sole comfort at home was in the absence of Arthur Wynne, and in the fact that Darthea was in the city, as I learned from Mason.

After this I went at once to see my aunt, but could give her only a few minutes, as I knew McLane would need my knowledge of the neighbourhood. In fact, I was busy for two days looking after the Tory bands who were plundering farms to west of the city.

As soon as possible I went again to see my Aunt Gainor. The good old lady was lamenting her scanty toilet, and the dirt in which the Hessians had left her house. "I have drunk no tea since Lexington," she said, "and I have bought no gowns. My gowns, sir, are on the backs of our poor soldiers. I am not fit to be seen beside that minx Darthea. And how is Jack? The Ferguson woman has been here. I hate her, but she has all the news. If one has no gowns, it is at least a comfort to hear gossip. I told her so, but Lord! the woman does not care a rap if you do but let her talk. She says Joseph Warder is smit with Darthea's aunt, and what a fine courtship that will be! Old Duché, our preacher, is gone away with Sir William; and now we have my beautiful young man, Mr. White, at Christ Church."

So the dear lady rattled on, her great form moving among her battered furniture, and her clear voice, not without fine tones, rising and falling, until at last she dropped into a chair, and would hear all my adventures. It was dangerous to wait long when my aunt invited replies, and before I had time to think she began anew to tell me that Darthea had come at once to see her, and of how respectful she was. At this I encouraged my aunt, which was rarely needed, and then heard further that Mrs. Peniston would remain in town, perhaps because of Friend Joseph Warder.

Darthea had also spoken eagerly of Arthur. His people in Wales had written to her: Arthur's father and his brother, who was so ill. "I could not but

thank her," said my aunt, "for that brave visit to the
jail, as to which she might have written to me. I told
her as much, but she said I was a Whig, and outside
the lines, and she did not wish to get her aunt into
trouble. 'Stuff!' said I; 'how came it Mr. Arthur
never knew Hugh?' 'How could he? You should
have seen him,' says my little lady, 'and even after
he was well. I did not know him, and how should
Mr. Wynne?'

"But," said my aunt, "I made such little additions
to his tale as I dared, but not all I wanted to. I
promise you they set my miss to thinking, for she
got very red and said it was sheer nonsense. She
would ask you herself. She had a pretty picture to
show me of Wyncote, and the present man was to be
made a baronet. Can a good girl be captured by
such things? But the man has some charm, Hugh.
These black men"—so we called those of dark complexion—"are always dangerous, and this special
devil has a tongue, and can use it well."

I listened to my aunt, but said little. What chance
had I to make Darthea credit me? She had a girl's
desire for the court and kings' houses and rank;
or was this only one Darthea? Could that other be
made to listen to a plain lieutenant in a rebel army?
Perhaps I had better go back and get knocked on
the head. Would she love me the better for proving
Arthur a rascal?

I said as much to Aunt Gainor. At this she got
up, crying, "Good heavens! there is a Hessian cock-
roach! They are twice as big as they were. What

a fool you are! The girl is beginning to be in doubt. I am sorry you have driven the man away. A pretty tale your mother had in French of her dear Midi, of the man who would have Love see, and pulled the kerchief off his eyes, whereon the boy's wings tumbled off, and he sat down and cried because he could no longer fly. When a scamp loves a good girl, let him thank the devil that love is blind."

Here was Aunt Gainor sentimental, and clever too. I shook my head sadly, being, as a man should be, humble-minded as to women. She said next she would see my father at once, and I must come at eight and bring Mr. McLane. Darthea would be with her, and a friend or two.

I went, but this time I did not bring my commanding officer. Miss Peniston was late. In all her life she was never punctual, nor could she be. While we waited my aunt went on to tell me that Darthea wished me to know how glad Mr. Wynne was I had escaped at the Mischianza. An impulse of a soldier's duty had made him seize upon me, and he had been happy in the accident which aided my escape. I had done a brave thing to venture into the city, and she and Mr. Wynne felt strongly what a calamity my capture would have been. Darthea's friends were his friends. "And he is jealous too," says my lady, "of De Lancey, and Montresor—and—of Mr. Hugh Wynne."

You must have known Mistress Wynne to comprehend what scorn she put into poor Darthea's sad excuses, and her explanations of what could not be

explained. I felt sorry for the little lady who was
absent and was getting such small mercy. It was
vain to try to stop my aunt. That no man and few
women could do. I did at last contrive to learn that
she had said no more of the visit of Arthur to the
jail than that I did not seem satisfied.

I had rather my aunt should have let my luckless
love-affair alone. I had been in a way to tell her of
it, but now I wanted no interference. I feared to
talk even to Jack Warder of my dear Darthea. That
he saw through me and her I have, after many years,
come to know, as these pages must have shown. If
to speak of her to this delicate-minded friend was
not at this time to my taste, you may rest assured I
liked not my aunt's queer way of treating the matter
as she would have done a hand at piquet. She ended
this wandering talk with her usual shrewd bits of
advice, asking me, as she stopped short in her walk,
"Have you a little sense left?"

"I hope so."

"Then get your head to help that idiot your heart.
Leave Darthea to herself. Ride with Miss Chew or
Miss Redman. Women are like children. Let them
alone, and by and by they will sidle up to you for
notice."

When the town was in Sir William Howe's hands,
my aunt had rejected all her Tory, and even her
neutral, friends. But now that Sir Henry Clinton
was flying across the Jerseys, harassed by militia, and
our general was on the way to cross the Delaware
after them, things were different. Her Tory friends

might come to see her if they pleased. Most of these dames came gladly, liking my aunt, and having always had of her much generous kindness. Bessy Ferguson was cross, and Mistress Wynne had been forced to visit her first. What manner of peace was made I did not hear; but no one else was a match at piquet for my Aunt Gainor, and doubtless this helped to reconcile the lady. I grieve that no historian has recorded their interview.

When I wrote of it to Jack, he was much delighted, and just before the fight at Monmouth wrote me a laughing letter, all about what my aunt and Mrs. Ferguson must have said on this occasion. As he knew no word of it, I could never see how he was able to imagine it. Once, later, when their war broke out anew, my aunt told me all about her former encounter; and so much like was it to what Jack had writ that I laughed outright. My aunt said there was nothing to grin at. But a one-sided laugh is ever the merrier. I could not always tell what Mistress Wynne would do, and never what she would say; but Jack could. He should have writ books, but he never did.

I had heard my aunt's wail over her wardrobe, and was struck dumb at her appearance when, in the evening, I returned as she desired. The gods and the china dragons were out, and, the Hessian devils having been driven forth, the mansion had been swept and garnished, the rugs were down, and the floor was dangerously polished.

My Aunt Gainor was in a brocade which she told

me was flowered beautiful with colours very lively.
I thought they were. As to the rest of her toilet, I
am at a loss for words. The overskirt was lute-
string silk, I was told. The hoops were vast; the
dress cut square, with a "modesty-fence" of stiff
lace. A huge high cap "with wings is the last
thing," cried the lady, turning round to be seen,
and well pleased at my admiration. She was an
immense and an amazing figure. I did wonder, so
big she was, where she meant to put the other women
— and I said as much.

"Here is one," she whispered, "who will like your
uniform more than will the rest. Mr. Wynne of the
army, my nephew, Miss Morris. And how is Mr.
Gouverneur Morris?"

We fell to talking, but when others came and
were presented or named by me to the Whig lady,
my young woman said, "Are there none but Tories?"
And she was short, I thought, with Mrs. Ferguson,
who came in high good humour and a gown of
Venice silk. I saw Aunt Gainor glance at her gold-
laced handkerchief.

I was glad to see them all. Very soon the rooms
were well filled, and here were Dr. Rush and Charles
Thomson, the secretary of Congress, who stayed but
a little while, leaving the great doctor to growl over
the war with Miss Morris, and to tell her how ill read
was our great chief, and how he could not spell, and
had to have his letters writ for him to copy like a boy.
Mr. Adams had said as much. I ventured to remark,
having by this time come to understand our doctor,

that we knew better in camp, and that at least our
chief understood the art of war. The doctor was
not of this opinion, and considered General Gates
the greater man.

Then I left them to welcome Mrs. Chew and the
lovely Margaret, and Miss Shippen, and last my Darthea with her aunt, who was as thin as a book-marker.

"Aunt," I said slyly, "what is this? Tories again?"

"Be quiet, child! You have pulled their teeth.
You will see they are meek enough. The dog on top
can always forgive, and I must have my cards. Behave yourself! How handsome you are! Here they
come." And now there was a cross-fire of welcomes
and "We have missed you so much," and "How well
you look!" and fine sweep of curtseys, very pretty
and refreshing to a war-worn veteran.

I bent to kiss Mrs. Shippen's hand. Mrs. Ferguson tapped me on the arm with her fan, whispering
I was grown past the kissing-age, at which I cried
that would never be. I took Darthea's little hand
with a formal word or two, and, biding my time, sat
down to talk with the two Margarets, whom folks
called Peggy, although both were like stately lilies,
and the pet name had no kind of fitness.

The ombre-tables were set out and ready, and it
was all gay and merry, and as if there might never
have been war, either civil or social. "It is all as
meek as doves' milk," whispered Mistress Wynne over
my shoulder. "Gossip and cards against the world
for peacemakers, eh, Hugh?" Assuredly here was
a beautiful truce, and all the world amiable.

The powdered heads wagged; brocade and silk rustled; the counters rattled. Fans huge as sails set little breezes going; there was wise neutrality of speech, King Ombre being on the throne and everybody happy.

Meanwhile I set my young women laughing with an account of how a Quaker looked in on them through the window at the redcoat ball, but of the incident in the garden I said nothing, nor was it known beyond those immediately concerned. The two Margarets were curious to hear what Mr. Washington looked like, and one miss would know if Mr. Arnold was a dark man, hearing with the delight of girls how his Excellency gave dinners in camp and sat on one side, with Mr. Hamilton or Mr. Tilghman at the top, and for diet potatoes and salt herring, with beef when it was to be had, and neither plates nor spoons nor knives and forks for all, so that we had to borrow, and eat by turns.

Miss Morris, just come to town with good Whig opinions, was uneasy in this society, and said, "We shall have enough of everything when we catch Sir Henry Clinton." In a minute there would have been more war had not my aunt risen, and the party turned to drink chocolate and eat cakes.

After a world of little gossip they settled their debts and went away, all but Mrs. Peniston and her niece, my aunt declaring that she wanted the elder lady's advice about the proper mode to cool blackberry jam. For this sage purpose the shadow-like form of Darthea's aunt in gray silk went out under cover of my aunt's large figure, and Darthea and I were left alone.

How pretty she was in fair white muslin with long gloves, a red rosebud in each sleeve, and only a trace of powder on her hair, smiling, and above all women graceful! She had seemed older when we met in the Provostry, and now to-day was slim and girl-like. I do not know where she got that trick of change, for in after-days, when in the fuller bloom of middle age, she still had a way of looking at times a gay and heedless young woman. She had now so innocent an air of being merely a sweet child that a kind of wonder possessed me, and I could not but look at her with a gaze perhaps too fixed to be mannerly.

"Darthea," I said, as we sat down, "I owe my life to you twice—twice."

"No, no!" she cried. "What could I do but go to the jail? Miss Wynne was away."

"You might have told my father," I said. Why had she not?

"Mr. Wynne is grown older, and—I— There was no time to be lost, and Arthur was gone on duty for I know not what." She was seeing and answering what further might have seemed strange to me. "Aunt Peniston was in a rage, I assure you. My aunt in a rage, Mr. Wynne, is a tempest in a thimble. All in a minute it boils over and puts out the little fire, and there is an end of it, and she asks what ought to be done. But now I am penitent, and have been scolded by Arthur. I will never, never do it any more. My aunt was right, sir."

II.—7

"I think you gave me more than life, Darthea, that day. And did you think I would take the parole?"

"Never for a moment!" she cried, with flashing eyes. "I would have taken it, but I want my friends to be wiser and stronger than I. I—I was proud of you in your misery and ragged blanket." And with this the wonderful face went tender in a moment, and for my part I could only say, "Darthea! Darthea!"

She was quick to see and to fear, and to avoid that which was ever on my lips when with her, and which she seemed to bid to live, and then to fly from as if she had never tempted me.

"Ah, you were a droll figure, and Arthur could not but laugh when I described this hero in a blanket. It was then he told me more fully what before he had wrote, how in the hurry of an inspection he saw many men dying, and one so like you that he asked who it was, and was given another name; but now he thought it must have been you, and that you had perhaps chosen, why he knew not, a name not your own, or you had been misnamed by the turnkey. It was little wonder where men were dying in scores and changed past recognition; it was no wonder, I say, he did not know you, Mr. Wynne. He was so sorry, for he says frankly that just because you and he are not very good friends—and why are you not?—he feels the worse about it. After he had scolded me well, and I made believe to cry, he said it was a noble and brave thing I had done, and he

felt he should have been the one to do it had he
known in season. He did really mean to get the
parole, but then you ran away. And you do see, Mr.
Wynne, that it was all a frightful mistake of Arthur's,
and he is—he must be sorry?"

I would then and there have said to her that the
man was a liar, and had meanly left me to die; but
it was my word against his, and Delaney had long
ago gotten out and been exchanged and gone South,
whither I knew not. As of course she must trust
the man she loved, if I were to say I did not believe him we should quarrel, and I should see her
no more.

"My dear lady," I said, keeping myself well in hand,
"the moral is that women should be sent to inspect
the hungry, the ragged, the frozen, and the dying."

I saw she did not relish my answer. Was she
herself quite satisfied? Did she want to be fortified in her love and trust by me, who had suffered?
A shadow of a frown was on her brow for a moment,
and then she said, "He will write to you. He promised me he would write to you. And that dear old
Sister of Charity!—you must go and thank her at the
little convent beside St. Joseph's, in Willing's Alley.
You upset her as you went out in that rude fashion.
Any but a Quaker would have stayed to apologise.
Mr. Wynne was pleased I went to the jail with the
dear sister. I believe the man really thought I
would have gone alone. And I would; I would!
When he told me it was clever and modest to get the
sweet old papist for company, I swept him a mighty

curtsey and thanked him and puzzled him, which is
what men are for."

Sitting in the open bow-window above the garden,
my Darthea had most of the talk, while, when I
dared no longer stare at her changeful face, I looked
past her at the June roses swaying in the open win-
dow-space.

"Yes," I laughed, "that is what men are for; but
I have not done with you. I have also to thank you
for my escape in the garden—you and Mr. André.
He has a good memory, I fancy."

"Oh, the fainting—yes," said Miss Peniston, lightly.
"It was fortunate it came just then. And Mr. Wynne
was glad enough of it later. He said it had saved
him from the most horrible regret life could bring.
If he had but had time to think—or had known—"

"Known what?"

"No matter; I was in time to stop myself from
saying a foolish thing. Let me give thanks for my
escape. I have a restless tongue, and am apt to say
what I do not mean; and I do faint at nothing."

"It was very opportune, my dear Miss Peniston."

"La! la! as aunt says, one would think I went
faint on purpose, in place of its being the heat, and
a providential accident, and very annoying too; not
a woman anywhere near me."

"It saved a worthless life," I said; "and but for it
I should have had short shrift and the gallows on
the Common."

"Hush!" she returned. "That is not pretty talk.
Your cousin is unlucky, he says, to have had you fall

in his way when it was impossible to escape from arresting you. He told me Mr. André assured him he could have done no other thing, and that it was vain to regret what was the inevitable duty of a soldier. I think Arthur was the most pleased of all when you got away. I must say you went very fast for so grave a Quaker."

"And could you see?" said I, slyly.

"No, of course not. How should I, and I in a dead faint? Mr. André told me next day he thought that dreadful rebel, Mr. McLane, saved your life when he was mean enough, just in the middle of that beautiful ball, to set fire to something. At first we took it for the fireworks. But tell me about Miss Gainor's girl-boy—our own dear Jack."

"He can still blush to beat Miss Franks, and he still believes me to be a great man, and—but you do not want to hear about battles."

"Do I not, indeed! I should like to see Mr. Jack in a battle; I cannot imagine him hurting a fly."

"The last I saw, at Germantown, of Jack, he was raging in a furious mob of redcoats, with no hat, and that sword my aunt presented cutting and parrying. I gave him up for lost, but he never got a scratch. I like him best in camp with starving, half-naked men. I have seen him give his last loaf away. You should hear Mr. Hamilton—that is his Excellency's aide—talk of Jack; how like a tender woman he was among men who were sick and starving. Hamilton told me how once, when Jack said prayers beside a dying soldier and some fellow laughed,—men get hard in war,—our old Quaker friend Colonel Forest would have had the beast out and shot him, if the fool had not gone to Jack and said he was sorry. Every one loves the man, and no wonder."

" He is fortunate in his friend, Mr. Wynne. Men do not often talk thus of one another. I have heard him say as much or more' of you. Mistress Wynne says it is a love-affair. Are men's friendships or women's the best, I wonder?" I said that was a question beyond me, and went on to tell her that I should be in town but a few days, and must join my regiment as soon as General Arnold could do without us, which I believed would be within a week.

She was as serious as need be now, asking intelligent questions as to the movements of the armies and the chances of peace. I had to show her why we lost the fight at Germantown, and then explain that but for the fog we should have won it, which now I doubt.

Mr. André had told her that it was because of our long rifles that the enemy lost so many officers, picked off out of range of musket, and did I think this was true? It seemed to her unfair and like murder.

I thought she might be thinking of my cousin's chances, for here, after a pause, she rose suddenly and said it was late and that the strawberry jam must be cool, or the discussion over it hot, to keep Mrs. Peniston so long. My aunt would have had me stay for further talk, but I said I was tired, and went away home feeling that the day had been full enough for me.

A little later, one afternoon in this June, I found my aunt seated so deep in thought that I asked her the cause.

"Presently," she said. "I have meant to tell you, but I have delayed; I have delayed. Now you must know." Here she rose and began to stride restlessly among the furniture, walking to and fro with apparent disregard of the china gods and Delft cows. She reminded me once more of my father in his better days. Her hands were clasped behind her, which is, I think, a rare attitude with women. Her large head, crowned with a great coil of gray hair which seemed to suit its massive build, was bent forward as if in thought.

"What is it, Aunt Gainor?"

She did not pause in her walk or look up, and only motioned me to a seat, saying, "Sit down. I must think; I must think."

It was unlike her. Generally, no matter how serious the thing on her mind, she was apt to come at it through some trivial chat; but now her long absence of speech troubled me.

I sat at least ten minutes, and then, uneasy, said, "Aunt Gainor, is it Darthea?"

"No, you fool!" And she went on her wandering way among the crackled gods. "Now I will talk, Hugh, and do not interrupt me. You always do;" but, as Jack Warder says, no one ever did successfully interrupt Miss Wynne except Miss Wynne.

She sat down, crossed one leg over the other, as men do when alone with men, and went on, as I recall it, to this effect, and quite in her ordinary manner: "When the British were still here, late in May I had a note through the lines from Mr. Warder as to the confusion in my house, and some other matters. He got for me a pass to come in and attend to these things. I stayed three days with Mrs. Peniston and Darthea. While here the second day I was bid to sup at Parson Duché's, and though I hated the lot of them, I had had no news nor so much as a game of cards for an age, and so I went. Now don't grin at me.

"When I was to leave no coach came, as I had ordered, and no chair, either. There was Mrs. Ferguson had set up a chaise. She must offer me to be set down at home. I said my two legs were as good as her horses', and one of them—I mean of hers—has a fine spavin; as to Mrs. Mischief's own legs, they are so thin her garters will not stay above her ankles.

"I walked from Third street over Society Hill, thinking to see your father, and to find a big stick for company across the bridges."

She was given to going at night where she had need to go, with a great stick for privateersmen, the vagabond, drunken Hessians, and other street pirates. I can see her now, shod with goloe-shoes against mud or snow, with her manlike walk and independent air, quite too formidable to suggest attack.

"I went in at the back way," she continued; "not a servant about but Tom, sound asleep at the kitchen fire. I went by him, and from the hall saw your father, also in deep slumber in his arm-chair. I got

me a candle and went upstairs to look how things
were. The house was in vile disorder, and dirty past
belief. As to your own chamber, where that scamp
Arthur slept, it was—well, no matter.

"As I went downstairs and into the back dining-
room I heard the latch of the hall door rattle. 'Is
it Arthur?' thought I; and of no mind to see him, I
sat down and put out my candle, meaning to wait till
he was come in, and then to slip out the back way.
The next moment I heard Arthur's voice and your
father's. Both doors into the front room were wide
open, and down I sat quietly, with a good mind to
hear. It is well I did. I suppose you would have
marched in and said, 'Take care how you talk; I am
listening.' Very fine, sir. But this was an enemy.
You lie, cheat, spy, steal, and murder in war. How
was I worse than you?"

"But, dear Aunt Gainor—"

"Don't interrupt me, sir. I sat still as a mouse."
My aunt as a mouse tickled my fancy. There may
be such in my friend Mr. Swift's Brobdingnag.

"I listened. Master Wynne is pleasant, and has
had a trifle too much of Mr. Somebody's Madeira.
He is affectionate, and your father sits up, and, as
Dr. Rush tells me, is clear of head after his sleep,
or at least for a time.

"My gentleman says, 'I may have to leave you
soon, my dear cousin. I want to talk to you a little.
Is there any one in the back room?' As there is no
one, he goes on, and asks his cousin to tell him about
the title to Wyncote as he had promised. His brother

was ill and uneasy, and it was all they had, and it was a poor thing after all. Your father roused up, and seemed to me to fully understand all that followed. He said how fond he was of Arthur, and how much he wished it was he who was to have the old place. Arthur replied that it was only in his father's interest he spoke.

"Then they talked on, and the amount of it was pretty much this. How many lies Arthur got into the talk the Lord—or the devil—knows! This was what I gathered: Your grandfather Hugh, under stress of circumstances, as you know, was let out of Shrewsbury jail with some understanding that he was to sell his estate to his brother, who had no scruples as to tithes, and to go away to Pennsylvania. This I knew, but it seems that this brother William was a Wynne of the best, and, as is supposed, sold back the estate privately to Hugh for a trifle, so that at any time the elder brother could reclaim his home. What became of the second deed thus made was what Arthur wanted to know.

"Your father must have it somewhere, Hugh. Now says Arthur, 'We are poor, cousin; the place is heavily encumbered; some coal has been found. It is desirable to sell parts of the estate; how honestly can my father make a title?' Your great-uncle William died, as we know, Hugh, and the next brother's son, who was Owen and is Arthur's father, had a long minority. When he got the place, being come of age, some memoranda of the transaction turned up. It was not a rare one in older Roundhead days. Nothing was done, and time ran on. Now the occupant is getting on in years, and as his second son Arthur is ordered hither on service, it was thought as well that he should make inquiry. The older squires had some vague tradition about it. It was become worth while, as I inferred, to clear the business, or at need to effect a compromise. Half of this I heard, and the rest I got by thinking it over. Am I plain, Hugh?" She was, as usual. "Your father surprised me. He spoke out in his old deliberate way. He said the deed—some such deed—was among his father's papers; he had seen it long ago. He did not want the place. He was old and had enough, and it should be settled to Master Arthur's liking.

"Your cousin then said some few words about you. I did not hear what, but your father at once broke out in a fierce voice, and cried, 'It is too true!' Well, Hugh," she went on, "it is of no use to make things worse between you."

"No," I said; "do not tell me. Was that all?"

"Not quite. Master Arthur is to have the deed if ever it be found, and with your father's and your grandfather's methodical ways, that is pretty sure to happen."

"I do not care much, Aunt Gainor, except that—"

"I know," she cried; "anybody else might have it, but not Arthur."

"Yes; unless Darthea—"

"I understand, sir; and now I see it all. The elder brother will die. The father is old, the estate valu-

able, and this lying scamp with his winning ways
will be master of Wyncote, and with a clear title if
your father is able to bring it about. He can, Hugh,
unless—"

"What, aunt?"

"Unless you intervene on account of my brother's
mental state."

"That I will never do! Never!"

"Then you will lose it."

"Yes; it must go. I care but little, aunt."

"But I do, sir. You are Wynne of Wyncote."

I smiled, and made no reply.

"The man stayed awhile longer, but your father
after that soon talked at random, and addressed
Arthur as Mr. Montresor. I doubt if he remembered
a word of it the day after. When he left and went
upstairs your father fell into sleep again. I went
away home alone, and the day after to the Hill Farm."

"It is a strange story," I said. "And did he get
the deed before the army left?"

My aunt thought not. "Mason says all the papers
are at the counting-house, and that up to this time
your father has made no special search. It was but
two weeks or less before they left town."

It was a simple way to trap an over-cunning man,
and it much amused me, who did not take the deed
and estate matter to heart as did my aunt. When
she said, "We must find it," I could but say that it
was my father's business, and could wait; so far, at
least, as I was concerned, I would do nothing. Of
course I told it all to Jack when next we met.

VII

N Sunday, the 21st of June, while our chief was crossing into the Jerseys, I was hearing at Christ Church, for the first time, the words of prayer in which William White commended Congress and our armies and their great leader to the protecting mercy of Almighty God. General Arnold was already busy with the great household and equipage which soon did so much to involve him in temptations growing out of his fondness for display. The militia were unwilling to act as a body-guard, or to stand sentries beside the great lamp-posts at his door. Nor did McLane and the rest of us fancy the social and guard duties which the general exacted; but we had to obey orders, and were likely, I feared, to remain long in this ungrateful service.

On June 30 we heard of the glorious battle at Monmouth, and with surprise of General Lee's disgrace. On the 3d of July came Jack with a bayonet-thrust in his right shoulder and a nasty cut over the left temple. He was able to be afoot, but was quite unfit for service. I heard from him of the splendid courage and judgment shown by his Excellency, and of the profane and terrible language he had used to that traitor Lee. Jack said: "I was in the midst of a lot of scared men, with a leader who wanted only to get away. And then the general rode up, and all was changed. I think, Hugh, he was like an angry god of war. I should have died of the things he said to Mr. Lee."

When, long after this, in July, '79, his Excellency issued that severe order about swearing, how it was against all religion, decency, and order, Jack was much amused. Like the army in Flanders, our own army solaced their empty stomachs with much bad language. But, as Jack observed, "There is a time for everything; Mr. Lee did catch it hot."

McLane soon left us, glad to get away. Had he stayed much longer there would have been one more sad moth in the pretty net into which fell all who were long in the company of our fatal Darthea. I too applied for active duty, but some influence, probably that of General Arnold, came in the way and kept me in the city.

Very soon, to my pleasure, I received a letter from Mr. Hamilton, inclosing my commission as captain in the Third Regiment of the Pennsylvania line, and with it, not to my pleasure, an order to recruit in and near the city. Rather later the general asked me, as I was but little occupied, to act as an extra aide on his staff, a position which might have been my ruin, as I shall by and by relate.

Jack's hurts turning out worse than was anticipated, he was of no use in camp, and remained at home to be petted and fussed over by my Aunt Gainor.

After a month or two he was able to go about with
his arm in a sling, and to be greatly noticed by the
Whig women. Very soon he was caught, like me,
in a ceaseless round of all manner of gaieties. He
shortly grew weary of it, and fell back on his books
and the society of the many who loved him—above
all, that of my aunt and Darthea. For me there was
no escape, as my own dissipations were chiefly those
of official duty, and in company with my chief.

Congress was still in session, but from it were missing Adams, Franklin, Henry, Jay, and Rutledge, who
were elsewhere filling posts of importance. It had
no fully recognised powers, and the want of more
distinct union was beginning to be sadly felt. Had
not the ruin of the Conway cabal and the profound
trust of the people lifted Washington into a position
of authority, the fears and predictions of men like
my friend Wilson would have been fully justified.
Intrigues, ruinous methods of finance, appointments
given to untried foreign officers who were mere ad-
venturers—all these and baser influences were working toward the ruin of our cause.

Our own city went wild that winter. The Tories
were sharply dealt with at first, but, as many of
them were favoured by the general in command,
they soon came back in mischievous numbers. The
more moderate neutrals opened their doors to all
parties. The general began to be at ease in the
homes of the proprietary set, and, buying the great
house of Mount Pleasant, made court to the lovely
Margaret Shippen, and was foremost in a display of

excess and luxury such as annoyed and troubled
those who saw him hand and glove with the Tory
gentlemen, and extravagant beyond anything hith-
erto seen in the quiet old city of Penn.

At this time the Congress often sat with but a
dozen members. It was no longer the dignified body
of seventy-six. Officers came and went. Men like
Robert Morris and Dr. Rush shook their heads.
Clinton lay in New York, watched by Washington,
and in the South there was disaster after disaster,
while even our best men wearied of the war, and
asked anxiously how it was to end.

Recruiting in the face of such a state of things
was slow indeed. I had little to do but wait on the
general, read to my aunt, ride with her and Darthea,
or shoot ducks with Jack when weather permitted;
and so the long winter wore on.

With Darthea I restrained my useless passion, and
contented myself with knowing that we were day by
day becoming closer friends. If Arthur wrote to her
or not, I could not tell. She avoided mentioning
him, and I asked no questions.

I shall let Jack's diary tell—at this time it was
very full—what chanced in midwinter. Alas, my
dear Jack!

"It has," he wrote, "been a season of foolish dis-
sipation. While the army suffers for everything,
these fools are dancing and gambling, and General
A—— the worst of all, which seems a pity in so good
a soldier. He is doing us a mighty harm.

"To-day has been for me a sad one. I shall think

ever of my folly with remorse. I set it down as a
lesson to be read. We had a great sleighing-frolic
to Cliveden. There were all the Tories, and few
else—the general driving Peggy Shippen, and I Darthea. Mistress Wynne would have none of it. 'We
were no worse off under Howe,' she says; 'Mr. Arnold
has no sense and no judgment.' It is true, I fear.
Mrs. Peniston, half froze, went along in our old
sleigh. We drove up to the stone steps of Cliveden
about seven at night—a fine moonlight, so that the
stone vases on the roof, crowned with their carved
pineapples, stood out against the sky. The windows
were all aglow, and neither doors nor shutters were
as yet fully repaired.

"We had a warm welcome, and stood about the
ample fires while the ladies went merrily upstairs
to leave their cloaks. I looked about me curiously, for there were dozens of bullet-marks on the
plaster and the woodwork. It had been a gallant
defence, and cleverly contrived. Soon came down
the stairs a bevy of laughing girls to look, with
hushed voices, at the blood-stains on the floor and the
dents the muskets had made. They did think to
tease me by praising Colonel Musgrave, who had
commanded the British; but I, not to be outdone,
declared him the bravest man alive. Darthea smiled,
but said nothing, and for that I loved her better than
ever.

"Then we fell to chatting, and presently she said,
'Madam Chew, Mr. Warder is to show me where the
troops lay, and Mr. Wayne's brigade; and who will
II.—8

come too?' There were volunteers, but once outside
they found it cold, and Darthea, saying, 'We shall
be gone but a minute,' walked with me around the
stone outbuilding to northwest. She was very
thoughtful and quiet this night, looking as sweet as
ever a woman could in a gray fur coat against the
moon-lit drifts of snow. 'Over there,' I said, 'across
the road, were our poor little four-pounders; and beyond yonder wall our chief held a brief council of
war; and just there in the garden lay my own men
and Hugh, and some Maryland troops, among the
box where we used to play hide-and-find.'

"On this Darthea said, 'Let me see the place,' and
we walked down the garden, a gentle excitement
showing in her ways and talk; and I—ah me, that
night!

"'I must see,' she said, 'where the dead lie; near
the garden wall, is it?'

"'Here,' said I—'ours and theirs.'

"'In the peace which is past understanding,' said
Darthea. Then, deep in thought, she turned from
the house and into the woods a little beyond, not
saying a word. Indeed, not a sound was to be heard,
except the creak and craunch of the dry snow under
our feet. A few paces farther we came to the sum-
mer-house, set on circular stone steps, and big enough
to dine in. There she stood, saying, 'I cannot go
back yet; oh, those still, still dead! Don't speak to
me—not for a little while.' She stayed thus, looking
up at the great white moon, while I stood by, and
none other near.

" 'I am better now, Jack, and you will not tell of
how foolish I was—but—'

" I said there was some sweet folly, if she liked
so to call it, which was better than wisdom. And
then how it was I know not, nor ever shall. I felt
myself flush and tremble. It is my foolish way when
in danger, being by nature timid, and forced to exercise rule over myself at such seasons.

"She said, 'What is it, Jack?' for so she often
called me when we were alone, although Hugh was
Mr. Wynne. The ways of women are strange.

"I could not help it, and yet I knew Hugh loved
her. I knew also that she was surely to marry Mr.
Arthur Wynne. I was wrong, but, God help us!
who is not wrong at times? I said: 'Darthea, I love
you. If it were to be Hugh I should never say so.'
I cared nothing about the other man; he hates my
Hugh.

" 'Oh, Jack, Jack! you hurt me!' Never was anything so sweet and tender. Her great eyes—like
Madam Wynne's that were—filled and ran over.
'Oh, Jack!' she cried, 'must I hurt you too, and is it
my fault? Oh, my dear Jack, whom I love and
honour, I can't love you this way. I can't—I can't.
And I am sorry. I must marry Arthur Wynne; I
have promised. You men think we women give our
hearts lightly, and take them again, as if they were
mere counters; and I am troubled, Jack, and no one
knows it. I must not talk of that. I wish you would
all go away. I can't marry you all.' And she began
to be agitated, and to laugh in a way that seemed to

me quite strange and out of place; but then I know
little about women.

"I could but say: 'Forgive me; I have hurt you
whom I love. I will never do it more—never. But,
dear Darthea, you will let me love you, because I cannot help it, and this will all be as if it had never been.
To hurt you—to hurt you of all the world! I had
no right to ask you.'

" 'Don't,' she said, with a great sob, which seemed
to break my heart.

" 'Darthea,' I said—'Darthea, do not marry that
man! He is cruel; he is hard; he does not love you
as my Hugh loves you.'

" 'Sir,' she said, with such sudden dignity that I
was overcome, and fell back a pace, 'I am promised;
let that suffice. It is cold; let us go in. It is cold—
it is cold!'

"I had never seen her like this. I said: 'Certainly; I should not have kept you. I was thought-
less.' And as she said nothing in reply, I went after
her, having said my say as I never intended, and
more than was perhaps wise. At the door she turned
about, and, facing me, said abruptly, with her dear ·
face all of a flush: 'Do not let this trouble you. I
am not good enough to make it worth while. I have
been a foolish girl, discontented with our simple
ways, wanting what I have not. I have cried for
toys, and have got them, and now I don't care for
them; but I have promised. Do you hear, sir? I
have promised—I have promised.'

"She stayed for no answer, but went in. It seemed

to me a singular speech, and to mean more than was said. The repeating of one phrase over and over appeared meant to reinforce a doubtful purpose. I think she cares little for Mr. Arthur Wynne, but who can say? Darthea is full of surprises.

"Can it be that she loves Hugh and knows it not, or that she has such a strong sense of honour that it is hard for her to break her word? She does not believe this man to be bad. That is sure. If ever I can make her see him as I see him, he will hold her not an hour. I shall disturb her life no more. Had she taken me to-day, I know not what would have come of it. I am not strong of will, like Hugh. God knows best. I will ask no more."

I was an old man when I, Hugh Wynne, read these pages, and I am not ashamed to say they cost me some tears.

So far as I remember, neither Jack nor Darthea betrayed by their manner what I learned naught of for so many years. Neither did my Aunt Gainor's shrewdness get any hint of what passed at Cliveden. I recall, however, that Jack became more and more eager to rejoin his regiment, and this he did some two weeks later.

My father's condition was such as at times to alarm me, and at last I proposed to him to see Dr. Rush. To my surprise, he consented. I say to my surprise, for he had a vast distrust of doctors, and, to tell the truth, had never needed their help. The day after the doctor's visit I saw our great physician, whom now all the world has learned to revere, and

who was ever more wise in matters of medicine than
in matters of state.

He told me that my father was beginning to have
some failure of brain because of his arteries being
older than the rest of him, which I did not quite comprehend. He had, he said, losses of memory which
were not constant. Especially was he affected with
forgetfulness as to people, and for a time mistook
them, so that for a while he had taken Dr. Rush for
his old clerk Mason. The doctor said it was more
common to lack remembrance of places. In my
father's condition he might take one man for another, and to-morrow be as clear as to his acquaintance as ever he had been; but that as to business,
as was in such cases rare, his mind continued to be
lucid, except at times, when his memory would suddenly fail him for a few minutes. The doctor saw
no remedy for his condition, and I mention it only
because my father's varying peculiarities came in a
measure to affect me and others in a way of which
I shall have occasion to speak.

My sense of his state did much to make me more
tender and more able to endure the sad outbreaks of
passion which Dr. Rush taught me were to be looked
for. Nor was my aunt less troubled than I. Indeed,
from this time she showed as regarded my father all
of that gentleness which lay beneath the exterior
roughness of her masculine nature. I observed that
she looked after his house, paying him frequent
visits, and in all ways was solicitous that he should
be made comfortable.

Near about the 1st of March—I am not quite sure of the date—I was asked in the absence of Major Clarkson, chief of the staff, to take his duties for a few days. I then saw how needlessly the general was creating enmities. His worst foe, Mr. Joseph Reed, had become in December president of the Council of State, and we—I say we—were thenceforward forever at outs with the body over which he presided. When at last, thoroughly disgusted, General Arnold was about to resign from the army, those unpleasant charges were made against him which came to little or nothing, but which embittered a life already harassed by disappointed ambition and want of means, and now also by the need to show a fair face to Mr. Shippen, whose daughter's hand he had asked.

General Arnold's indifference as to privacy in his affairs amazed me, and I saw enough to make me both wonder and grieve. The friend of Schuyler and of Warren, the soldier whom Washington at one time absolutely trusted, attached me to him by his kindness and lavish generosity, and as an officer he had my unbounded admiration. Surely his place was in the field, and not at the dinner-tables of Tories, whose society, as I have said, he much affected. It was a sign of weakness that he overesteemed the homage of a merely gay and fashionable set, and took with avidity the dangerous flattery of the Tory dames.

He was withal a somewhat coarse man, with a vast amount of vanity. It was a blow to his self-estimate when he was unjustly passed over in the promotions

to major-general. He felt it deeply, and was at no
pains to hide his disgust. I did not wonder that the
Shippens did all they could to break off this strange
love-affair. They failed; for when a delicate-minded,
sensitive, well-bred woman falls in love with a
strong, coarse, passionate man, there is no more to
be said except, "Take her."

VIII

S the spring came on my father's condition seemed to me to grow worse. At times he had great gusts of passion or of tears, quite unlike himself; for a day he would think I was my cousin, and be more affectionate than I had ever seen him. Once or twice he talked in a confused way of our estate in Wales, and so, what with this and my annoyance over the irregularities at our headquarters, I had enough to trouble me.

The office duties were, as I have said, not much to my taste, but I learned a good deal which was of future use to me. It was a dull life, and but once did I come upon anything worth narrating. This, in fact, seemed to me at the time of less moment than it grew to be thereafter.

Neither I nor Major Clarkson, his chief of staff, had all of the general's confidence. Men came and went now and then with letters, or what not, of which naturally I learned nothing. One—a lean, small man, ill disguised as a Quaker—I saw twice. The last time he found the general absent. I offered to take charge of a letter he said he had, but he declined, saying he would return, and on this put it

back in his pocket, or tried to; for he let it fall, and
in quick haste secured it, although not before I
thought I had recognised Arthur Wynne's peculiar
handwriting. This astounded me, as you may imagine. But how could I dream of what it meant? I
concluded at last that I must have been mistaken,
and I did not feel at liberty to ask the general. It
was none of my business, after all.

The fellow—I had always supposed him one of our
spies—came again in an hour, and saw the general.
I heard the man say, "From Mr. Anderson, sir," and
then the door was closed, and the matter passed from
my mind for many a day.

Jack very soon after left us, and Darthea became
more and more reserved, and unlike her merry,
changeful self.

On March 25, '79, I came in late in the afternoon
and sat down to read. My father, seated at the table,
was tying up or untying bundles of old papers.
Looking up, he said abruptly, "Your cousin has been
here to-day." It was said so naturally as for a moment to surprise me. I made no reply. A few
minutes later he looked up again.

"Arthur, Arthur—"

I turned from a book on tactics issued by Baron
Steuben. "I am not Arthur, father."

He took no notice of this, but went on to say that
I ought to have come long ago. And what would I
do with it?

I asked what he meant by *it*, and if I could help
him with his papers.

No, no; he needed no help. Did I ever hear from Wyncote, and how was William? I made sure he had once again taken me for my cousin. I found it was vain to insist upon my being his son. For a moment he would seem puzzled, and would then call me Arthur. At last, when he became vexed, and said angrily that I was behaving worse than Hugh, I recalled Dr. Rush's advice, and humouring his delusion, said, "Uncle, let me help you." Meanwhile he was fumbling nervously at the papers, tying and untying the same bundle, which seemed to be chiefly old bills and invoices.

"Here it is," he went on. "Take it, and have a care that thou hast it duly considered by James Wilson, or another as good. Then we will see."

"What is it, uncle?" I returned.

He said it was the reconveyance of Wyncote to my grandfather; and with entirely clear language, and no fault of thought that I could observe, he stated that at need he would execute a proper title to Godfrey, the present man.

I was struck dumb with astonishment and pity. Here was a man acting within a world of delusion as to who I was, and with as much competence as ever in his best days. I did not know what to say, nor even what to do. At last I rose, and put the old yellow parchment in my coat pocket, saying I was greatly obliged by his kindness.

Then, his business habits acting as was their wont, he said, "But it will be proper for thee to give me a receipt."

I said it was not needed, but he insisted; and at this I was puzzled. I did not want the deed, still less did I want it to pass into Arthur's hands. I said, "Very good, sir," and sitting down again, wrote a receipt, and, calmly signing my own name, gave it to him. He did not look at it, but folded and indorsed it, and threw it into the little red leather trunk on the table.

I went away to my aunt's without more delay, a much-astounded man. The good lady was no less astonished. We read the deed over with care, but its legal turns and its great length puzzled us both, and at last my aunt said:

"Let me keep it, Hugh. It is a queer tangle. Just now we can do nothing, and later we shall see. There will be needed some wiser legal head than mine or yours, and what will come of it who can say? At all events, Mr. Arthur has it not, and in your father's condition he himself will hardly be able to make a competent conveyance. Indeed, I think he will forget the whole business. I presume Master Wynne is not likely to return in a hurry."

In the beginning of April General Arnold married our beautiful Margaret Shippen, and took her to the new home, Mount Pleasant, above the shaded waters of the quiet Schuylkill. Tea-parties and punch-drinking followed, as was the custom.

Mr. Arnold, as my aunt called him, after a fashion learned in London, and also common in the colonies, gave his bride Mount Pleasant as a dowry, and none knew—not even the fair Margaret—that it was hopelessly mortgaged. Hither came guests in scores for a week after the marriage to drink tea with madam, the men taking punch upstairs with the groom, while the women waited below, and had cakes and gossip, in which this winter was rich enough to satisfy those of all parties.

It was a year of defeat, and again the weaker folk, like Joseph Warder and some much better known,—I mention no names,—were talking of terms, or, by their firesides with a jug of Hollands, were criticising our leader, and asking why he did not move. Meanwhile the army was as ill off as ever it had been since the camping at Valley Forge, while the air here in the city was full of vague rumours of defection and what not. I was of necessity caught in the vortex of gaiety which my chief loved and did much to keep up. He liked to see his aides at his table, and used them as a part of the excessive state we thought at this time most unseemly.

I remember well an afternoon in April of this year, when, the spring being early, all manner of green things were peeping forth, while I walked to and fro in the hall at Mount Pleasant, that I might receive those who called and excuse the absence of the host. I wandered out, for as yet none came to call. The air was soft like summer, and, sweeter than birds overhead or the fragrant arbutus on the upland slopes, came Darthea in virgin white, and a great hat tied under her chin with long breadths of blue ribbon. My aunt walked with her from her coach, and close after them came a laughing throng of men and women, for the most part of the governor's set. There was bad news from the South, which was by no means unwelcome to these people, if I might judge from their comments. My aunt walked with them in silent wrath, and after I had met them at the door, turned aside with me and bade me go with her on the lawn, where the grass was already green.

"I have held my tongue," she said. "These people have neither manners nor hearts. I told Mr. Shippen as much. And where does your general get all his money? It is vulgar, this waste. Look!" she said; "look there! It is well to feed the poor after a wedding; I like the old custom; but this is mere ostentation." It was true; there was a crowd of the neighbouring farm people about the detached kitchen, eager for the food and rum which I saw given daily in absurd profusion. My Aunt Gainor shook her head.

"It will turn out badly, Hugh. This comes of a woman marrying beneath her. The man may be a good soldier,—oh, no doubt he is,—but he is not a gentleman. You must get away, Hugh." Indeed, I much desired to do so, but until now had been detained, despite repeated applications to my chief.

My aunt said no more, but went into the house, leaving me to await the coming of the many guests, men and women, gentlemen of the Congress, with officers in uniform, who flocked to this too hospitable mansion. I had just heard from Jack, and the contrast shown by his account of the want of arms, clothing, and food seemed to me most sad when I reflected upon the extravagance and useless excess I had seen throughout the winter now at an end. I did not wonder at my aunt's anger. Her fears were but the vague anticipations of a wise old woman who had seen the world and used good eyes and a sagacious brain. How little did she or I dream of the tragedy of dishonour into which the mad waste, the growing debts, the bitterness of an insulted and ambitious spirit, were to lead the host of this gay house!

As I turned in my walk I saw the general dismount, and went to meet him. He said: "I shall want you at nine to-night at my quarters in town— an errand of moment into the Jerseys. You must leave early to-morrow. Are you well horsed?"

I said yes, and was, in fact, glad of any more active life. Before nine that night I went to headquarters, and found a number of invitations to dine or sup. It may amuse those for whom I write to know that nearly all were writ on the white backs of playing-cards; but one from Madam Arnold was printed. I sat down, facing the open doorway into the general's room, and began to write refusals, not knowing how long I might be absent.

Presently looking up, I saw the general at his desk. I had not heard him enter. Two candles were in front of him. He was sitting with his cheeks resting on his hands and his elbows on the desk, facing me, and so deep in thought that I did not think fit to interrupt him. His large, ruddy features now were

pale and sombre, and twice I saw him use his kerchief
to mop his brow as if it were moist from overheating.

At last he called me, and I went in. His forehead
and the powdered hair about it were in fact wet, like
those of a man who is coming out of an ague. Indeed, he looked so ill that I ventured to ask after his
health. He replied that he was well. That infamous
court-martial business annoyed him, and as to Mr.
Reed, if there were any fight in the man, he would
have him out and get done with him—which seemed
imprudent talk, to say no more.

"Captain Wynne," he went on, "early to-morrow
you will ride through Bristol to the ferry below
Trenton. Cross and proceed with all haste to South
Amboy. At the Lamb Tavern you will meet an
officer from Sir Henry Clinton. Deliver to him this
despatch in regard to exchange of prisoners. He
may or may not have a letter for you to bring back.
In this package are passes from me, and one from
Sir Henry Clinton, in case you meet with any Tory
parties."

"I shall be sure to meet them in west Jersey.
Pardon me, sir, but would it not be easier to pass
through our own lines in the middle Jerseys?"

"You have your orders, Mr. Wynne," he replied
severely.

I bowed.

Then he seemed to hesitate, and I stood waiting
his will. "The despatch," he said, "is open in case
it becomes needful to show it. Perhaps you had
better read it."

This sounded unusual, but I opened it, and read to the effect that the exchanges would go on if Sir Henry did not see fit to alter his former proposal, but that some time might elapse before the lists on our side were made out. "The officer charged with this letter will be unable to give any further information, as he has no powers to act for me.

"I have the honour to be
"Your obedient, humble servant,
"BENEDICT ARNOLD,
"*Major-General in command of*
Philadelphia and the western Jerseys."

I looked up. "Is that all?"

"Not quite. If it chance that no officer appears to meet you at Amboy, you will return at once."

Very glad of relief from the routine of rather distasteful duties, I rode away at dawn the next day up the Bristol road. I was stopped, as I supposed I should be, by a small band of Tory partisans, but after exhibiting my British pass I was permitted to proceed. Between Trenton and Amboy I met a party of our own horse, and had some trouble until I allowed their leader, a stupid lout, to read my open despatch, when he seemed satisfied, and sent on two troopers with me, whom I left near Amboy.

At the inn I waited a day, when a ketch appeared, and an officer, stepping ashore, came up from the beach to meet me. I saw, as he drew near, that it was Arthur Wynne.

"Glad to see you," he cried, in a quite hearty way.

II.—9

"It is an unexpected pleasure. André was to have come, but he is ill. He desires his regards and particular compliments."

Was I always to meet this man when I was so hampered that to have my will of him was out of the question? I said the meeting could not be unexpected, or how could André have known? At this I saw him look a bit queer, and I went on to add that the pleasure was all on his side.

"I am sorry," he returned.

Not caring to hear further, I said abruptly: "Let us proceed to business. Here is a despatch for Sir Henry. Have you any letter for me?"

"None," he replied.

"Then I am free to go."

"Pardon me; not yet," he said. "I beg that for once you will hear what I in person have to say. I have been greatly misrepresented."

"Indeed?"

"Yes. Pray be patient. I meant to write to you, but that has been difficult, as you know."

"Of course. And what have you to say, sir?"

"You have misunderstood me. There have been reasons of difference between us which, I am happy to say, are at an end for me." He meant as to Darthea. "I made a mistake in the prison such as any man might have made. I have been sorry ever since. I made an effort to arrest you in the garden; I did my duty, and was glad you escaped. If you are not satisfied, a time may come when I can put myself at your disposal. Our present service and our relationship make me hope that you may never desire it."

He was quiet, cool, and perfectly master of himself. It did not suit him to have a break with me, and I well knew why. It would end all chance of his future intercourse with my father, and why he did not wish this to happen I now knew pretty well.

I said, "Mr. Wynne, the arrest is a small matter. Thanks to Miss Peniston and to Major André, it came to nothing." At my use of Darthea's name I saw him frown, and I went on:

"You have lied about the prison, sir. If Mr. Delaney, who heard you ask my name, were here, I should long ago have exposed you and your conduct to all who cared to hear. You were shrewd enough to provide against the possibility of my telling my own story. I can only hope, at no distant day, to have the means of unmasking a man who—why, I know not—has made himself my enemy. Then, sir, and always I shall hope to ask of you another form of satisfaction."

"Cousin Hugh," he returned, "I shall be able to prove to you and to Mr. Delaney, when he can be found, that you are both mistaken. I trust that you will not for so slight a reason see fit to disturb my pleasant relations with your father." They were, I thought, profitable as well as pleasant.

"I shall use my judgment," said I.

"I am sorry. I hoped for a more agreeable ending to our talk. Good-evening." And he walked away.

Before nightfall of the day after I was again at home, and had made my report, little dreaming of the innocent part I had played in a sorrowful drama, nor how great was the risk I had run. Concerning this I was not made clear for many a day. I had carried a letter which was not what it seemed to be, but was really a means of satisfying Clinton that Arnold intended to betray us, and had accepted his terms. Had this been known when the great treason came, I should no doubt have got into serious difficulties. The unreasoning storm of anger which followed General Arnold's treachery spared no one who was in any way involved, and no appearance of innocence would have saved even so loyal and blameless a soldier as I from certain disgrace.

I have at times wondered that a man to outward seeming so kindly and so plainly attached to me as Arnold apparently was should have used me for such an errand; but he who could value lightly the respect and friendship of Washington and Schuyler may have had few scruples as to the perils to which he might expose a simple officer like myself. Who bore his later missives no one knows. I have never thought, as some do, that any Eve was active in the temptation which led to the dark treachery of the saddest hour of that weary war. Arnold's first downward step was taken months before he knew Margaret Shippen, as Sir Henry Clinton's papers have now most clearly shown.

Of my personal regret as to Arnold's disgrace I have said little in these pages, and shall say but little more. His generosity may have been but a part of his lavishness in all directions; but this was he who for years cared liberally for the destitute children of his friend Warren after his death at Bunker Hill; and this was he who, as Schuyler has told me, saved the life of the soldier who had just shot him on the field at Saratoga. Surely the good and the bad are wonderfully mingled in our humanity!

Early in June of '79, and after repeated requests on my part to rejoin my regiment, I received orders to report to the colonel in command of the Third Pennsylvania foot, then lying at Ramapo, New York. I took leave of my people, and, alas! of Darthea, and set out with a number of recruits. I was glad indeed to be away. Darthea was clearly unhappy, and no longer the gay enchantress of un-numbered moods; neither did my home life offer me comfort or affection.

If, however, I looked for activity in the army, I was greatly mistaken. Sir Henry held New York; our own people had the Jerseys. A great chain of forts limited the movements of the British on the Hudson. Our general seemed to me to have a paralysing influence on whatever British commander was matched against him. As it had been with Gage in Boston and with Howe in Philadelphia, so was it now with Clinton in New York. From Danbury in Connecticut to Elizabeth in New Jersey, a thin line watched the pent-up enemy, who to seaward was guarded by a great fleet. North of the Potomac he held New York alone, but on the frontier a savage contest raged, and in the South the war everywhere went against us.

Occasional skirmishes, incessant drill, and a life of expedients to shelter, clothe, and feed my men, filled the tedious winter of '79 and '80, but affords me nothing of interest to add to the story of my life. In August General Arnold passed through our forces to take command of the forts at West Point, having declined a command in the field on account, as he said, of continued suffering from his wounded leg. I fear it was a mere pretence.

We were lying about Middlebrook, New Jersey, when, a few days later, Colonel Alexander Hamilton came to my quarters, evidently much amused. He said the videttes had captured a batch of letters, mostly of no moment, but some too mischievous to be let to pass.

"Here," he said, "is one which concerns you, Wynne. You need have no scruple as to the reading of it. It has much entertained the mess of the headquarters guard."

He sat down with Jack and a pipe to keep off the Tory mosquitos, while I fell to reading the letter. The same buzzing Tories were busy about me also with bugle and beak, but when, as I glanced at the letter, I caught Darthea's name on the second page, I forgot them and hesitated. "Still," thought I, "others have read it, and it may be well that I should do so." It was no longer private. I went on to learn what it said. It was from Miss Franks in New York to some young woman of her set in my

own city, but to whom was not clear, as an outer
cover seemed to have been lost or cast away.

"My dear Pussy," it began: "I hope you will
get this despite the rebels, else you will lose much
that is useful in the warfare with our dear enemy,
the unfair sex." After this was an amusing record
of the latest modes and much about gowns, pin-
cushion hoops, and face-patches. "Also the gentlemen of New York wear two watches, which with you
is not considered genteel, and the admiral has intro-
duced the fashion of dining by candle-light at four.
It is very becoming, I do assure you.

"How is the pretty boy-captain? Does he still
blush?" This was clearly Jack, but who was Pussy?
"And Mr. Wynne—not Darthea's Mr. Wynne, but
the perverted Quaker with the blue eyes?" It was
plain who this was.

"Darthea's captain—but I must not tell tales out
of school;—indeed he needs to be dealt with. Tell
the witch if she *will* stay among the R. R.'s—which
is what we call them—Ragged Rebels it is—she
must look to suffer. I am not as sure she does. Oh,
these men! Between us, there is a certain Olivia
L—— who is great friends with Mr. Wynne. She
hath a winning air of artless youth. I am pleased to
hear from *my* colonel, whom you must soon know,
that we shall soon be with you in our dear Philadelphia, and Mr. G. W. hoeing tobacco, or worse, poor
man. Dear me! I have quite lost my way, and must
look back.

"I can fancy Darthea weeping. She hath small

need. It is my way to love to tease whom I love, and the more I do love the more I do love to tease. I cannot believe any would be false to Darthea, nor is he, I am sure; but *thou* dost know (as Mistress Wynne's Captain Blushes would word it. 'Thou' and 'thee' are sweet. I would I had a Quaker lover) —*thou* dost know that the she who is *here* is always more dangerous than the she who is *there*. That is Darthea, dear.

"I forgot- to say stays is wore looser, which is a mercy; also the garters *must* be one red and one blue."

When, amused, I read a bit to Jack, he declared we ought to read no more, and if he had been of the mess which did read it, he would have had reason out of some one. Indeed, he was angry-red, and beginning to twitch in his queer way, so that I feared he would bring about a quarrel with Mr. Hamilton, who knew neither woman and was still shaking with laughter.

I liked it no better than Jack did, but he had said enough, and I shook my head at Hamilton as I lay on the floor of the hut behind Jack. Mr. Hamilton, who was a very model of good breeding, and despite his vivacity never forgot what was due to others, said at once: "I ask pardon, Mr. Warder. I did not know either of the ladies was known to you. Had I been aware, no one should have read the letter."

Then Jack said he had been hasty, and hoped Mr. Hamilton would excuse him.

"There is nothing to excuse, Mr. Warder; but I

must tell you the rest, for it much delighted his Excellency. It is but a madcap account of how Miss Franks tied our own colours all over Mr. André's black poodle, and let him loose at a ball the De Lanceys had in honour of Sir Henry Clinton. Our Excellency says it is a pity we had not captured the fair writer. That is as near to a jest as he ever comes, but he can enjoy our staff nonsense for all his gravity. I leave you the letter; you may like some day to deliver it. I hope we shall move soon. This camp life is devilish dull. And here is the British mouse in a hole and won't come out, and our serious old cat a-watching. Lord, the patience of the man! Come over and see us soon, Mr. Warder, and you too, Wynne."

"I wish Miss Darthea had the letter. But she never can have it now," said I.

"Hardly," says Jack, blushing sweetly. I think the garters were on his mind.

Early in August Jack's command was sent to join the army on the Hudson, and, as I learned later, was camped with the bulk of our forces about the former seat of the Tappan Indians, among the old Dutch farms. These changes of troops from place to place were most perplexing to us, who did not comprehend the game, and were now at Hartford, and a month later at Elizabeth in the Jerseys. My own regiment had seen little service beyond the Jersey line, and was willing enough to get out of reach of those summer pests, the mosquitos. We were soon gratified.

IX

N the 20th of September I was desired by my colonel to conduct two companies from Newark, where we lay, through the gap at Ramapo, New York, to the main army, which at this date was camped, as I have said, about Tappan. Being stout and well, I was glad to move, and glad of a chance to see the great river Hudson. We were assigned camp-ground back from the river, on a hill slope, in a long-settled country, where since early in the seventeenth century the Dutch had possessed the land. Having no tents, on arriving we set to work at the old business of hut-building, so that it was not until the 26th of September that I had an idle hour in which to look up Jack, who lay somewhere between Tappan and the river.

It was, as usual, a joyous meeting, and we never did less lack for talk. Jack told me that he was ordered on an unpleasant bit of business, and asked if I could not get leave to go with him. Orders were come from West Point to seize and destroy all periaguas, canoes, and boats in the possession of the few and often doubtfully loyal people between us and King's Ferry. He had for this duty two sail-

138

rigged dories with slide-keels, and would take two soldiers in each.

Upon his representing my skill as a sailor, and the need for two officers, I was allowed to turn over my command to the junior captain and to join Jack.

We set off on the 27th of September with provender and two small tents, and went away up the river with a fine wind. The water was a dull gray, and the heavens clouded. The far shore of Dobb's Ferry and Tarrytown was already gaily tinted with the hues of the autumn, and to south the bleak gray lines of the Palisades below Sneedon's Landing lay sombre and stern under a sunless sky. One of my men was a good sailor, and I was thus enabled to spend most of the day in Jack's boat.

I mention all these details because of a curious coincidence. I said to Jack—I was steering—that I had had since dawn a feeling that some calamity was about to happen. Now this was, as I recall it, a notion quite new to me, and far more like Jack himself. He laughed and said it was the east wind. Then after a pause he added : " I was trying to recall something I once heard, and now I have it. This waiting for an idea is like fishing in the deep waters of the mind : sometimes one gets only a nibble, and sometimes a bite ; but I have my fish. It was Dr. Rush who told me that the liver was the mother of ghosts and presentiments. When I told him I was afflicted with these latter, he put on his glasses, looked at me, and said I was of a presentimental temperament."

"And he was right," said I, laughing. Then Jack declared the weather was sorry enough to account for my notion. I made answer, as I remember, that I was not subject to the rule of the weather-cock, like some fellows I knew, nor to thinking I was going to be shot. This shut up Jack for a while, and we got off on to our own wise plans for capturing Sir Henry and all his host.

At last we ran ashore at a settled point called Nyack, and thence we went to and fro wherever we saw the smoke of men's homes. We broke up or burned many boats and dugouts, amid the lamentations of their owners, because with the aid of these they were enabled to take fish, and were ill off for other diet. We had an ugly task, and could only regret the sad but inexorable necessities of war.

We camped ten miles above Tappan, and next day, near to dusk, got as far as King's Landing, having pretty thoroughly attended to our ungracious task.

As the tall promontory of Stony Point rose before us, dim in the evening light, we talked of Wayne's gallant storming of this formidable fort, and of his affection for the bayonet, which, he said, was to be preferred to the musket because it was always loaded.

"We of our State had most of that glory," said Jack; "and all our best generals, save the great chief, are men of the North," which was true and strange.

We had at this place a strong force of horse and foot, and here we meant to pass the night with some of our officers, friends of Jack's.

It was quite dark, when, running in with a free sheet, we came close to a large barge rowed by six men. As we approached I heard a stern order to keep off, and recognised in the boat, where were also armed men, Major Tallmadge, whom I knew. I called to him, but as he only repeated his order, I answered, "Very well, sir;" and we drew in to the shore some hundred feet away.

Jack said it was queer; what could it mean? We walked toward the small blockhouse in time to see Tallmadge and several soldiers conduct a cloaked prisoner into the fort. A little later the major came out, and at once asked me to excuse his abruptness, saying that he had in charge Sir Henry Clinton's adjutant-general, who had been caught acting as a spy, and was now about to be taken to Tappan. I exclaimed, "Not Major André!"

"Yes," he returned; "André. A bad business." And I was hastily told the miserable story of Arnold's treason and flight. I turned to Jack. "There it is," said I. "What of my presentiment?" He was silent. "You know," I added, "that to this man I owed my life at the Mischianza ball; here he is in the same trap from which his refusal to aid my cousin saved me." I was terribly distressed, and at my urgent desire, in place of remaining at the fort, we set out after supper, and pulled down the river against the flood-tide, while my unfortunate friend André was hurried away to Tappan, guarded by a strong escort of light horse.

We reached Sneedon's Landing about 5 A. M., and

I went up with Jack to his hut. Here I got a bit of
uneasy sleep, and thence set off to find Hamilton;
for the whole staff, with his Excellency, had made
haste to reach the camp at Tappan so soon as the
general felt reassured as to the safety of West
Point.

I walked a half-mile up a gentle rise of ground to
the main road, about which were set, close to the old
Dutch church, a few modest, one-story stone houses,
with far and near the cantonments of the armies.
At the bridge over a noisy brook I was stopped
by sentries set around a low brick building then
used as headquarters. It stood amid scattered
apple-trees on a slight rise of ground, and was, as I
recall it, built of red and black brick. Behind the
house was the little camp of the mounted guard, and
on all sides were stationed sentinels, who kept the
immediate grounds clear from intrusion. For this
there was need; soldiers and officers were continually coming hither in hopes to gather fresh news
of the great treason, or curious as to this strange
capture of Sir Henry Clinton's adjutant. General
officers came and went with grave faces; aides
mounted and rode away in haste; all was excitement and anxious interest, every one asking questions, and none much the wiser. With difficulty I
succeeded in sending in a note to Hamilton along
with Jack's report. This was nigh to nine in the
morning, but it was after midday before I got a
chance to see my friend.

Meanwhile I walked up and down in a state of

such agitation and distress as never before nor since
have I known. When I had seen Major Tallmadge,
he knew but little of those details of Arnold's treason
which later became the property of all men; but he
did tell me that the correspondence had been carried
on for Sir Henry by André in the name of Anderson, and this brought to my mind the letter which
the Quaker farmer declined to surrender to me at the
time I was serving as Arnold's aide. I went back
at last to Jack's hut in the valley near the river and
waited. I leave Jack to say how I felt and acted that
day and evening, as I lay and thought of André
and of poor Margaret Shippen, Arnold's wife:

"Never have I seen my dear Hugh in such trouble.
Here was a broken-hearted woman, the companion
of his childhood; and André, who, at a moment which
must have called upon his every instinct as a soldier,
held back and saved my friend from a fate but too
likely to be his own. Hugh all that evening lay in
our hut, and now and then would break out declaring he must do something; but what he knew not,
nor did I. He was even so mad as to think he might
plan some way to assist André to escape. I listened,
but said nothing, being assured from long knowledge
that his judgment would correct the influence of the
emotion which did at first seem to disturb it.

"Now all this miserable business is over, I ask
myself if our chief would have tried to buy an English general, or if so, would I or Hugh have gone
on such an errand as André's. To be a spy is but
a simple duty, and no shame in it; but as to the

shape this other matter took, I do not feel able to decide."

Still later he adds:

"Nor is my mind more fully settled as to it to-day; some think one way, some another. I had rather André had not gone on this errand with the promise of a great reward. Yet I think he did believe he was only doing his duty."

After an hour or more of fruitless thinking, not hearing from Mr. Hamilton, I walked back to headquarters. Neither in the joy and pride of glad news, nor when disaster on disaster fell on us, have I ever seen anything like the intensity of expectation and of anxiety which at this time reigned in our camps. The capture of the adjutant-general was grave enough; his fate hung in no doubtful balance; but the feeling aroused by the fall of a great soldier, the dishonour of one greatly esteemed in the ranks, the fear of what else might come, all served to foster uneasiness and to feed suspicion. As the great chief had said, whom now could he trust, or could we? The men talked in half-whispers about the camp-fires; an hundred wild rumours were afloat; and now and again eager eyes looked toward the low brick church where twelve general officers were holding the court-martial which was to decide the fate of my friend.

It was evening before the decision of the court-martial became generally known. I wandered about all that day in the utmost depression of mind. About two in the afternoon of this 29th of September I met Hamilton near the creek. He said he had been busy all day, and was free for an hour; would I come and dine at his quarters? What was the matter with me? I was glad of a chance to speak freely. We had a long and a sad talk, and he then learned why this miserable affair affected me so deeply. He had no belief that the court could do other than condemn Mr. André to die. I asked anxiously if the chief were certain to approve the sentence. He replied gloomily, "As surely as there is a God in heaven."

I could only wait. A hundred schemes were in my mind, each as useless as the others. In fact, I knew not what to do.

On the 30th his Excellency signed the death-warrant, and, all hope being at an end, I determined to make an effort to see the man to whom I believe I owed my life. When I represented the matter to Mr. Hamilton and to the Marquis de Lafayette, I put my request on the ground that Mr. André had here no one who could be called a friend, excepting only myself, and that to refuse me an interview were needlessly cruel. I wrote my application with care, the marquis, who was most kind throughout, charging himself with the business of placing it favourably before our chief. The execution had been ordered for October 1, but, upon receipt of some communication from Sir Henry Clinton, it was postponed until noon on October 2.

On the 30th I rode out into the hills back of Tappan, and tried to compose myself by my usual and effective remedy of a hard ride. It was useless now.

II.—10

I came back to my friend's quarters and tried to read, finding a stray volume of the " Rambler " on his table. It was as vain a resort.

Never at any time in my memory have I spent two days of such unhappiness. I could get no rest and no peace of mind. To be thus terribly in the grip of events over which you have no control is to men of my temper a maddening affliction. My heart seemed all the time to say, " Do something," and my reason to reply, " There is nothing to do." It was thus in the jail when my cousin was on my mind; now it was as to André, and as to the great debt I owed him, and how to pay it. People who despair easily do not fall into the clutches of this intense craving for some practical means of relief where none can be. It is the hopeful, the resolute, and such as are educated by success who suffer thus. But why inflict on others the story of these two days, except to let those who come after me learn how one of their blood looked upon a noble debt which, alas! like many debts, must go to be settled in another world, and in other ways than ours.

Hamilton, who saw my agitation, begged me to prepare for disappointment. I, however, could see no reason to deny a man access to one doomed, when no other friend was near. Nor was I wrong. About seven in the evening of the 1st, the marquis came in haste to find me. He had asked for my interview with Mr. André as a favour to himself. His Excellency had granted the request in the face of objections from two general officers, whom the marquis did not name. As I thanked him he gave me this order:

"*To Major Tallmadge:*

"The bearer, Hugh Wynne, Esq., Captain, Second Company, Third Regiment of Pennsylvania foot, has herewith permission to visit Major André.

"GEO^E WASHINGTON.

"October 1, 1780."

I went at once—it was now close to eight in the evening—to the small house of one Maby, where the prisoner was kept. It was but an hundred yards from his Excellency's quarters. Six sentries marched to and fro around it, and within the room two officers remained day and night with drawn swords. My pass was taken at the door of the house, while I waited on the road without. In a few minutes an officer came to me with Major Tallmadge's compliments, and would I be pleased to enter?

I sometimes think it strange how, even in particulars, the natural and other scenery of this dark drama remains distinct in my memory, unaffected by the obliterating influence of the years which have effaced so much else I had been more glad to keep.

I can see to-day the rising moon, the yellowish road, the long, gray stone farm-house of one story, with windows set in an irregular frame of brickwork. The door opens, and I find myself in a short hall, where two officers salute as I pass. My conductor says, "This way, Captain Wynne," and I enter a

long, cheerless-looking apartment, the sitting-room
of a Dutch farm-house. Two lieutenants, seated
within at the doorway, rose as I entered, and, saluting me, sat down again. I stood an instant looking
about me. A huge log fire roared on the hearth, so
lighting the room that I saw its glow catch the bayonet tips of the sentinels outside as they went and
came. There were a half-dozen wooden chairs, and
on a pine table four candles burning, a bottle of
Hollands, a decanter and glasses. In a high-backed
chair sat a man with his face to the fire. It was
André. He was tranquilly sketching, with a quill
pen, a likeness of himself.[1] He did not turn or leave
off drawing until Captain Tomlinson, one of the
officers in charge, seeing me pause, said:

"Your pardon, major. Here is a gentleman come
to visit you."

As he spoke the prisoner turned, and I was at once
struck by the extreme pallor of his face even as seen
in the red light of the fire. His death-like whiteness
at this time brought out the regular beauty of his
features as his usual ruddiness of colour never did.
I have since seen strong men near to certain
death, but I recall no one who, with a serene and untroubled visage, was yet as white as was this gentleman.

The captain did not present me, and for a moment
I stood with a kind of choking in the throat, which
came, I suppose, of the great shock André's appearance gave me. He was thus the first to speak:

[1] My acquaintance, Captain Tomlinson, has it.

"Pardon me," he said, as he rose; "the name escaped me."

"Mr. Hugh Wynne," I said, getting myself pulled together—it was much needed.

"Oh, Wynne!" he cried quite joyously; "I did not know you. How delightful to see a friend; how good of you to come! Sit down. Our accommodations are slight. Thanks to his Excellency, here are Madeira and Hollands; may I offer you a glass?"

"No, no," I said, as we took chairs by the fire, on which he cast a log, remarking how cold it was. Then he added:

"Well, Wynne, what can I do for you?" And then, smiling, "Pshaw! what a thing is habit! What can I do for you, or, indeed, my dear Wynne, for any one? But, Lord! I am as glad as a child."

It was all so sweet and natural that I was again quite overcome. "My God!" I cried, "I am so sorry, Mr. André! I came down from King's Ferry in haste when I heard of this, and have been three days getting leave to see you. I have never forgotten your great kindness at the Mischianza. If there be any service I can render you, I am come to offer it."

He smiled and said: "How strange is fate, Mr. Wynne! Here am I in the same sad trap in which you might have been. I was thinking this very evening of your happier escape." Then he went on to tell me that he had instantly recognised me at the ball, and also—what in my confusion at the time I did not hear—that Miss Peniston had cried out as she was about to faint, "No, no, Mr. André!" Afterward he had wondered at what seemed an appeal to him rather than to my cousin.

At last he said it would be a relief to him if he might speak to me out of ear-shot of the officers. I said as much to these gentlemen, and after a moment's hesitation they retired outside of the still open doorway of the room, leaving us freer to say what we pleased. He was quiet and, as always, courteous to a fault; but I did not fail to observe that at times, as we talked and he spoke a word of his mother, his eyes filled with tears. In general he was far more composed than I.

He said: "Mr. Wynne, I have writ a letter, which I am allowed to send to General Washington. Will you see that he has it in person? It asks that I may die a soldier's death. All else is done. My mother —but no matter. I have wound up my earthly affairs. I am assured, through the kindness of his Excellency, that my letters and effects will reach my friends and those who are still closer to me. I had hoped to see Mr. Hamilton to-night, that I might ask him to deliver to your chief the letter I now give you. But he has not yet returned, and I must trust it to you to make sure that it does not fail to be considered. That is all, I think."

I said I would do my best, and was there no more —no errand of confidence—nothing else?

"No," he replied thoughtfully; "no, I think not. I shall never forget your kindness." Then he smiled and added, "My 'never' is a brief day for me,

Wynne, unless God permits us to remember in the
world where I shall be to-morrow."

I hardly recall what answer I made. I was ready
to cry like a child. He went on to bid me say to the
good Attorney-General Chew that he had not forgotten his pleasant hospitalities, and he sent also some
amiable message to the women of his house and to
my aunt and to the Shippens, speaking with the
ease and unrestraint of a man who looks to meet
you at dinner next week, and merely says a brief
good-by.

I promised to charge myself with his messages,
and said at last that many officers desired me to express to him their sorrow at his unhappy situation,
and that all men thought it hard that the life of an
honest soldier was to be taken in place of that of a
villain and coward who, if he had an atom of honour,
would give himself up.

"May I beg of you, sir," he returned, "to thank
these gentlemen of your army? 'Tis all I can do;
and as to General Arnold—no, Wynne, he is not one
to do that; I could not expect it."

Before I rose to go on his errand I said,—and I was
a little embarrassed,—"May I be pardoned, sir, if I
put to you a quite personal question?"

"Assuredly," he returned. "What is it, and how
can a poor devil in my situation oblige you?"

I said: "I have but of late learned that the exchanges were all settled when I met my cousin,
Arthur Wynne, at Amboy. Could it have been that
the letter I bore had anything to do with this treason

of General Arnold? Within a day or two this
thought has come to me."

Seeing that he hesitated, I added, " Do not answer
me unless you see fit; it is a matter quite personal
to myself."

"No," he replied; "I see no reason why I should
not. Yes, it was the first of the letters sent to Sir
Henry over General Arnold's signature. Your cousin
suggested you as a messenger whose undoubted position and name would insure the safe carriage of
what meant more to us than its mere contents seemed
to imply. Other messengers had become unsafe; it
was needful at once to find a certain way to reply to
us. The letter you bore was such as an officer might
carry, as it dealt seemingly with nothing beyond
questions of exchange of prisoners. For these reasons, on a hint from Captain Wynne, you were selected as a person beyond suspicion. I was ill at the
time, as I believe Mr. Wynne told you."

"It is only too plain," said I. "It must have been
well known at our headquarters in Jersey that this
exchange business was long since settled. Had I
been overhauled by any shrewd or suspicious officer,
the letter might well have excited doubt and have
led to inquiry."

"Probably; that was why you were chosen—as a
man of known character. By the way, sir, I had no
share in the selection, nor did I know how it came
about, until my recovery. I had no part in it."

I thanked him for thus telling me of his having
no share in the matter.

"You were ordered," he continued, "as I recall it, to avoid your main army in the Jerseys; you can now see why. There is no need of further concealment."

It was clear enough. "I owe you," I said, "my excuses for intruding a business so personal."

"And why not? I am glad to serve you. It is rather a relief, sir, to talk of something else than my own hopeless case. Is there anything else? Pray go on; I am at your service."

"You are most kind. I have but one word to add; Arthur Wynne was—nay, must have been—deep in this business?"

"Ah, now you have asked too much," he replied; "but it is I who am to blame. I had no right to name Captain Wynne."

"You must not feel uneasy. I owe him no love, Mr. André; but I will take care that you do not suffer. His suggestion that I should be made use of put in peril not my life, but my honour. It is not to my interest that the matter should ever get noised abroad."

"I see," he said. "Your cousin must be a strange person. Do with what I have said as seems right to you. I shall be—or rather," and he smiled quite cheerfully, "I *am* content. One's grammar forgets to-morrow sometimes."

His ease and quiet seemed to me amazing. But it was getting late, and I said I must go at once.

As I was in act to leave, he took my hand and said: "There are no thanks a man about to die can give

that I do not offer you, Mr. Wynne. Be assured
your visit has helped me. It is much to see the face
of a friend. All men have been good to me and kind,
and none more so than his Excellency. If to-morrow
I could see, as I go to death, one face I have known
in happier hours—it is much to ask—I may count on
you, I am sure. Ah, I see I can! And my letter—
you will be sure to do your best?"

"Yes," I said, not trusting myself to speak further,
and only adding, "Good-by," as I wrung his hand.
Then I went out into the cold October starlight.

It was long after ten when I found Hamilton. I
told him briefly of my interview, and asked if it
would be possible for me to deliver in person to the
general Mr. André's letter. I had, in fact, that on
my mind which, if but a crude product of despair, I
yet did wish to say where alone it might help or be
considered.

Hamilton shook his head. "I have so troubled
his Excellency as to this poor fellow that I fear I can
do no more. Men who do not know my chief cannot
imagine the distress of heart this business has caused.
I do not mean, Wynne, that he has or had the least
indecision concerning the sentence; but I can tell you
this—the signature of approval of the court's finding
is tremulous and unlike his usual writing. We will
talk of this again. Will you wait at my quarters?
I will do my best for you."

I said I would take a pipe and walk on the road
at the foot of the slope below the house in which
Washington resided. With this he left me.

The night was clear and beautiful; from the low hills far and near the camp bugle-calls and the sound of horses neighing filled the air. Uneasy and restless, I walked to and fro up and down the road below the little farm-house. Once or twice I fancied I saw the tall figure of the chief pass across the window-panes. A hundred yards away was the house I had just left. There sat a gallant gentleman awaiting death. Here, in the house above me, was he in whose hands lay his fate. I pitied him too, and wondered if in his place I could be sternly just. At my feet the little brook babbled in the night, while the camp noises slowly died away. Meantime, intent on my purpose, I tried to arrange in my mind what I would say or how plead a lost cause. I have often thus pre-arranged the mode of saying what some serious occasion made needful. I always get ready, but when the time comes I am apt to say things altogether different, and to find, too, that the wisdom of the minute is apt to be the better wisdom.

At last I saw Hamilton approaching me through the gloom. "Come," he said. "His Excellency will see you, but I fear it will be of no use. He himself would agree to a change in the form of death, but Generals Greene and Sullivan are strongly of opinion that to do so in the present state of exasperation would be unwise and impolitic. I cannot say what I should do were I he. I am glad, Wynne, that it is not I who have to decide. I lose my sense of the equities of life in the face of so sad a business. At least I would give him a gentleman's death. The

generals who tried the case say that to condemn a
man as a spy, and not at last to deal with him as
Hale was dealt with, would be impolitic, and unfair
to men who were as gallant as the poor fellow in
yonder farm-house."

"It is only too clear," I said.

"Yes, they are right, I suppose; but it is a horrible
business."

As we discussed, I went with him past the sentinels
around the old stone house and through a hall, and
to left into a large room.

"The general sleeps here," Hamilton said, in a
lowered voice. "We have but these two apartments;
across the passage is his dining-room, which he uses
as his office. Wait here," and so saying, he left me.
The room was large, some fifteen by eighteen feet,
but so low-ceiled that the Dutch builder had need to
contrive a recess in the ceiling to permit of a place
for the tall Dutch clock he had brought from Holland. Around the chimney-piece were Dutch tiles.
Black Billy, the general's servant, sat asleep in the
corner, and two aides slumbered on the floor, tired
out, I fancy. I walked to and fro over the creaking
boards, and watched the Dutch clock. As it struck
eleven the figure of Time, seated below the dial, swung
a scythe and turned a tiny hour-glass. A bell rang;
an orderly came in and woke up an aide: "Despatch
for West Point, sir, in haste." The young fellow
groaned, stuck the paper in his belt, and went out
for his long night ride.

At last my friend returned. "The general will see

you presently, Wynne, but it is a useless errand.
Give me André's letter." With this he left me again,
and I continued my impatient walk. In a quarter
of an hour he came back. "Come," said he; "I have
done my best, but I have failed as I expected to fail.
Speak your mind freely; he likes frankness." I went
after him, and in a moment was in the farther room
and alone with the chief.

A huge fire of logs blazed on the great kitchen
hearth, and at a table covered with maps and papers,
neatly set in order, the general sat writing.

He looked up, and with quiet courtesy said, "Take
a seat, Captain Wynne. I must be held excused for
a little." I bowed and sat down, while he continued
to write.

His pen moved slowly, and he paused at times, and
then went on apparently with the utmost deliberation. I was favourably placed to watch him without
appearing to do so, his face being strongly lighted
by the candles in front of him. He was dressed with
his usual care, in a buff waistcoat and a blue-and-buff
uniform, with powdered hair drawn back to a queue
and carefully tied with black ribbon.

The face, with its light-blue eyes, ruddy cheeks,
and rather heavy nose above a strong jaw, was now
grave and, I thought, stern. At least a half-hour
went by before he pushed back his chair and looked
up.

I am fortunate as regards this conversation, since
on my return I set it down in a diary which, however, has many gaps, and is elsewhere incomplete.

" Captain Wynne," he said, " I have refused to see several gentlemen in regard to this sad business, but I learn that Mr. André was your friend, and I have not forgotten your aunt's timely aid at a moment when it was sorely needed. For these reasons and at the earnest request of Captain Hamilton and the marquis, I am willing to listen to you. May I ask you to be brief?" He spoke slowly, as if weighing his words.

I replied that I was most grateful—that I owed it to Major André that I had not long ago endured the fate which was now to be his.

"Permit me, sir," he said, "to ask when this occurred."

I replied that it was when, at his Excellency's desire, I had entered Philadelphia as a spy; and then I went on briefly to relate what had happened.

"Sir," he returned, "you owed your danger to folly, not to what your duty brought. You were false, for the time, to that duty. But this does not concern us now. It may have served as a lesson, and I am free to admit that you did your country a great service. What now can I do for you? As to this unhappy gentleman, his fate is out of my hands. I have read the letter which Captain Hamilton gave me." As he spoke he took it from the table and deliberately read it again, while I watched him. Then he laid it down and looked up. I saw that his big, patient eyes were overfull as he spoke.

"I regret, sir, to have to refuse this most natural request; I have told Mr. Hamilton that it is not to be thought of. Neither shall I reply. It is not fitting that I should do so, nor is it necessary or even proper that I assign reasons which must already be plain to every man of sense. Is that all?"

I said, "Your Excellency, may I ask but a minute more?"

"I am at your disposal, sir, for so long. What is it?"

I hesitated, and, I suspect, showed plainly in my face my doubt as to the propriety of what was most on my mind when I sought this interview. He instantly guessed that I was embarrassed, and said, with the gentlest manner and a slight smile:

"Ah, Mr. Wynne, there is nothing which can be done to save your friend, nor indeed to alter his fate; but if you desire to say more do not hesitate. You have suffered much for the cause which is dear to us both. Go on, sir."

Thus encouraged, I said, "If on any pretext the execution can be delayed a week, I am ready to go with a friend"—I counted on Jack—"to enter New York in disguise, and to bring out General Arnold. I have been his aide, I know all his habits, and I am confident that we shall succeed if only I can control near New York a detachment of tried men. I have thought over my plan, and am willing to risk my life upon it."

"You propose a gallant venture, sir, but it would be certain to fail; the service would lose another brave man, and I should seem to have been wanting in decision for no just or assignable cause."

I was profoundly disappointed; and in the grief

of my failure I forgot for a moment the august presence which imposed on all men the respect which no sovereign could have inspired.

"My God! sir," I exclaimed, "and this traitor must live unpunished, and a man who did but what he believed to be his duty must suffer a death of shame!" Then, half scared, I looked up, feeling that I had said too much. He had risen before I spoke, meaning, no doubt, to bring my visit to an end, and was standing with his back to the fire, his admirable figure giving the impression of greater height than was really his.

When, after my passionate speech, I looked up, having of course also risen, his face wore a look that was more solemn than any face of man I have ever yet seen in all my length of years.

"There is a God, Mr. Wynne," he said, "who punishes the traitor. Let us leave this man to the shame which every year must bring. Your scheme I cannot consider. I have no wish to conceal from you or from any gentleman what it has cost me to do that which, as God lives, I believe to be right. You, sir, have done your duty to your friend. And now may I ask of you not to prolong a too painful interview?"

I bowed, saying, "I cannot thank your Excellency too much for the kindness with which you have listened to a rash young man."

"You have said nothing, sir, which does not do you honour. Make my humble compliments to Mistress Wynne."

I bowed, and, backing a pace or two, was about
to leave, when he said, "Permit me to detain you
a moment. Ask Mr. Harrison—the secretary—to
come to me."

I obeyed, and then in some wonder stood still,
waiting.

"Mr. Harrison, fetch me Captain Wynne's papers."
A moment later he sat down again, wrote the free
signature, "Geo⁰ Washington," at the foot of a parchment, and gave it to me, saying, "That boy Hamilton
has been troubling me for a month about this business.
The commission is but now come to hand from
Congress. You will report, at your early conve-
nience, as major, to the colonel of the Third Pennsylvania foot; I hope it will gratify your aunt. Ah,
Colonel Hamilton," for here the favourite aide entered, "I have just signed Mr. Wynne's commission."
Then he put a hand affectionately on the shoulder
of the small, slight figure. "You will see that the
orders are all given for the execution at noon. Not
less than eighty files from each wing must attend.
See that none of my staff be present, and that this
house be kept closed to-morrow until night. I shall
transact no business that is not such as to ask instant attention. See, in any case, that I am alone
from eleven until one. Good-evening, Mr. Wynne;
I hope that you will shortly honour me with your
company at dinner. Pray, remember it, Mr. Hamilton."

I bowed and went out, overcome with the kindliness of this great and noble gentleman.

II.—11

"He likes young men," said Hamilton to me long afterward. "An old officer would have been sent away with small comfort."

It was now late in the night, and, thinking to compose myself, I walked up and down the road and at last past the Dutch church, and up the hill between rows of huts and rarer tents. It was a clear, starlit night, and the noises of the great camp were for the most part stilled. A gentle slope carried me up the hill, back of André's prison, and at the top I came out on a space clear of these camp homes, and stood awhile under the quiet of the star-peopled sky. I lighted my pipe with help of flint and steel, and, walking to and fro, set myself resolutely to calm the storm of trouble and helpless dismay in which I had been for two weary days. At last, as I turned in my walk, I came on two upright posts with a cross-beam above. It was the gallows. I moved away horror-stricken. and with swift steps went down the hill and regained Jack's quarters.

Of the horrible scene at noon on the 2d of October I shall say very little. A too early death never took from earth a more amiable and accomplished soldier. I asked and had leave to stand by the door as he came out. He paused, very white in his scarlet coat, smiled, and said, "Thank you, Wynne; God bless you!" and went on, recognising with a bow the members of the court, and so with a firm step to his ignoble death. As I had promised, I fell in behind the sad procession to the top of the hill. No fairer

scene could a man look upon for his last of earth.
The green range of the Piermont hills rose to north.
On all sides, near and far, was the splendour of the
autumn-tinted woods, and to west the land swept
downward past the headquarters to where the cliffs
rose above the Hudson. I can see it all now—the
loveliness of nature, the waiting thousands, mute and
pitiful. I shut my eyes and prayed for this passing
soul. A deathful stillness came upon the assembled
multitude. I heard Colonel Scammel read the sentence. Then there was the rumble of the cart, a low
murmur broke forth, and the sound of moving steps
was heard. It was over. The great assemblage of
farmers and soldiers went away strangely silent, and
many in tears.

The effort I so earnestly desired to make for the
capture of Arnold was afterward made by Sergeant
Champe, but failed, as all men now know. Yet I am
honestly of opinion that I should have succeeded.

Years afterward I was walking along the Strand
in London, when, looking up, I saw a man and
woman approaching. It was Arnold with his wife.
His face was thin and wasted, a countenance writ
over with gloom and disappointment. His masculine
vigour was gone. Cain could have borne no plainer
marks of vain remorse. He looked straight before
him. As I crossed the way, with no desire to meet
him, I saw the woman look up at him, a strange,
melancholy sweetness in the pale, worn face of our
once beautiful Margaret. Her love was all that time

had left him ; poor, broken, shunned, insulted, he was
fast going to his grave.   Where now he lies I know
not.   Did he repent with bitter tears on that gentle
breast ?   God only knows.   I walked on through the
crowded street, and thought of the words of my great
chief, "There is a God who punishes the traitor."

X

HE long winter of 1780 and 1781, with its changeful fortunes in the South, went by without alteration in mine. There were constant alarms, and leaves of absence were not to be had. We drilled our men, marched hither and thither, and criticised our leaders over the winter camp-fires, envying the men who, under Williams, Marion, and Morgan, were keeping my Lord Cornwallis uncomfortably busy in the Carolinas. By the end of January we knew with joy of the thrashing Tarleton got at the Cowpens, and at last, in April, of the fight at Guilford. It began to dawn on the wiseacres of the camp-fires why we were now here and now there. In fact, we were no sooner hutted than we were on the march, if there were but the least excuse in the way of a bit of open weather, or a Tory raid.

Sir Henry was kept in doubt as to whether our chief meant for New York from the north or from Jersey, and when at last he began to suspect that it was not a city but an army which he intended to strike, it was too late. Our brave old hawk, so long half asleep, as it looked, had begun to flutter his wings, and to contemplate one of those sudden swoops

upon his prey which did to me attest the soldier of
genius within this patient, ceremonious gentleman.
He was fast learning the art of war.

At last, as I have said, even we who were but
simple pawns in the game of empire knew in a measure why we had been thus used to bother and detain
this unlucky Sir Henry, who had failed to help Burgoyne, and was now being well fooled again, to the
ruin of Lord Cornwallis.

But all of this was chiefly in the spring. The winter
up to February was sad enough in our waiting camps,
what with low diet, desertions, mutinies, and the
typhus fever, which cost us many more men than
we lost in battle. It brought us at last one day the
pleasure of a visit from the great physician, Benjamin
Rush, now come to Morristown to see after the sick,
who were many.

This gentleman was a prime favourite with my Aunt
Gainor, although they had but one opinion in common, and fought and scratched like the far-famed
Irish cats. I think, too, the doctor liked your humble
servant, chiefly because I admired and reverenced
him for his learning and his unflinching love of his
country.

At this time we lay about Morristown in New
Jersey. There was to be a great ball on the night of
the doctor's arrival. And just now, when his delicate
features appeared at the door of our hut, Jack and I
—for Jack was with me for a day—had used the
last of our flour to powder our hair, and Jack was
carefully tying my queue.

"Good-evening, Master Hugh, and you, John Warder. Can I have a bite?"

We gave a shout of welcome, and offered him a herring—very dried it was—and one of Master Baker Ludwick's hard biscuits. He said we were luxurious scamps with our powder, until we explained it to be the end of a rather mouldy bag of meal. He thought powdering a fine custom for young doctors, for it gave them a look of gray hair and wisdom; and he was, as usual, amusing, cynical, and at times bitter.

When we were seated and had his leave for a pipe, he told us there was now constant good news from the South, and that General Greene seemed to be somehow doing well, losing fights and winning strategetic victories. Probably it was more by luck than genius. By and by Gates would be heard from, and then we should see. On which my naughty Jack winked at me through the fog of his pipe smoke.

"And why," said the doctor, "does your general keep so quiet? Was an army made to sit still?"

I could not but remind him that the only lucky winter campaign of the war had been made by his Excellency, and that it was not usually possible to fight in the cold season; not even Marlborough could do that. I was most respectful, you may be sure.

He assured me that our general would never end the war; for in revolutions it was not they who began them who ever did bring them to auspicious conclusions. Our general, the doctor went on to tell us, was a weak man, and soon all would be of this opinion.

As he spoke I saw Hamilton in the doorway, and
I made haste to present him to the doctor.

The young aide said modestly that he must venture
to differ as to our chief. He was a man dull in talk,
not entertaining, given to cautious silence, but surely
not weak, only slow in judgment, although most decisive in action.

"No great soldier, sir," said the doctor, "and never
will be."

"He is learning the business, like the rest of us,
Dr. Rush. 'T is a hard school, sir, but it is character
that wins at last; may I venture to say this man has
character, and can restrain both his tongue and his
own nature, which is quick to wrath."

"Nonsense!" cried the doctor. "The whole country is discontented. We should elect a commander-
in-chief once a year."

In fact, many were of this strange opinion. Hamilton smiled, but made no reply.

I saw Jack flush, and I shook my head at him. I
thought what was said foolish and ignorant, but it
became not men as young as we to contradict the
doctor. It was Rush who, in '77, with Adams and
others, sustained Gates, and put him in the Board
of War, to the bewilderment of affairs. How deep
he was in the scheme of that officer and Conway
and Lee to displace our chief none know. My aunt
insists he had naught to do with it. He was an
honourable, honest man, but he was also a good,
permanent hater, and sustained his hatreds with a

fine escort of rancorous words, where Jack or I would
have been profane and brief.

The cabal broke up with Lee's trial, and when
Cadwalader shot Conway through the mouth, and,
as he said, stopped one d—— lying tongue, it did not
change our doctor's views. When he and Dr. Shippen, who was no Tory like the rest of his family,
quarrelled, as all doctors do, Rush preferred charges,
and was disgusted because his Excellency approved
the acquittal with some not very agreeable comments.
I think he never forgave the slight, but yet I liked
him, and shall ever revere his memory as that of a
man who deserved well of his country, and had the
noble courage of his profession, as he showed amply
in the great yellow-fever plague of '98.

He told me of my father as still much the same,
and of my Aunt Gainor, and of Darthea, who, he
thought, was troubled in mind, although why he
knew not. She had long since ceased answering the
messages we sent her through my aunt. Mr. Warder,
he told me later, had given up his suit to Madam
Peniston, and was now an outspoken Whig. The
lady was disposed to seek refuge again with her De
Lancey cousins in New York, but Darthea was obstinate, and not to be moved. And so we got all the
gossip of our old town, and heard of Mrs. Arnold's
having been ordered to leave, and of how the doctor,
like our own Wayne, had always distrusted her husband. Indeed, we had asked a thousand questions
before we let the doctor get to my bed, and we our-

selves, pulling on our sherry-vallies, a kind of overalls, to protect our silk stockings from the mud, were
away to the ball.

Despite our many cares and former low diet, we
danced till late in the night; the good people of
Morristown contriving, I know not how, to give us
such a supper as we had not had for many a day. I
had the pleasure to converse, in their own tongue,
with Comte de Rochambeau and the Duc de Lauzun,
who made me many compliments on my accent, and
brought back to me, in this bright scene, the thought
of her to whom I owed this and all else of what is
best in me.

It was indeed a gay and pleasant evening. Even
our general seemed to forget the anxieties of war,
and walked a minuet with Lady Stirling, and then
with Mrs. Greene. Very quiet and courteous he was,
but not greatly interested, or so it seemed to me.

Again in May we were in motion, now here, now
there; and, with a skirmish or two, the summer was
upon us. Meanwhile, as I have said, things went
more happily in the South.

Greene, continually beaten, was ever a better soldier; and at last, early in this summer of '81, my
Lord Cornwallis, driven to despair by incessant foes
who led him a wearisome and fruitless chase through
States not rich enough to feed him, turned from the
"boy" Lafayette he so much despised, and finally
sought rest and supplies on the seaboard at Yorktown, while the "boy general," planted in a position
to command the peninsula at Malvern Hill, sat down

to intrench and watch the older nobleman. I have no
wish to write more history than is involved in my own
humble fortunes, and I must leave those for whom
I write these memoirs to read the story of the war
on other pages than mine. Enough to say that when
his Excellency was sure of the French fleet and knew
of his lordship's position, he made one of those swift
decisions which contrasted strangely with his patient,
and even elaborate, businesslike fashion of attending
to all the minor affairs of life. Nor less secret and
subtle was the way in which he carried out his plan
of action. Leaving a force at West Point, he swept
in haste through the Jerseys.

Even the generals in immediate command knew
nothing of his real intention until we were turned
southward and hurried through the middle colonies.
Then all men knew and wondered at the daring, and,
as some thought, the rashness of this movement.
Sir Henry had been well fooled to the end, for now
it was far on in August.

At Trenton I received an appointment which much
amazed me. The army of our allies was marching
with us. De Grasse, with a great fleet, was off Chesa-
peake Bay; despatches were coming and going daily.
His Excellency had little knowledge of the French
tongue, and had suffered for it in his youth. Mr.
Duponceau, of the Marquis de Lafayette's staff, was
competent in both French and English, but, save one
other officer, no one of his Excellency's staff spoke
and wrote French well; and this aide was, as a consequence, much overworked.

Seeing this difficulty, which occasioned much confusion, the Duc de Lauzun suggested that I be asked to serve as a special aide-de-camp. I believe I owed this chance, in part, to Lafayette, and also to the fact, stated elsewhere, that I had had the fortune to be presented to the duke at our famous ball in Morristown, where he was pleased to talk with me in French.

My appointment reached me on August 29. His Excellency was then with us at Trenton, despatching couriers, urging haste, and filling all men with the great hope which his audacious action excited.

I was ordered to turn over my command, to join his Excellency's headquarters staff at Philadelphia, and there to report to Colonel Tilghman as extra aide-de-camp with the brevet rank of lieutenant-colonel. A note from Hamilton, now with his regiment, congratulated me, and related the cause of my unlooked-for promotion.

Would you see what my lifelong friend Jack had to say?

"I thank God for the happy fortune which has again fallen to Hugh. Had it not been for his assiduity in youth, and the love and respect he bore his mother, he would never have come by this promotion. Thus God rewards us for that we do without thought of profit." Alas! my dear Jack, those French lessons were sometimes but ungratefully learned.

Early on September 2, having borrowed a horse from one of the staff, I was ferried over the Delaware, and, once across the river, pushed on in haste to my own dear city. I found the French about to enter the town.

I had left home in 1777 a raw youth, and it was not without a sense of just pride that I returned a lieutenant-colonel at twenty-eight, having, as I felt, done my country honest service.

Our allies halted in the suburbs to clean off the dust, and as they began their march I fell in beside De Lauzun. They made a brilliant show in neat white uniforms, colours flying and bands playing. Front street was densely crowded, and at Vine they turned westward to camp on the common at Centre Square. As they wheeled I bowed to the French gentlemen, and kept on down Front street to Arch, soon halting before my aunt's door. The house was closed. All had gone forth to welcome the marching troops. I mounted again and rode down Second street to my own home, left my horse at the stable, and, seeing no one, passed into the sitting-room. My father was seated at the open window, but to see him dismayed me. He rose with an uneasy look as I went toward him. He was so wasted that his large features stood out gaunt and prominent. His clothes hung about him in folds, and his vast, bony frame was like a rack from which they seemed ready to fall.

I caught him in my arms, and kissed his shrunken cheeks, utterly overcome at the sight of this splendid body in ruins. Meanwhile he stayed quite passive, and at last pushed me off and looked at me steadily.

"It is Hugh," he said. "Thy mother will be glad to see thee."

I was shocked. This delusion of my mother's being alive greatly increased the grief I had in seeing this wreck of a strong, masterful man.

I said something, I hardly know what. He repeated, "Thy mother will be glad to see thee. She is upstairs—upstairs. She is with thy little sister. Ellin has been troublesome in the night."

After this he sat down and took no more notice of me. I stood watching him. The dead alone seemed to be alive to him: my mother, and the little sister who died thirty years back, and whose name I heard now from my father for the first time in all my life. As I stood amazed and disturbed at these resurrections, he sat speechless, either looking out of the window in a dull way, or now and then at me with no larger interest. At last, with some difficulty as to finding words, he said: "Thy mother wearies for thy letters. Thou hast been remiss not to write."

I said I had written him, as indeed I had, and with regularity, but with never an answer. After this he was long silent, and then said, "I told her it was but for a week thou wert to be away. She thinks it more." The long years of war were lost to him, and as though they had not been.

I made a vain effort to recall him to the present and the living, telling him of the army and the war, and at last asked news of my aunt. He soon ceased to hear me, and his great head fell forward, the gray locks dropping over his forehead, as he sat breathing deeply and long.

I found it a sorry spectacle, and after giving some orders to Tom I went away.

I learned later that my father never went out, but sat at the window all day with his pipe, drawing on it as if it were lighted, and heeding neither the friends who still came to see him nor the vacant days which went by. I had lost my father, even that little of his true self he had let me see.

I went thence and reported to Colonel Tilghman at the City Tavern, where his Excellency had alighted, and after performing that duty made haste to see my aunt.

There I found the love and tender welcome for which I so much yearned, and I also had news of Darthea. She, my aunt said, was well and still in the city, but out of spirits; as to that "villain," my cousin, my Aunt Gainor knew nothing, nor indeed Mistress Peniston much. Letters were difficult to get through our lines, and if he or Darthea still wrote, my aunt knew no more than I. When I told her in confidence of the errand on which, at my cousin's prompting, General Arnold had sent me, she exclaimed:

"Could he have wished to get you into trouble? It seems incredible, Hugh. I hope you may never meet."

"Aunt Gainor," said I, "to meet that man is the dearest wish of my life."

"The dearest?"

"Not quite," said I, "but it will be for me a happy hour."

"Then God forbid it, Hugh; and it is most unlikely. You must go and see Darthea. I suppose you will hardly tarry here long—and get your epaulets, sir. I want to see my boy in his uniform. Bring Mr. Hamilton here, and the French gentlemen. Fetch some of them to dinner to-morrow."

Then she kissed me again, and told me how strong and well I looked, and so on, with all the kind prettiness of affectionate speech women keep for those they love.

As I knew not when we should leave, nor how busy I might be while still in the city, I thought it well to talk to my aunt of my father's sad condition, and of some other matters of moment. Of the deed so strangely come into my possession she also spoke. It seemed to be much on her mind. I still told her I cared little for the Welsh lands, and this was true. Nevertheless I discovered in myself no desire to be pleasant to Mr. Arthur Wynne, and I began to suspect with my aunt that more than Darthea, or stupid jealousy, or the memory of a blow, might be at the bottom of his disposition to injure me.

It may seem strange to those who read what a quiet old fellow writes, that I should so frankly confess my hatred of my cousin. Nowadays men lie about one another, and stab with words, and no one resents it. Is the power to hate to the death fading out? and are we the better for this? It may be so. Think of the weary months in jail, of starvation, insult, and the miseries of cold, raggedness, filth, and fever. Think, too, of my father set against me, of

the Mischianza business,—but for that I blame him
not,—and, last, of his involving me in the vile net of
Arnold's treason. I could as soon forgive a snake
that had bit me as this reptile.

"Mr. James Wilson has the deed," said my aunt;
"and of that we shall learn more when Mr. Cornwallis is took, and you come home a general. And
now go and see Darthea, and let me hear how many
will be to dine, and send me, too, a half-dozen of
good old wine from my brother's cellar—the old
Wynne Madeira. Decant it with care, and don't
trust that black animal Tom. Mind, sir!"

Darthea lived but a little way from my aunt's, and
with my heart knocking at my ribs as it never had
done at sight of levelled muskets, I found my way
into Mistress Peniston's parlour, and waited, as it
seemed to me, an age.

It was a large back room with an open fireplace
and high-backed chairs, claw-toed tables bare of
books or china, with the floor polished like glass.
Penistons and De Lanceys, in hoop and hood, and
liberal of neck and bosom, looked down on me. It
was all stiff and formal, but to me pleasantly familiar.
Would she never come?

Then I heard a slow step on the stair, and the rustle
of skirts, and here was Darthea, pale and grave, but
more full in bud, and, I thought, more lovely in her
maturing womanhood.

She paused at the doorway, and made as it were
to greet me with a formal curtsey, but then—how
like her it did seem!—ran forward and gave me both

II.—12

her hands, saying: "You are welcome, Mr. Wynne. I am most glad to see you. You are all for the South, I hear. Is it not so?"

I said yes, and how delightful it was to be here if but for a day or two; and then, being pretty vain, must tell her of my good fortune.

"I am glad of my friend's success, but I wish it were with the other side. Oh, I am a mighty Tory yet," shaking her head. "I have seen your Mr. Washington. What a fine man! and favours Mr. Arnold a trifle."

"Fie for shame!" said I, pleased to see her merry; and then I went on to tell her the sad story of André, but not of what he told me concerning Arthur. The tears came to her eyes, although of course it was no new tale, and she went white again, so that I would have turned the talk aside, but she stopped me, and, hesitating a little, said:

"Did that miserable treachery begin when Mr. Arnold was in the town?"

I said it was thought to have done so. For my own part, I believed it began here, but just when I could not say. "But why do you ask?" I added, being for a reason curious.

For a little she sat still, her hands, in delicate white lace mittens, on her lap. Then she spoke, at first not looking up. "Men are strange to me, Mr. Wynne. I suppose in war they must do things which in peace would be shameful."

I said yes, and began to wonder if she had divined that Arthur had been deep in that wretched plot. I

do not know to this day. She kept her counsel if
she did. Women see through us at times as if we
were glass, and then again are caught by a man-trap
that one would think must be perfectly visible.

"And was poor Peggy Shippen in it?"

"Oh, no! no!" I replied.

"I am glad of that; but had I been she, I would
never have seen him again—never! never! To think
of life with one who is as black a creature as that
man!"

"But, after all, he is her husband." I wanted to
see what she would say.

"Her husband! Yes. But a husband without
honour! No! no! I should have to respect the man
I loved, or love would be dead—dead! Let us talk
of something else. Poor Peggy! Must you go?"
she added, as I rose. "This horrid war! We may
never meet again." And then quickly, "How is
Captain Blushes, and shall we see him too?"

I thought not. Already the army was making
for Chester, and so toward the Head of Elk. "No;
I must go." On this she rose.

"Is it the same, Darthea, and am I to go away with
no more hope than the years have brought me?"

"Why," she said, colouring, "do you make it so
hard for me—your friend?"

"Do I make it hard?"

"Yes. I used to say no to men, and think no more
of the thing or of them, but I am troubled; and this
awful war! I am grown older, and to hurt a man—a
man like you—gives me pain as it did not use to do."

"But you have not said no," said I; "and I am an obstinate man."

"Why will you force me to say no? Why should I? You know well enough what I think and feel. Why insist that I put it in words? It were kinder —not to urge me."

It seemed a strange speech. I said I did not understand her.

"Then you had better go. I am engaged to Mr. Arthur Wynne, sir. I have had no word of him for a year, and can get no letter to him."

I might have given her Miss Franks's letter, and poured out to her the story of his treachery and baseness. I may have been wrong, but something in me forbade it, and I preferred to wait yet longer.

"Shall I get you a letter through the lines? I can."

"You are a strange man, Mr. Wynne, and an honest gentleman. No, you cannot do me this service. I thank you."

"Then good-by; and it is love to the end, Darthea."

"I wish you would go," she said faintly.

"Good-by," I repeated, and rose.

"Come and see me some day when you can,—not now, not this time,—and do not think ill of me."

"Think ill of you! Why should I?"

"Yes! yes!"

I did not understand her, but I saw that she was shaken by some great emotion. Then she spoke:

"I have given my word, Mr. Wynne, and I do not lightly break it. Perhaps, like some men, you may

think that women have no such sense of honour as
men believe to be theirs."

"But do you love him, Darthea?"

"He is not here to answer you," she cried, looking
up at me steadily, her eyes ablaze. "Nor will I.
You have no right to question me—none!"

"I have every right," I said.

"Oh, will you never go away?" And she stamped
one little foot impatiently. "If you don't go I shall
hate you, and I—I don't want to hate you, Hugh
Wynne."

I stood a moment, and once more the temptation
to tell her all I knew was strong upon me, but, as
she said, Arthur was not here; first I must tell him
face to face, and after that God alone knew what
might come. I must tell him, too, with such proof
as neither her love nor his subtlety could gainsay.
And when this hour came—what then? If I killed
him,—and I meant to,—what of Darthea? That
would end my slender chance, and yet I knew myself
so surely as to be certain that, when the hour came,
no human consideration would be listened to for a
moment. I could hate in those days, and I did. If
I had had the assured love of Darthea, I should perhaps have hesitated; but not having it, I only longed
once to have that man at the point of the sword. It
is all very savage and brutal, but in those my young
days men loved and hated as I do not think they do
of late. It was a strong and a choleric generation,
but we did some things for which the world should
thank us.

XI

Y the 7th of September Marquis Lafayette was holding the neck of the peninsula of York. A more daring man than Cornwallis would have tried a fall with this army, but he waited for a fleet to relieve him, and behold! none came save that of De Grasse. By September 26 sixteen thousand men were added to those of the marquis, and lay about Williamsburg. Our quiet old hawk had my lord in his clutches, and meant no long delay.

Not to be in advance of the army, his Excellency, who left Philadelphia before us, lingered a few days on the way to visit the home he had not seen for six long years, and we of the staff followed him the day after. Both in town and on the march through Delaware I was occupied as I had never been in my life. The French marched with us, and to keep things straight duplicate orders in both tongues were needed, and there were notes, letters, and despatches to be done into French or English. An aide who spoke French fluently was apt to be in the saddle whenever his pen was not in use.

The life was to me of advantage, because I came daily into contact with officers, young and old, who had seen the finest company in Europe, and from whom there was much to learn. It is Chastellux, I think, who has said that Mr. Washington possessed the charm of such manners as were rare among our officers. With these gentlemen, our allies, the way of doing every little act of the life of society seemed to have been studied and taught, until these gracious and amiable forms were become, as one may say, a part of the man.

No wonder they found us clumsy fellows. Too many of our gentry were not in the war, or were opposed to it. Many regiments were strangely officered, and this, as Graydon says in his memoirs, was especially the case as to the New England troops. But a man with no manners and with brutal habits may fight as well as a marquis.

Now toward the close of the war, if we were still as to looks but a Falstaffian contingent, the material in men and officers had been notably sifted, and was in all essential ways fit for the perilous service to which we were about to address ourselves.

At Mount Vernon we camped—we of the staff— in and out of the house, and were bountifully fed, nor did I ever see his Excellency more to advantage than here. He personally looked after our wants, and lost for a time much of the official reserve with which he guarded himself elsewhere.

At table after dinner he was in the habit of asking one of his aides to propose toasts for him. The day before we left, as we were about to rise from table, Colonel Tilghman said, "One more toast, with your permission, Excellency," and cried out, "My Lord Cornwallis, and may he enjoy the hospitalities of our army."

Our host laughed as he rarely did, saying, "We must first catch our fish, Mr. Tilghman."

I ventured to say, "He is in the net already."

His Excellency, looking round at me, said gravely, "Pray God the net hold good!" After I had offered the toast of Lady Washington's health, and our thanks for the pleasant days of rest and good cheer, he left us, desiring Mr. Tilghman to see that we had wine enough.

On the 14th we reached Williamsburg. The army rapidly came in by divisions, French and American. Before the 25th we had from the fleet cannon and intrenching-tools, and all our available force was to hand.

I can make clear in a few words the situation of the enemy. The peninsula of York lies between the James and the York rivers. On the south bank of the latter sits the little town of York. Seven redoubts surrounded it. The town was flanked right and left by deep ravines and creeks falling into the York River. Intrenchments, field-works, and abatis, with felled trees, lay to landward.

Gloucester Point, on the opposite shore of the river, was well fortified, and before it lay a small force of British war-ships, the channel being obstructed lower down by sunken vessels. The French fleet held the river below the town, and we the peninsula.

On the night of the 25th, after a brief visit to the

fleet, our chief lay down in the open under a mulberry-tree with one of its roots for a pillow, and slept well, as was audible enough to us who lay at a distance.

That night his lordship abandoned his outworks and drew within the town. We seized these lines next day, losing Colonel Scammel, formerly of the staff, in whose amusing songs and gay talk our chief had used to take much pleasure. On the 28th the armies marched twelve miles down the peninsula, and camped two miles from the town, driving in the pickets and some parties of horse.

By October 1, the weather being fine, we had completed a half-moon of intrenchments, resting at each wing on the river. Two advanced redoubts we threw up were severely cannonaded, so as to interrupt the men at work.

His Excellency, somewhat anxious, came out of his tent, and calling Mr. Tilghman and me, who were writing, rode forth, followed by his faithful black Billy, whom we used to credit with knowing more of what went on than did we of the staff. Mr. Evans, a chaplain, was fain to see more of the war than concerned him, and came after us. As we approached, Billy, riding behind me, said as the cannon-shot went over us:

"Dem redcoats is p'intin' us mighty well."

Then a shot ricochetted, striking the ground in front and covering us with dust. Mr. Evans, who was standing by, and had now seen quite enough of it, said, "We shall all be killed," and then looked ruefully at his new beaver, well dusted and dirty.

"You had better carry that home to your wife and children," said the chief. "This is not the place for you, sir."

Neither was it much to my own liking, and I was not sorry when we rode back.

On the night of the 9th of October his Excellency put a match to the first gun, and for four days and nights a furious cannonade went on from both sides.

Late on the night of the 10th Jack came to my tent, and we walked out to see this terrible spectacle, climbing a little hill which lay well away from our lines. For a time we were quite alone.

A monstrous dome of smoke hung over the town. Now and then a gust of sea wind tore it apart, and through the rifts we saw the silver cup of the moon and the host of stars. We lay long on the hillock. I suppose the hour and the mighty fates involved made us serious and silent. Far away seventy cannon thundered from our works, and the enemy's batteries roared their incessant fury of reply.

Presently I said, "Jack, how still the heavens are, and under them this rage of war! How strange!"

"Yes," said Jack; "once I said something of this tranquilness in the skies to our great Dr. Franklin. He is very patient with young fellows, but he said to me: 'Yes, it is a pleasing thing, even to be wrong about it. It is only to the eye of man that there is calm and peace in the heavens; no shot of cannon can fly as these worlds fly, and comets whirl, and suns blaze; and if there is yonder, as with us, war and murder and ravage, none can say.' It all comes

back to me now," said Jack, "and I thought to tell
you."

"It is a terrible sight," said I, as the great tumult
of sound grew louder. "Let us thank God the cause
is a just one."

"And there are the stars again," said Jack, "and
the moon." And we were silent once more, watching the death-struggle of a failing cause.

Our own mad world was far other than at peace.
The great bombs rose in vast curves overhead, with
trails of light, and, seeming to hesitate in mid-air,
exploded, or fell on town or ship or in the stream
between. As we looked, awe-struck, hot shot set fire
to the "Charon," a forty-four-gun ship, nigh to
Gloucester, and soon a red rush of fire twining about
mast and spar rose in air, lighting the sublime spectacle, amid the crash of guns, the rattle of musketry,
and multitudinous inexplicable noises, through which
we heard now and then the wild howl of a dog from
some distant farm-yard.

At last the war-ship blew up, and a wonderful
strong light lighted the town, the river, and the camp.
As it fell the dog bayed again, a long, sharp, waver-
ing cry.

This seemed to me to impress Jack Warder more
than anything else in this din of war. He said now
and again, "There is that dog," and wondered what
the beast thought of it all. It is curious upon what
the minds of men fix on grave occasions. I meant
to ask Jack why he spoke over and over of the dog
when before us was the bloody close of a great his-

toric tragedy : a king humbled ; a young republic at
sword-point with an ancient monarchy.

It seemed to me a man's mind must grow in the
presence of such might of events. The hill, a half-mile
from the lines, was a good vantage-ground whence
to see and hear. Jack and I smoked many pipes, and,
as he was not for duty in the trenches, lay here most
of that cool October night, wrapped in our cloaks.
Sometimes we talked; more often we were silent,
and ever the great cannon roared from trench and
bastion, or were quiet awhile to let their hot lips cool.

Once Jack fell to talk of how he and I were changed
from the quiet Quaker lads we had been, and did I
remember our first fight, and Colonel Rupert Forest,
and Master Dove ? That greater master, War, since
then had educated and broadened us. He was more
philosophic than I, and liked thus to speculate; but
of Darthea he said never a word, though we spoke
of many things that memorable night.

At last, when it was near to dawn, Jack jumped
up, crying, "Oh, confound that dog !" He had,
what I never had, some remnant of the superstitions
of our ancestors, and I suspect that the howl of the
poor beast troubled him. I guessed at this when he
said presently, "I suppose we shall have to carry the
place by storm."

"Now don't tell me you will get hit," said I. "You
always say that. There are enough dead men to set
every dog in Virginia a-howling."

Jack laughed, but I had shamed him out of any
desire to repeat his predictions of disaster, and with

the signal-rockets in air, and the resounding thunder of this storm of war ever rising and falling, we went at last to our tents.

For two or three days his Excellency kept me busy; but since, except every third or fourth day, Jack had no active work, his diary at this time is very fully kept. I see from its pages that he thought over and over in this leisure of what we had so largely discussed on that night when we lay upon the hill.

"October 11," I find written.—"Hugh and I had a long talk over our own lives. It is a good thing and wise at times to take stock, as merchants say, of one's self and of one's friends. Indeed, if a man could contrive a moral likeness of his inner self such as he may have of his body, and this at different ages, it were an interesting and perhaps, too, a useful thing. It might much surprise him as the years went on. I think of myself as not so changed as Hugh. I am indeed more shy. As time goes on I arrange to hide it. I am less ambitious. Duty seems to me more and more a thing which I must do by reason of habit, that being strong with me owing much to the constant example set by my friend's life. If I have in me something of the woman's nature, as Mistress Wynne used to declare, I do not now so much dislike the notion. It may explain why, as I mature, nothing in life seems to me so greatly to be desired as the love of my fellows. If I think a man I esteem has no affection for me, I will fetch and carry to get it. Thank God I need not for Hugh. For him I would give my life, should he want it, and what more can

a man do for his friend? Yes, there is a greater
test, but of that I need not think, since she does not
love me, nor ever could I think to win her love.

"My Hugh is a big handsome fellow nowadays,
builded to be of the bigness of his father, but cleaner
fashioned, from early use of his muscles. He has
the strong passions of these hot Welsh, but is disci-
plined to control them, though not always. He is
more serious of late, and has thoughts which surprise
me, and show that his mind has grown. I used to
think he was too abrupt with people, but he has a
gift I have not—the power to capture the fine ways
which these French gentlemen possess, so that nowadays he has quite lost the stiff ways in which we
were brought up. But this art I have not, nor ever
shall have."

Now all this is more or less true, and as I have
said whatever was ill of myself, I like to let another,
if a too partial judge, say of me, for the flattery of
our blood, what may one day pleasure my children
to read.

On the night of the 12th of October our second
parallel was opened by Baron Steuben's division, in
which was Jack's command. It brought us within
three hundred yards of the enemy's works. Here
our people, while at the labour of digging, were
greatly annoyed by the flanking fire of two redoubts,
one on each side, and lying nearly as far out to right
and left as were now our advanced trenches.

On the 13th Colonel Tilghman came to ask me to
write the needed orders for an assault on these two

redoubts. He told me that Marquis Lafayette had
asked that his own aide-de-camp, Captain Gimat,
should lead the storming-party of Americans from
the troops for duty on the 14th, but Lieutenant-
Colonel Hamilton had insisted on his own right to
this honourable risk, he being, on the day set for the
assault, in command in the trenches.

This officer, my lifelong friend, had, in February
of '81, resigned from the staff, of which resignation
too much has been said. It in no way affected the
regard for him which our chief entertained, and the
occasion of his leaving the staff was not one, I
thought, to justify my friend in so doing, as indeed
I made bold to tell him.

He had now written a spirited letter to our chief,
claiming the right of command, as he had that day
the tour of duty in the trenches. His Excellency,
with his strong sense of justice, had decided in Mr.
Hamilton's favour, and it was thus settled that he
should head our assaulting column, and the marquis
have command of the whole detachment, which was
to be made up of picked men from the divisions for
duty in our works.

I wrote the required orders, and set them forth in
the orderly-book. The same day toward nightfall
Jack appeared at my tent. He said his company
was selected to be of the assault, adding with a fine
colour and very cheerful, that here in a packet were
letters he had writ to his father and to my Aunt
Gainor, and here, too, another—this with a little hesitation—for Miss Darthea.

I laughed, and said I was a bad person to be his executor, as I meant in some way to contrive to be of the party; how, I did not yet know. He begged me not to risk myself on a business out of my line of duty, but I was firmly set as to the matter, and he went away more serious than I thought worth while. In fact, I was tired of the every-day sameness of staff-duty and incessant letter-writing.

Later in the evening I was sent for to the tent of his Excellency. I found him with the Comtes de Deuxponts and de Rochambeau. I was wanted to act as interpreter. Although his Excellency could comprehend what was said, he possessed no such knowledge of French as to be able to speak it.

The business was soon despatched, and as I lingered, the general asked what other matter needed attention. Upon this I replied that I greatly desired to be of the storming-party.

He returned, "I presume of course, sir, that you are not for duty on the 14th?"

I said, "No."

"Then your business is with the staff. I am unwilling to permit gentlemen to step aside out of their work." He spoke in his usual deliberate manner, and with a certain sternness such as he well knew how to assume.

I saluted, but stood still a moment, and then said, "I trust, Excellency, that I have fulfilled my duties to your satisfaction."

"Entirely. I should have made it plain to you had it been otherwise."

"And I have never asked a favour of your Excellency. I have been twice wounded, have had no home leave for four years, and have spent five months in a British jail."

I saw a faint smile come over his grave face. "You boys are all alike. Here is Colonel Hamilton in a rage because the marquis would have given his place to Captain Gimat, and now it is an obstinate Welshman must go and get into mischief. I wish the whole army had your spirit, sir."

I ventured to observe that Colonel Armand had been permitted to serve as a volunteer, and that I had hoped that I too should be allowed a like favour.

His Excellency smiled, and returned, "As a volunteer, Mr. Wynne—well, as a volunteer. Ask Colonel Hamilton. I trust that is satisfactory. Are the orders and detail all made out?"

I said yes, and, thanking him, went away.

Colonel Hamilton, whom I saw early on the 14th, was as much surprised at the result of my request as was I, and was pleased to say he should be glad of my company, and would I be on hand in the trenches before dark?

The French of the old regiment D'Auvergne, which that night won the right to be called D'Auvergne *sans tache*, were to carry the redoubt to the right of the enemy's line. The Baron de Viomenisle was to lead them. Gimat was to have a chance with us.

"There are Connecticut men, and Massachusetts
II.—13

and Rhode Island men, with a reserve from Pennsylvania. The North has the whole business," said Hamilton, "and your friend Warder has the luck to be with us."

The redoubt Number Ten on the enemy's left, and nearest the river, fell to us, and Hamilton by no means meant that we should be later in the work than our allies.

I am forced to be thus particular because, although in God's providence I knew it not, I was about to pass through another crisis of my adventurous life. Before dusk I was in the trenches, and lying down amid a crowd of silent men. Hamilton walked to and fro among them, seeing that all were ready, and at last tied a piece of surgeons' bandage around my left arm, a precaution also taken as to the men that they might be distinguished in the darkness from the enemy.

Pioneers with fascines and ladders were a little later put out in front of the trenches, and with them the sappers and axemen under Captain Kirkpatrick. Within the crowded trenches and behind them the detachment of four hundred men lay ready.

It was cold, and a drizzling rain would have made it needful, under ordinary circumstances, to keep the pans of the muskets dry; but all loads were drawn, and the marquis meant to trust to the bayonet alone. Jack was afoot, and in his gay fashion was saying something merry to his men. I heard the marquis cry, "Silence!" in queer English, and down the line I could hear officers repeating his order.

For a little while all was still.

"Good-by," said my Jack. His hand was damp, and shook.

"You dear old idiot!" said I.

It was now close to eight, and of a sudden our cannon ceased. I dimly saw, a few yards away in the deep trench, the marquis looking back toward our camp. The enemy, glad, I dare say, of a chance to cool their guns, also stopped firing. I wished to heaven this horror of waiting were over.

Then a rocket rose high in air over our camp. "Ready, men!" said Hamilton, while I drew my long Hessian blade.

Six bombs in quick succession rose and went over us. I heard the marquis cry out, "*En avant!* Forward!"

"Forward, sappers!" cried a voice in front.

"Come along, boys!" cried Jack. And not giving the sappers more than time to scramble up, we were off in a swift rush through the darkness. The quickly formed line broke irregularly, as we ran over the space between us and the abatis, the sappers vainly trying to keep ahead.

As we rushed forward, my legs serving me well, I saw that they in the redoubt knew what was coming. A dozen rockets went up, Bengal fires of a sudden lighted their works, a cannon-shot went close to my head, and all pandemonium seemed to break loose.

At the stockade, an hundred feet from their works, our men pushed aside the sappers, and tore down the rude barrier, or tumbled over it. They were used to fences. Here Gimat was hurt, and Kirkpatrick of the pioneers, and a moment later Colonel Barber.

The hundred feet beyond were passed at a run, and the men with fascines cast them into the ditch. It was already half full of the wreck the cannon had made in the earthwork. We jumped in, and out; it was all mud and water. Ladders were set against the parapet, but the slope was now not abrupt, having been crumbled away by our guns, so that most of us scrambled up without delay. I saw Captain Hunt fall, the enemy firing wildly. If Sergeant Brown of the Fourth Connecticut, or Mansfield of the Forlorn Hope, were first on the parapet, I do not know. Hamilton got by me, and I saw him set a foot on the shoulder of a man, and jump on to the top of the redoubt. Why more or all were not killed seems to me a wonder. I think if the enemy had been cooler we had been easily disposed of. I saw the girl-boy leap down among the bayonets, and we were at once in a hurly-burly of redcoats, our men with and after us.

For a little there was fierce resistance and a furious struggle, of which I recall only a remembrance of smoke, red flashes, yells, and a confusion of men striking and thrusting. A big Hessian caught me a smart thrust in the left leg—no great hurt. Another with his butt pretty nearly broke my left arm, as I put it up to save my head. I ran him through, and felt that they were giving way.

To left and right was still a mad struggle, and
what with the Bengal fires still blazing, and a heap
of brush in flames at one side of the redoubt, there
was light enough to see. Near about me was a clear
space, and a pause such as occurs now and then in
such a scrimmage. There were still men who held
back, and to whom, as I pushed on, I called, "Come
on! We have them!" A great wind from the sea
blew the smoke away, so that it was easy to see. As
I called out to the men who hesitated on the outer
slope, as some will, I heard before me a voice cry,
"This way, men!" and, turning, caught sight of the
face of Arthur Wynne. He too saw and knew me.
He uttered an oath, I remember, crying out, "At
last!" as I dashed at him.

I heard ahead of me cries for "Quarter! quarter!"
The mass of striving men had fallen back, and in
fact the business was at an end. I saw Jack run
from my left toward me, but he stood still when he
saw what was happening, and instantly, as he came,
Arthur and I crossed swords. What else chanced
or who else came near I knew not. I saw for the
time only that one face I so hated, for the heap of
brush in the work was still blazing.

As is true of every Wynne I ever knew, when in
danger I became cool at once. I lost no time, but
pressed him hard with a glad sense that he was no
longer my master at the game. I meant to kill
him, and as he fell back I knew that at last his hour
had come. I think he too knew it. He fenced with
caution, and was as cool as I. Just as I touched

him in the right shoulder I felt a wounded Hessian
clutch my leg. I fell squarely backward, my cousin
lunging savagely as I dropped. I had been done
for had not Jack struck up his blade as I lay, calling out:

"Coward!"

I was up in a moment, pretty savage, and caught
sight of my Jack fencing with my man, as calm as
if we were in old Pike's gallery. As I stood panting—it was but a moment—I saw Jack's blade whip
viciously round Arthur's and pass through his
breast, nearly to the guard.

My cousin cried I know not what, fell to one side,
and then in a heap across a dead grenadier.

"Better I than thou," cried Jack, blowing hard.
"He will play no more tricks. Come on!"

With a glance at my enemy I hurried past him
over dead and wounded men, a cannon upset, muskets cast away, and what not.

"This way, Wynne," said the marquis. "C'est fini!
Get those fellows together, gentlemen."

Our men were huddling the prisoners in a corner
and collecting their arms. A red-faced New Hamp-
shire captain was angrily threatening Major Campbell, the commander of the redoubt, who had just sur-
rendered. Colonel Hamilton struck up the captain's
blade, or I do believe he would have killed the major.
He was furious over the death of Colonel Scammel,
who was greatly beloved, and had been killed by
Hessians after having given up his sword.

It was over, and I went back to see what had

become of Arthur. He was alive, and having dragged himself to the inner wall of the redoubt, was now seated against it. Jack soon found a lantern, and by its light we looked at Arthur. He was covered with blood, but was conscious, and stared at me with dull eyes, without power to say a word.

"Take care of him, Jack," said I, and went away down the crumbled slope and through the broken abatis, while overhead the bombs howled with unearthly noises and the cannonry broke out anew.

I was still angry that I had not killed the man, and went off to my tent in no very happy state of mind, so tired in body that I could not sleep for hours.

Says Jack, "October 15.—I can never cease to be thankful that, when we had them driven like scared sheep into the far side of the redoubt, I ran back to see what had become of Hugh. It was but a minute I had missed him, and when I saw him slip I had only just time to catch that devil Arthur Wynne's blade. He was used in old days to play with me like a child, but either I am become more skilful or he was out of practice, for I knew pretty soon that he was delivered over to me, and had small chance to get away unhurt. If my friend had killed him,— and that was what he meant, I fear,—would Darthea ever have married Hugh? I know not, but it has been ordered otherwise. There was indeed a way opened, as Friends say. A nice Quaker I am become!"

I was not of his opinion that night. Just before

reveille I fell into a broken slumber. I awakened
in a sweat, having dreamed that I had put a sword
through my cousin, and was troubled that Jack
was to tell Darthea. Thus it came to my mind
—dulled before this with anger and unsatisfied hate
—that I had made a fortunate escape. The morning brought wisdom. I was beginning to think
that all was not well between Darthea and Arthur
Wynne, and that to kill him would do anything but
add to my chances with a woman so sensitive, nor
would it much improve matters that his death had
come out of the unhappy chances of war.

When in happier mood I began to dress at dawn,
I found my left arm very stiff and sore. I must
have been much distracted overnight not to have
felt it, and not to have seen that I was seriously
bruised; my breeches were starched stiff with blood
from a bayonet-prick. Jack's quarters were on the
extreme right, and as soon as the lines broke after
morning drill I rode over to find him.

He told me that Dr. Rush was come to camp the
day before with other surgeons, and that Arthur
was in a tent and cared for by our good doctor, who
informed Jack that his sword had traversed the right
lung, but had not gone through, as it seemed to me
it must have done. The doctor thought he might
possibly get over it. Out of his affection for my
aunt he would see that Arthur had such care as she
would desire for one of her kin, but was it not a
most unfortunate accident?

"I assured him," said Jack, "that it was most

lamentable, but might have been worse—as I intended it should be," added Jack, with a grin. He then asked me had I heard of that good Free Quaker, Colonel Forest, who had taken Major Campbell, saying, "I advise thee to surrender, or thou wilt repent it, d—— thee!" to the delight of Hamilton, who must tell his Excellency that night, having supped with him on his return.

I made haste to write to my aunt, and was able to send our letters North with the general's despatches to Congress. I said nothing of my own encounter with Arthur, but made mention of Jack's affair as one of the chances of war.

Dr. Rush dressed my arm, and I went back to duty with the member in a sling, and aching like mad. His Excellency, seeing my condition, asked me if my right arm was in good order, but made no reference to the left. After I took his commands for the morning he said, seeing me limp, "Were you much hurt?"

I said, "No; I ran against something sharp in the bastion."

He smiled, and that was the end of the matter. Fair women and brave men were to his Excellency's liking.

This was my last of active warfare. The marquis tried his hand at a sally, and made ready too late to get away over the York River; but the sally came to nothing, and the belated effort to run to still less.

I neglected to say that the French, having come to the abatis, waited in line while the pioneers used

their axes to clear it away. Meanwhile, thanks to
too good discipline, they suffered severely. As we
rushed the whole thing, we lost far less. "It was
very fine and *en règle*," said Hamilton, "but I like our
way better." And so, I think, do I.

The good doctor liked to come to my staff tent in
those days, to talk to me or to others. He seemed
to think it necessary to inform me as to my cousin,
and I dare say thought me cool about him.

"And if, doctor, I had stuck him through the left
side?" said Jack, lying at ease on a bearskin in my
tent.

"In that case," said our doctor, in a quite professional way, "the heart or the great arteries had like
enough been pierced."

"And what then?" asked Jack of the doctor, who
was sitting on the camp-bed.

"Probably death would have occurred."

On this Jack looked up with those innocent eyes,
and, pushing back the blond locks, said: "It is a
great thing to know anatomy. If only I had made
a little study of that science, Dr. Rush, I might have
had better success at this pig-sticking business we
call war." The sly humour of the fellow set Hamilton to laughing, but the doctor did not smile.

"It might have been better for Hugh's cousin," he
said.

"Yes," said Jack, sweetly; "perhaps."

As they talked I was automatically putting into
fine French a letter of his Excellency to Comte
d'Estaing, and I took in readily what was passing.

When Jack said, "Perhaps," I cried out, "It would be a fine thing, doctor, to have all this saving knowledge on both sides, so as to know where not to hurt one another."

Hamilton was on the side of Dr. Rush. "It were more to the purpose," he said, "to sit down and not to go to war at all." This was set forth demurely, the colonel seeing how serious a dose our fun was for the great physician, who did somewhat lack the capacity to discover the entertainment to be found in this manner of jesting.

He returned gravely that this was his opinion, and that had he his way, war and drinking of spirits should alike cease.

To this we agreed in part as one man, for of war we were tired enough. As to the other matter, we did not mention it. To think of such a revolution was too astonishing in those days, nor have we come to it yet.

After that the doctor discussed Arthur's case with much learning and evident satisfaction. I might like in a day or two to see Captain Wynne. I was of opinion that it would do him harm, and when the great doctor said, "Perhaps, perhaps," Jack began discreetly to talk war, and asked where was General Gates.

But by this time our doctor had become cautious. His favourite commander was dismissed with a word or two, and so our chat ended, Mr. Hamilton and the physician going away together, each pleased with the other, and, despite some differences in politics, to remain lifelong friends.

On the 17th of October, the Marquis Cornwallis having had a stomach full of fighting, and having failed of his schemes to get away across the York River, beat a parley, and after some discussion signed the articles of capitulation. The soldiers were to remain prisoners in Virginia and Maryland, the officers were to return to Europe upon parole. The beaten army at two on the 19th came down the road between the French and our lines, with the colours in their cases, and the bands playing a British march; for it is of the etiquette of such occasions that the captured army play none but their own tunes. Some wag must have chose the air, for they marched by to the good old English music of "The World Turned Upside Down"; such must have seemed sadly the case to these poor devils.

As I was of the staff, I was privileged to see well this wonderful and glorious conclusion of a mighty strife. Our chief sat straight in the saddle, with a face no man could read, for in it was neither elation nor show of satisfaction, as the sullen ranks came near.

At the head of the line rode General O'Hara. He paused beside our chief, and begged his Excellency to receive the excuses of my Lord Cornwallis, who was not well enough to be present, which no one believed nor thought a manly thing to do.

His Excellency bowed, trusted it was not very serious, but would not receive General O'Hara's sword. With quiet dignity he motioned him to deliver it to Major-General Lincoln, who now had these grateful amends for the misfortune of having had to surrender his own good blade at Charleston.

After this the long array of chagrined and beaten men went by, and, returning to York, were put under guard.

A day or two later a letter of my aunt's informed me of the disorder my father's condition had brought about on his tobacco-plantation in Maryland. This caused me to ask for leave, and, with the understanding that I might be recalled at any time, I received permission to be absent two months.

I set out on November 5 for Annapolis, with two horses and my servant. Arthur Wynne, being found unfit to go to Europe with the rest, was taken a week later by our doctor on a transport to the Head of Elk, and thence by coach to Philadelphia. There, as I heard, the doctor took him to his own house, much amazed that Mistress Gainor would not receive him. Arthur won the good doctor, as he did most people, and, despite all expectations, was said to be mending fast, being much petted by the Tory ladies; but if Darthea had seen him or not I did not then learn.

My affairs in Maryland, where we had many slaves and large interests, kept me busy until near the close of December, when I set out to rejoin the staff in Philadelphia, my leave being up.

During this winter of '81 and '82 my duties were light, and except to write a few despatches daily, and to attend his Excellency on occasions of festivity, I had little to do save to look after my father's affairs.

It is now fit that I return to the narration of such things as immediately concern my personal interests. Arthur Wynne was able to ride out by the end of January, as I heard, for I did not chance to see him. My father remained much as he had been for a year.

Darthea, to our great surprise, on Captain Wynne's return became desirous to yield to her aunt and to go to New York. My aunt said she would get them a pass through our lines in the Jerseys; but this proving difficult, they stayed in and about the city, spending much time at their old home in Bristol. Darthea was so clearly unwilling to see me that I was fain to give it up, and accept what I could not better. When I said I was sorry she wished to go away, my Aunt Gainor replied that I was a fool, and would never be anything else. I asked why, but she was away from my question at once, and went on to tell me what officers were to dine with her that day, and did his Excellency like Madeira? and why was her doctor so fond of quoting Mr. Adams's letters from Holland, where he now was on a mission, with his nasty sneers at Virginians and Mr. Washington? She gave me no time to reply. Indeed, this and much else I saw or heard in those days was quite beyond me.

My aunt's way of dismissing a question she liked not was to pour out matters which were quite irrelevant, when to stop her was altogether past hope. I had learned to wait. She, at my desire, made Jack her aid in her affairs, as I was fully occupied with my father's neglected business. Now, too, she was busy finding Jack a wife, and would tell me all about it, striding to and fro, and with vast shrewdness and humour discussing the young women we knew.

"Cat" Ferguson was very humble, and the Chews in great favour with his Excellency. I was fain to dismiss my wonder as to Darthea, and, unable to recur to the question I had asked, I went away to headquarters in the great Chew house in Third street.

The town was gone wild with feasting and dinners, and as the general liked his staff to attend him, I had more of these engagements than I cared about.

Arthur, still weak and on parole, lingered; but why he did not get permission to go to New York, as had been easy, I could not well understand.

In February, '82, I came home to my father's one morning at an earlier hour than usual, and to my surprise heard my cousin's voice.

"I fear, sir, I am not understood. I came for the deed you promised me."

My poor father, a huge, wasted framework of a big man, was looking at him with lack-lustre eyes. He said, "My wife will be with us presently. Wilt thou stay for dinner?"

I went in at once, saying, "I am more than amazed, sir, to see you here. As to the deed you would have stolen—"

"What!" he cried.

"I said 'stolen,' sir. As to the deed you would have stolen from a man too feeble in mind to guard his own property, I have only this to say " (amid constant duties it had gone from my mind): " I shall put no obstacle in the way of your seeing it."

" I have no other purpose," he said quietly—" none. To you I could not go, and, sir, if you choose to consider my effort in any other light than an honest one, I have no more to say. We have enough causes of difference without that."

" Quite enough," said I. I was beginning to lose grip of my patience. "Quite enough. That they were not settled long ago an accident alone prevented."

"I am not, sir, in a way fitly to answer you. Neither is this a place nor a presence for this discussion."

" At least we can agree as to that," said I; " but I did not seek it. At my own leisure I shall have to ask you certain questions which, as a gentleman and a man of honour, you will find it hard to answer."

"I fail to comprehend," he returned, with his grand air, looking all the better for his paleness.

I said it was not now needful that he should, and that in future he would understand that he was no longer a welcome guest.

" As you please," he said.

I thought he showed little anxiety to hear at length what was in my mind.

Meanwhile, as we spoke, my father looked vacantly from me to him and from him to me, and at last, his old hospitable instincts coming uppermost, he said, " Thou hast not asked thy cousin to take spirits, Hugh."

Arthur, smiling sadly, as I thought, said: "Thank you, none for me. Good-day, Cousin Wynne," and merely bowing to me, he went out, I ceremoniously opening the door.

I had said no more than I intended to say; I was resolutely bent upon telling this man what he seemed to me to be and what I knew of his baseness. To do this it was needful, above all, to find Delaney. After that, whether Darthea married my cousin or not, I meant that she should at last know what I knew. It was fair to her that some one should open her eyes to this man's character. When away from her, hope, the friend of the absent, was ever with me; but once face to face with Darthea, to think of her as by any possibility mine became impossible. Yet from first to last I was firm in my purpose, for this was the way I was made, and so I am to this day. But whether I had loved her or not, I should have done my best out of mere friendship to set her free from the bonds in which she was held.

I had heard of Delaney as being in the South, but whether he had come out alive from the tussles between Morgan, Marion, and Tarleton, I knew not. On asking Colonel Harrison, the general's secretary, he told me he thought he could discover his whereabouts. Next day he called to tell me that there was an officer of the name of Delaney at the London Inn, now called "The Flag," on Front street, and that he had been asking for me. I had missed him by five minutes. He had called with despatches from Major-General Greene.

II.—14

To my joy this proved to be the man I wanted,
nor was it surprising that he should thus luckily
appear, since the war was over in the South, and a
stream of officers was passing through Philadelphia
daily to join the Northern army.

For a moment he did not know me, but was delighted when I named myself.

I said I had no time to lose, and asked him to
meet me at my aunt's in the afternoon. I much
feared that Arthur would get away before I was
ready to talk to him.

Delaney had received my last letter and had answered it, but whither his reply went I cannot say.
At all events, he had lingered here to find me. When
we met at my Aunt Gainor's that afternoon, it took
but a few minutes to make clear to her the sad tale
of Arthur's visit to the jail.

My friend had no sooner done than the old lady
rose, and began as usual to walk about, saying: "You
will excuse me; I must think of this. Talk to Hugh."
What there was to think of I could not see.

Delaney looked on amused, and he and I chatted.
She was evidently much disturbed, and while the
captain and I talked, I saw her move a chair, and
pick up and set down some china beast. At last
she said: "Come in at nine to-night, Mr. Delaney.
I want to think this over. I have still much I desire
to ask you. It deeply concerns my nephew in a way
I cannot now explain to you. May I have the privilege of another half-hour?"

Delaney bowed.

"Of course I do not want you, Hugh," she added.

When you have known a woman as long as I had known my aunt, there are sometimes hints or warnings in her most casual expressions. When my aunt said I was not wanted that evening I knew at once that she was meditating something out of the common, but just what, I did not think to ask myself. My Aunt Gainor was all her life fond of what she called inventing chances, a fine phrase, of which she was proud. In fact, this sturdy old spinster liked to interfere authoritatively in the affairs of men and women, and believed that for this she had a special talent, which in fact she discovered no inclination to bury; but what now she had in hand to do I knew not.

She was deeply grieved for a season to find that her plans went awry, or that men were disappointed, or that women would not go her way. "When she hurts you," said Mrs. Ferguson, "she is like a child, and has a dozen silly devices for doctoring your wounds. We have fought many times, and made up as often. There is no real malice in her," which was true.

Jack Warder once remarked in his lively way that Mistress Wynne had a richly coloured character. I fear it may have looked at times very black to some and very rose-tinted to others, but assuredly never gray in its tones, nor other than positive.

With me she took all manner of liberties, and with Darthea too, and if ever she were in doubt if it were well to meddle in our affairs I know not. A vast richness of human love and an urgent desire of rule lay underneath the life she showed the outer world of quadrille and dinners and gossip.

When she hurt us, or, as Darthea said, broke her china in trying to wash it, she fell back on our love with a quite childlike astonishment that what was come out of affection should give rise to resentment.

With a slight puzzle in my mind I went away with Delaney to dine at the London Coffee-house, which now showed our own new flag, where so often I had passed in under the cross of St. George.

"We have a new St. George now," said Mr. John Adams, in one of those ill-natured letters to Dr. Rush which filled my aunt with rage. "*Sancte Washington, ora pro nobis.*" The Massachusetts statesman admired *our* grave and knightly St. George, but there are those who cannot fly a kite without the bobtail of a sneer—which is good wit, I think, but not my own; it was Jack said that.

When Delaney left me to call again upon my aunt, I little dreamed of what part she meant him to play. He left the town early next day, and had it not been for Jack I should not for a long while have known fully what an hour brought forth.

"On the afternoon of February 28 of this 1782," says Jack's diary, "I got a note from Mistress Wynne asking me to see her on business at nine. I found with her, to my pleasure, the good fellow Delaney, and was able to thank him for the service he had done us all in his noble care of Hugh. We talked over our battles, and presently comes in

Darthea, whom now we see but rarely, for reasons best known to herself.

"I do believe Hugh has given up his love-affair as a thing quite hopeless, and no wonder. I think she still sees that rascal of an English captain, and perhaps he will not have her keep up a closer friendship with such as no longer desire his own acquaintance.

"Mr. Delaney was, like all men, charmed with Miss Peniston, and the talk went on busily enough, the young woman in good spirits and the captain most amusing.

"By and by he spoke quite naturally of the horrors of their life in the provost's prison, and upon this Darthea, becoming of a sudden seriously attentive, listened with fixed gaze. Our hostess, seeing her chance, said: 'I meant to ask you more of that to-day, but my nephew hates even to hear of it. How long were you there?'

"'I was taken at Germantown like Mr. Wynne, and was kept until June. After Wynne nearly killed that rascal, Cunningham, things were worse than ever.'

"'And was Hugh so very ill?'

"'He could not have been worse to live at all.'

"'And was there no inspection amidst all those horrors? Do you suppose Sir William knew nothing of them? I can hardly credit that.'

"Darthea looked round at Mistress Wynne. She had been unusually silent. Now turning to Delaney, she said, with slow articulation: 'I also am curious,

Mr. Delaney. We heard many rumours and some unpleasant facts. Could Sir William Howe have known? I cannot think it.'

" 'But he must, after the inspections, and there were three to my knowledge.'

" 'Indeed?' said Mistress Wynne. ''T is most strange!'

" Delaney hesitated, not liking, I suppose, to mention Arthur, her cousin, of whose close relation to Darthea, however, he was not aware.

" 'And one,' Mistress Wynne went on, 'was, I hear, made by our kinsman.'

" 'Yes,' said Delaney, 'and that did certainly amaze me. Captain Wynne—'

" 'Captain Wynne!' exclaimed Darthea, and, turning her head, she looked sharply at Mistress Wynne and then at me. I think that Delaney, being unfamiliar with her habits of speech, did not notice how strange was the tone in which she added, 'We all know Mr. Arthur Wynne.'

" 'Indeed!' said Delaney; 'but of course I might have known that.'

" 'Yes, yes! I interrupted you. Pray, go on; it is most interesting.'

" 'Very,' said Mistress Wynne. And now I saw what a wicked trap our spinster-fox had laid for poor Darthea. Delaney, a bit puzzled, glanced at me. I made no sign. It must not stop here.

" 'It is a queer story, Miss Peniston, and not much to the credit of his Majesty's officers.'

" 'What next?' said Darthea.

"'Oh, the tale is brief and brutal. I was seated on the straw one day, with Hugh's head in my lap, putting water on his forehead and trying to quiet him, when the turnkey came in with an English officer. This gentleman looked about him at the few left alive, asked carelessly who broke the window-panes, and then suddenly seemed to notice Hugh. He asked who was this poor devil. The turnkey said, "Name of Wynne, sir." Then the captain stood still a moment, staring at us, and, as if curious, bent down, asking me what Hugh was saying. Now my poor friend was muttering over and over, "Dorothea! Dorothea!"—some woman's name, I suppose, but what woman he never told me.'

"At this I saw Darthea flush, but perhaps remembering that Mr. Delaney might know her only as Miss Peniston, which was the fact, she controlled herself and said quickly: 'He asked his name? Are you sure he asked his name? Could there have been no mistake?'

"Delaney looked the surprise he no doubt felt, and replied, 'Yes; of that I am sure.'

"'Do you think,' said Darthea, 'he knew how ill Mr. Hugh Wynne was?'

"'Certainly; I heard the turnkey tell him that a day or two would see Hugh in the potter's field with the rest. The doctor had said as much. This was true; he had told me it was useless for him to return, and indeed I thought so too. They buried a half-dozen a day. When told that this man Wynne had jail-fever, the captain seemed in haste to leave. At the door he turned and took another look at Hugh, and then went out. I asked his name next day, but the turnkey laughed, and said it was none of my business. I had a fancy that the inspector desired to remain unknown. I was sure of this when, a few days after, I described the officer to Hugh, who was then quite himself. When Hugh said at last, "Had he a scar over the left eye?" and I said he had, Hugh cried out in a rage that it was his cousin, and would talk of nothing else for days. I fear there can be no doubt that the inspecting officer was Captain Arthur Wynne.'

"'Horrible!' exclaimed Mistress Wynne. 'Incredible!'

"'Yes; it seems to me a quite inconceivable thing, but I am certain, though the man looked a gentleman all over.'

"'He looked a gentleman all over,' said Darthea, with strange deliberateness of speech.

"This while Mistress Wynne sat drawn up, her face set, and one hand moving on the arm of the chair, just the same queer trick her brother had. As for me, I watched Darthea. It was a merciless plot, and may have been needed; but in truth the way of it was cruel, and my heart bled for her I loved.

"As she spoke her tones were so strange that Mr. Delaney, who was clearly but an innocent though sharp tool, said: 'I beg pardon, Miss Peniston. These sad stories are too dreadful to repeat. Miss Wynne would have it—'

"But Darthea was now quite lost to the common

ways of life. She went on like a person questioning herself, as it sounded to me. 'Arthur Wynne asked his name. Is that so?'

"Delaney said, 'Yes,' now, as I saw, quite troubled, and wishing himself out of it, I dare say.

"'And he knew he was in rags, starved, dying, and he left him?' continued Darthea. 'He left him —to die.'

"'Yes; but—'

"'No matter. I must hear all—all!' she cried sharply—'all! I am the person most concerned.'

"'Darthea!' then exclaimed Miss Wynne, alarmed, I suppose, at her wild manner and breaking voice.

"But Darthea went on. 'This is my business, madam. You are sure, sir? This is no time to trifle. I—I am—I must know! I must know! Would you say this to Captain Wynne were he here? Answer me, sir!'

"'Certainly I would, Miss Peniston.'

"'Mistress Wynne,' said Darthea, rising, 'I have been brought here to let a stranger see my—my weakness. It is plain. Did you think I could hide it, madam? Pardon me, sir. You have done me a cruel service. I—I thank you. I bid you good-evening, Mistress Wynne. Was there no other way, no kinder way, to tell me? Will you take me home, Jack? I—I am tired.'

"We had all risen with her at the beginning of this last speech, I troubled, Miss Wynne very red, and only fit to say over and over, 'Darthea! Darthea!' Mr. Delaney annoyed, and lacking knowledge of the

situation; all of us awkward and confused save
Darthea, who passed out into the hall, followed by
Miss Wynne, and saying, as she went forth, 'I will
never forgive you, madam, never! never! You are
a wicked old woman! I shall never speak to you
again. I did not think it.'

"I walked in silence beside her to Mrs. Peniston's
home. 'Thank you, Jack,' said she, in a sweet, low
voice. 'You did not know, did you, of this sad
story?'

"'Yes, dear lady, but of this disgusting plot, no.'

"'But why did you, who are my friend, and Mr.
Hugh Wynne, and all of you, leave me in the dark
as to this—this man?'

"I said quickly that it was not well to have told
her until Mr. Delaney could be found. He had but
just now come. She had seemed to trust Captain
Wynne's story; Hugh's was but the hearsay of a
man just out of a deadly fever. We had waited.

"As I spoke, she stood with her calash bonnet
fallen back, clear to see by the full moonlight, and
looking with intent face across Arch street, as it
might be with envy of the untroubled dead of generations who lay around the meeting-house. As I
ended, she said:

"'I have been a fool, Jack, but I loved him; indeed
I did. Is there more? I know Hugh hates him. Is
there more?'

"'Too much, too much, Darthea,' I said.

"'Then come in. I must hear all—all.' And she
knocked impatiently.

"Presently we were in the parlour. 'Fetch a light,' she said to the black who opened for us. When we were alone and seated, she said quietly: 'Jack, you are my only friend. I do trust *you*—oh, entirely. Now what is it? I must know all. Why has Hugh Wynne been silent? It is not like him.'

"'I have already told you why. Partly because, Darthea, you were away, or would not see us. That you know. Partly because Hugh had only his own word to give; but this I have told you.'

"'Yes, yes,' she cried; 'but what else?'

"'I think,' said I, 'knowing him well, that Hugh meant, when once he had Delaney's evidence, to tell his cousin face to face, and so force him to release you.'

"'That is my business, not his,' she broke in. 'What has Hugh Wynne to do with it? Am I a child?'

"'It had been the kinder and the manlier way,' said I. 'Now there is no need; but Hugh will be furious with his aunt.'

"'I am glad of that. What else is there? You are hiding something.'

"'There was that scene in the garden, Darthea.'

"She coloured at this. 'Yes, I know; but there were reasonable excuses for that, and no one had time to think.'

"'Two people had, Darthea.'

"'We will let that pass, Jack. Don't play with me.'

"Then, driven to the wall, so to speak, I told her

of the sad revelation André had made to Hugh, and
how, being Hugh's enemy, Arthur had been base
enough to involve him in an affair which might have
been his ruin.

"'Yes, yes,' she said, 'I see; but who could know,
or who think to use such knowledge?'

"I was taken aback at her seeming to have any
doubt. I coldly set myself to tell her of Arthur's
double dealing about the estate, and of how he
had made Hugh's father believe he was minded
to consider the ways of Friends, and at last of how
he had borrowed money and had set poor Hugh's
half-demented father against him. I did not spare
her or him, and the half of what I said I have not
set down. The Arnold business I did return to, seeing that it struck her, or seemed to, less than it did
me; for to my mind it was the worst.

"'Darthea,' I said, 'how could a man of honour
or even of good feeling put any gentleman in such
peril of worse than death? There were Tories enough
to have done his shameful errand. But oh, dear
Darthea, to suggest to send on such business an open,
frank enemy,—his cousin too,—that was too bad for
the lowest and vilest!'

"'Hush!' she said, 'I know enough. You have
been both brave and good. You are the best man I
know, Jack Warder, and the kindest. I wish I loved
you. I am not worthy of you. Now go away.'

"I obeyed her, and this was so far the end of a
miserable affair. What Hugh will say to Miss Wynne,
God knows. I have given a thorough rascal his

dues; but I cannot do this and not tell him to his
face what I have said behind his back.

"This was at night, but I had no better counsel in
the morning.

"I went to find Mr. Delaney, but he was gone,
having, as I heard later, put on paper what he had
seen and heard in the Provostry."

XII

"HEN," continues Jack, "I found Delaney had gone away, I was in a quandary. I by no means desired to go alone to see Captain Wynne. At last I made up my mind to ask Hugh. If there came a quarrel it should be mine. I resolved there should be no fight if I could help it, and that there might be trouble if Hugh were first to see his cousin I felt sure. The small sword was out of the question, but the pistol was not. I intended no such ending, and believed I had the matter well in my own hands. When I found Hugh at the quarters I told him quietly the whole story.

"That he was in a mad rage at his aunt I saw. I hate to see Hugh smile in a certain way he has, with his lips set close. He said nothing save that he would go with me, and that I was altogether in the right. He was reluctant to promise he would leave me to speak alone, but at last I did get him to say so.

"Mr. Arthur Wynne was alone in his room at the inn, and would see us. He was writing, and turned from his table, rising as we entered. He looked red and angry, in a soiled dressing-gown, and I thought had been drinking. He did not ask us to be seated, and we remained standing until our unpleasant talk came to a close.

"He said at once, 'My good cousin, I presume I owe to you the note I have had from Miss Peniston to-day.'

"'You do not,' said Hugh, not looking at all displeased.

"'Indeed? I had hoped you had come to offer me the only satisfaction in life your slanders have left me. My health is no longer such as to forbid the use of a pistol.'

"'Pardon me,' said I, 'this is my affair, and not Mr. Wynne's. I have had the honour of late to hear Mr. Delaney relate what passed in the jail.'

"'Have you, indeed? An old story,' said Arthur Wynne.

"'None the less a nasty one. I had also the pleasure to tell Miss Peniston that you suggested to the traitor Arnold to use my friend's known loyalty as a safe means of getting to Sir Henry Clinton a letter which was presumably a despatch as to exchange of prisoners, but was really intended to convey to Sir Henry the news that the scoundrel Arnold was willing to sell his soul and betray his country.'

"'Who told you this nonsense?' said the captain, coming toward us.

"'Major André,' said I. 'You may have my friend's word for that.'

"'It is a lie!' he cried.

"'Men about to die do not lie, Mr. Wynne. It is true.'

"The man's face changed, and he got that slack look about the jaw I have heard Hugh describe. To my astonishment he did not further insist on his denial, but said coldly, 'And what then?'

"'Nothing,' said I. 'Having told what I knew to a woman, I had no mind to have you say I had slandered you behind your back. That is all.'

"'Is it, indeed? And which of you will give me the honour of your company to-morrow?'

"'Neither,' said I. 'We do not meet men like you.'

"His face flushed. 'Coward!' he said.

"'If I am that,' said I, pretty cool, and shaking a little after my silly way, 'you know best, and will remember, I fancy, for many a day. Good-morning, sir.'

"On this he cried out, 'By —— ! this shall not pass! I—I will post you in every inn in town, and my cousin too. No man shall dare—'

"'Stop a little,' said Hugh. 'If it comes to that I shall know what to do, and well enough. I have no desire to put my own blood to open shame, but if this matter goes further, I shall publish Mr. Delaney's statement, and that, sir, will close to you every gentleman's house here and in London too.'

"'And shall you like it better to have it known that you were General Arnold's agent?'

"I saw Hugh's face lose its quiet look, and again he smiled. 'In that case,' he said, 'I should tell my own story and Mr. André's to his Excellency, and then, my good cousin, I should kill you like a mad dog, and with no ceremony of a duel. You warned

me once when I was a mere boy. It is my turn now.
As there is a God in heaven, I will do as I have
said.'

" ' Two can play at that game,' said Arthur. Hugh
made no reply.

" And on this we left the man standing, and went
forth without another word.

" ' I think his fangs are drawn,' said Hugh. And
indeed that was my opinion. I made up my mind,
however, that at the least unpleasant rumour of any
kind, I would take such a hand in the matter as would
save Hugh from having to go to extremities."

With the date of a week or so later I find added :
" The man thought better of it, I dare say, when the
drink wore off; how much of his folly was due to
that I cannot tell. It was plain that my dear Darthea had let him go at last. Was it because her sweet
pity distressed her to wound a man once dear that
she was held so long in this bondage ? or was it that
absence, said to be the enemy of love, was, in a
woman of her sense of honour, a reason why she
should not break her word until she had a more full
assurance of being right ?

" I think he slowly lost his place in the heart won
when Darthea was younger, and perhaps carried
away by vain notions, which lost value as time went
on. Such men have for the best of women a charm
we cannot understand."

I have left Jack to tell a part of my life which I
am glad to leave to another than I. I heard no
more of my cousin except that he had made up

his mind to go home under his parole. This did not fill me with grief. I had the sense to know that for many a day Darthea were better left alone.

My Aunt Gainor had recovered from the remorse which, as usual with her, followed upon some futile attempt to improve the machinery of other folks' fates. In fact, although Darthea closed her doors upon Mistress Wynne and would on no account see her, my aunt was already beginning to be pleased with the abominable trap she had set, and was good enough to tell me as much.

For three days after Jack had informed me as to the drama my aunt had planned I stayed away from her, being myself in no very happy state of mind, and unwilling to trust myself. When at last, of a Saturday afternoon, I came in on Mistress Wynne, she got up from her accounts, which she kept with care, saying at once: "It is a week since you were here, sir, and of course I know why. That long-tongued girl-boy has been prating, and your lordship is pleased to be angry, and Darthea is worse, and will not see me because I had the courage to do what you were afraid to do."

"Upon my word, Aunt Gainor," said I, "you are a little too bad. I was here four days ago, and have I said an impatient word? If I was angry I have had no chance to say so." Nor had I.

"Then if you are not angry you ought to be." She seemed to me bigger than ever, and to have more nose than usual. "You ought to be. I made a fool of myself, and all for you; and because I have

burned my fingers in pulling your goose out of the
fire, you must get into a passion. You have no need
to smile, sir. I suppose it were finer to say chestnuts,
but a goose she is, and always will be, and I love her
like a child. Your soft-hearted Excellency was to
see me last week, and saying that he had no children,
I, that have no right to any, said I was as ill off, and
we looked at each other and said nothing for a little,
because God had given to neither the completeness
of life. Is he stern, sir? I don't think it. We
talked of General Arnold, and of poor Peggy his
wife, and as to all this he was willing enough, and
frank too. Despite Dr. Rush and Mr. Adams, he
can talk well when he has a mind to. But when I
said a word of poor André, I had better have kept
my tongue quiet, for he said quickly: 'Mistress
Wynne, that is a matter I will never hear of willingly.
I ask your pardon, madam.' I could do no more
than excuse my want of thought, and we fell to discussing tobacco-growing."

"But what more of Darthea?" said I, for all the
generals in the world were to me as nothing compared with one little woman.

"Oh, there is no more, except that I am unhappy.
I will never again be kind to anybody. I am only a
miserable, useless old maid." And here she began to
cry, and to wet a fine lace handkerchief.

Just now comes in saucy Miss Margaret Chew,—
we call her Peggy,—and is rather flustered by my
aunt in tears. "O Mistress Wynne," she says, "I beg
pardon. I—"

"What for?" says my aunt. "My Manx cat has eaten the raspberry jam. That is all." Whereon we laugh, and the little lady, being pretty-spoken, says she wishes she was Mistress Wynne's cat, and while my aunt dries her eyes goes on to say, "Here is a note for you to dine with us and Mr. Washington, and I was bid write it, and so I did on the back of the queen of hearts for a compliment, madam," and with this she drops a curtsey.

My aunt, liking beauty and wit combined, kissed her, and said she would come.

This diversion cleared the sky, which much needed clearing, and Miss Chew being gone away, my aunt detained me who would willingly have followed her.

After that I comforted her a little as to Darthea, and said she could no more keep up being angry than a June sky could keep cloudy, and that, after all, it was just as well Darthea knew the worst of the man. I related, too, what Jack had told, and said that now my cousin would, I thought, go away, and we—thank Heaven!—be quit of him forever.

"And yet I must see him once," she said, "and you too. I have put that deed in the hands of James Wilson, and he has taken counsel of our friend Mr. Attorney-General Chew."

"I suppose you are right, Aunt Gainor," said I. "The man is bad past belief, but he has lost Darthea, which is as much punishment as I or any could desire. I think with you this estate business should some way be settled, and if it is to be his, I have no mind to leave the thing in doubt, and if it be mine

or my father's, I for one do not want it. I have
enough, and no wish to muddle away my life as a
Welsh squire."

"We shall see," said my aunt, not at all of my
opinion, as I readily perceived. "We shall see. He
shall have justice at our hands, and James Wilson
will be here at four to-morrow, and you too, Hugh,
whether you like it or not."

I did not, and I said so. She had written my
cousin that she desired to see him concerning the
deed. Whether from interest, or what, I know not,
he had replied that he would be with her at half-
past four.

Thus it happened that I was to see Arthur Wynne
once more, and indeed I felt that my aunt was right,
and that it were as well all our accounts with this
man were closed. Just how this would come about
I knew not yet, but closed they should be; as to that
I was fully advised in my own mind.

XIII

T four punctually arrived my friend the famous lawyer. He was not a handsome man, but possessed a certain distinction, which he owed to a strong face, well-modelled head, and a neatly powdered wig, the hair being tied back, after the fashion of the bar, in a black queue-bag with, at the end, a broad black ribbon. He took the snuff my aunt offered, carefully dusting the excess off the collar of his brown velvet coat, and sat down, saying, as he took some papers from a silk bag, that it was altogether an interesting and curious question, this we had set before him. And why had we held this deed so long and said nothing?

I told him of my father's and my grandfather's disinclination to open the matter, and why and how the estate had seemed of little worth, but was now, as I believed, more valuable.

Hearing this he began to question my aunt and me. He learned from our replies that at the time I got the deed from my father none but my parent had any clear idea of what this old family compact meant, but that now we were in possession of such facts as enabled us to understand it. I then went on

230

to make plain that my aunt was full of the matter, and eager, but that I had no inclination at any time to enter on a long and doubtful litigation in another country.

To myself I confessed that I desired no immediate settlement until I saw what Arthur meant to be at. It was one more hold on a scamp still able to do me mischief. If it was clearly his father's estate and not ours, he should soon or late be relieved of any possible doubt this deed might still make as to questions of title.

When Mr. Wilson turned to my aunt he found a more warlike witness. She delighted in the prospect of a legal contest.

"When a child," she said, "I used to hear of my father's having consented to make over or give away to his brother William an embarrassed estate, and that the crown officers were in some way consenting parties to the agreement, my father engaging himself to go to America when let out of jail.

"There is no doubt," she went on, "that Wyncote was under this arrangement legally transferred by my father to his next brother. Our Welsh cousins must have this conveyance. It seems, from the deed you have examined, that privately a retransfer was made, so as, after all, to leave my father possessed of his ancestral estate. If ever he chose to reclaim it he was free to do so. The affair seems to have become more or less known to the squires in that part of Merionethshire. William was, we presume, unwilling to take an unfair advantage of his brother's misfortune, and hence the arrangement thus made between them."

"You state the case admirably," said the lawyer. "And what else is there?"

"But little. Letters of affection and esteem came and went at long intervals. I recollect hearing bits of them, but cannot say if the estate matter were ever mentioned. After William's death the correspondence may or may not have ceased. His brother Owen came into the property without interference, and, dying, left a young son, Owen, who is still alive. His son Arthur, Captain Wynne, is to be here to-day. There are personal matters involved, into which there is no need to go. The Welsh branch is no doubt desirous in some way to clear the matter; but having held the estate for a century, they are, we may presume, not very eager to give it up. In justice to Owen Wynne, I may say that it is probable that because of a long minority he only began, as I think, a few years ago to have any doubt as to his title. I may add," my aunt went on, "that Captain Wynne came and went during the war, and that only of late has this deed turned up."

"And your brother is quite unfit to help us?" said Wilson.

"Yes; and unwilling if he were able."

"I see, madam, I see; a difficult business."

"And this deed?" said my aunt; "you were about to speak of it."

"It is," he replied, "a simple act of sale for one shilling, a reconveyance of Wyncote from William

to Hugh, the date October 9, 1671. It is in order,
and duly witnessed."

"Well?"

"As to its present value, Mistress Wynne, there is
a consensus of opinion between the Attorney-General
and myself."

"That is to say, you agree," said my aunt.

"Precisely, madam. It is our belief that the lapse
of time has probably destroyed the title. There is
no annexed trust, on William's part, to hold for his
brother's use, and the length of undisputed, or what
we lawyers call adverse, possession—something like
an hundred years or more—*seems* to make it impossible for my friends to oust the present holder. Am
I clear?"

"Too clear, sir," said my aunt. "Is that all?"

"No; I said, 'seems.' There are other questions,
such as the mention of the matter in letters. If the
succeeding brothers in letters or otherwise from time
to time acknowledged the rights of Hugh Wynne,
that might serve to keep alive the claim; if, too, it
can be proved that at any time they paid over to
Hugh or his son, your brother, madam, rents or dues,
as belonging to these American claimants, this too
would serve to give some validity to your present
claim. It is a question of dates, letters, and of your
possession of evidence in the direction of repeated
admissions on the part of the Welsh holders."

My Aunt Gainor was at once confident. Search
should be made. She had some remembrance in her
childhood of this and that. In fact, my aunt never

admitted the existence of obstacles, and commonly refused to see them. Mr. Wilson shook his head dubiously. "There seems to have been negligence or a quite culpable indifference, madam. The time to be covered by admissions is long, and the statutes of 32 Henry VIII. and 21 James I., 1623, do, I fear, settle the matter. The lapse in the continuity of evidence will be found after the death of Hugh. Twenty years will suffice, and I am forced to admit that your claim seems to me of small value. It was simply an estate given away, owing to want of the simplest legal advice."

"Wait until I look through our papers," said my aunt. "We are not done with it yet, nor shall be, if I have my way, until the courts have had a chance to decide."

"It will be mere waste of money, my dear lady. Now, at least, you can do nothing. The war is not over, and when it is, none but an English court can settle the title. I confess it seems to be a case for amicable compromise."

"There shall be none—none," said my aunt.

"And we are just where we began," said I.

"Not quite," he returned. "You may have a case, but it seems to me a weak one, and may lie in chancery a man's lifetime. I, as a friend as well as a lawyer, knowing you have no need of the estate, hesitate to advise you to engage in a suit of eject-ment. I should rather counsel—ah, that may be Mr. Wynne."

It was a clamorous knock at the hall door, which

caused Mr. Wilson to cut short his advice with the statement that it would need longer discussion, and that this must be the other party.

It was, in fact, my cousin, who was set down in a chair, as I saw by a glance through the window. When Jack and I had seen him at his inn he had been a little in liquor, and wore a sort of long chintz bedgown wrapper, with his waistcoat buttoned awry —not a very nice figure. He was now Arthur Wynne at his best. He stood a moment in the doorway, as beautiful a piece of manhood as ever did the devil's work. His taste in all matters of dress and outer conduct was beyond dispute, and for this family meeting he had apparently made ready with unusual care. Indeed this, my last remembrance of Arthur Wynne, is of a figure so striking that I cannot resist to say just how he looked. His raiment was costly enough to have satisfied Polonius; if it bore any relation to his purse, I know not. It was not "expressed in fancy," as was that of the macaroni dandy of those early days. He knew better. As he stood he carried in his left hand a dark beaver edged with gold lace. His wig was small, and with side rolls well powdered, the queue tied with a lace-bordered red ribbon. In front a full Mechlin lace jabot, with the white wig above, set his regular features and dark skin in a frame, as it were, his paleness and a look of melancholy in the eyes helping the natural beauty and distinction of a face high bred and haughty. The white silk flowered waistcoat, the bunch of gold seals below it, the claret-tinted velvet

coat and breeches, the black silk clocked hose with
gold buckles at ankle and knee, and a silver-hilted
dress-sword in a green shagreen sheath, complete my
picture. I wish you to see him as I saw him, that in a
measure you may comprehend why his mere personal
charms were such as to attract and captivate women.

He came forward with his right hand on his heart
and bowed to my aunt, who swept him a space-filling
curtsey, as he said quite pleasantly, "Good-afternoon,
Cousin Gainor; your servant, Mr. Wilson." To me
he bent slightly, but gave no other greeting. It was
all easy, tranquil, and without sign of embarrassment.
As he spoke he moved toward the table, on which
Mr. Wilson had laid his papers and bag. Now, as
always, a certain deliberate feline grace was in all
his movements.

"For a truth, he is a beauty," said my Aunt Gainor after our meeting was over. "And well-proportioned, but no bit of him Wynne. He has not our
build." Nor had he.

"Pray be seated," said my aunt. "I have asked
my friend and counsel, Mr. James Wilson, to be
present, that he may impartially set before you a
family matter, in which your father may have interest. My nephew, Hugh Wynne, is here at my earnest
solicitation. I regret that Mr. Chew is unable, by
reason of engagements, to do me a like favour. Mr.
Wilson will have the kindness to set before you the
nature of the case."

Mistress Wynne, sitting straight and tall in a high
cap, spoke with dignified calmness.

"At your service, madam," said the lawyer, looking Arthur over with the quick glance of a ready
observer. Before he could go on to do as he was
bidden I found my chance to say, "You will be so
good, Mr. Wilson, as to state Mr. Owen Wynne's case,
as well as our own, with entire frankness; we have
no desire to wrong any, and least of all one of our
blood."

"I think I understand you fully," said Wilson.
"A deed has been put in the hands of Mr. Attorney-
General Chew and myself, and as to its value and
present validity an opinion has been asked by Mistress Wynne and her nephew."

"Pardon me," said Arthur; "is not my Cousin
John the proper person to consider this question?"

"Assuredly," returned Mr. Wilson, "if his state
of mind permitted either his presence or an opinion.
No interests will be affected by his absence, nor can
we do more than acquaint those who are now here
with what, as lawyers, we think."

"I see," said Arthur. "Pray go on."

"This deed seems to convey to my client's grandfather—that is to say, Mistress Wynne's father—
certain lands situate in Merionethshire, Wales. I
understand that you, sir, represent the present
holder."

"I am," said Arthur, "the son of the gentleman
now in possession of Wyncote, and have full permission to act for him. If, indeed, you desire further
to learn on what authority—"

"Not at all, not at all," interposed Wilson. "Your

presence suffices; no more is needed. This meeting commits no one."

"I was about to ask the date of this document," said Arthur.

"Certainly; here it is." And so saying the lawyer spread the deed out on the table. "It is a conveyance from William Wynne to Hugh of that name; the date, 1671, October 9; the witnesses are Henry Owen and Thomas ap Roberts. It is voluminous. Do you desire to hear it?"

"No; oh no! What next?"

"We believe," continued the lawyer, "that this deed has ceased to have effect, owing to lapse of time and the appearance—pray note my words—the *appearance* of undisputed ownership by the younger branch. Neither is there any trust to hold the estate for Hugh; it is a mere conveyance."

"There can be, of course, no doubt," returned Arthur—"I mean as to a century of unquestioned possession."

"I am not secure as to the point you make," said Mr. Wilson, courteously. "I cannot now decide. I am asked to state the matter impartially. My clients wish justice done to all, and will take no unfair advantage. It may be you have no case. There may have passed frequent letters on both sides, admitting the claim or reasserting it, and thus keeping it alive. Rents may have been paid. Facts like these may open questions as to the length of undisputed holding. Only your own courts can decide it, and that with all the evidence before them."

"I am obliged by your frankness," said my cousin. "I had hoped to see the matter fully settled."

"That will never be," said my aunt, "until I have carried it through every court in England."

"As you please," replied Arthur.

"Mr. Wynne," said I, "while my father lives we shall do nothing; nor even afterward, perhaps. I do not want the money, nor the old home. What is done may depend much on your own actions, sir." I had no desire to lose this hold on him. As I spoke I saw him look up astonished, as was also, I thought, the lawyer, who knew nothing of our quarrels.

"If," said I, "you had come to us frankly at first, and stated why you came, we should have said what I now say. No, *I* should have said far more. I believe this ends the matter for the present." My aunt lifted her hand, but I added, "I pray you let it rest here, aunt," and for a wonder she held her peace.

Arthur, too, seemed about to speak, but his worse or better angel, I know not which, prevailed, and quietly saluting us all, he rose and took his leave.

"We shall see when this war is over," said my aunt, taking the deed. "Many thanks, Mr. Wilson; I should like to have your opinion in writing."

"I shall send it in a week or two. Mr. Arthur Wynne seems to have come over, as I judge from what he said, with authority to act for his father. Why he did not at once relate his errand I cannot see. Had you had no deed it would have closed the matter. If he found you had one he would have been only in the position he is now in to-day."

"I fancy he may have been fearful and over-cautious, not comprehending the nature of those he had to deal with," said I. "You must have known him as I do, Mr. Wilson, to understand his actions. I was sorry you did not let him tell us what powers he really had. I was curious."

"Yes, yes, I interrupted him. It was a mistake." And so saying he rose.

"It shall not rest here," said my aunt. "Something shall be done." And on this I too went away, declining further talk.

When Arthur came over to learn what he could as to their title to Wyncote, he failed to see that we were people whom no prospect of gain could lead into the taking of an advantage. He thus lost the chance a little honest directness would have given him. When later my father threw in his way the opportunity of absolute security as to the title, the temptation to get secretly from him a legal transfer, or—God knows—perhaps the power to destroy the deed, was too much for a morally weak and quite reckless nature. I was the sole obstacle, or I seemed to be. We loved the same woman; she had begun to doubt her English lover. If I had died he had become assured, not only of the possession of Wyncote, but of being ultimately my father's heir.

Of this Jack writes: "Here was a whole brigade of temptations, and he could not stand it. He would have broken that tender heart I loved. God help me! I think I should have killed him before he had the cruel chance."

If to the estate and other worldly baits was added the remembrance of the blow a mere boy gave, I do not know. It is certain that at last he hated me, and as sure that I had as little love for him.

XIV

ARLY in March of 1782 Jack and I concluded that the war was over, or was to be
but a waiting game, as indeed it proved.
After some thought over the matter we
both resigned, and as it was desired to
lessen the list of officers, we were promptly released
from service.

On March 22 his Excellency rode away from town
under escort of Captain Morris's troop of light horse.
I went along as far as Burlington, being honoured
when I left by the personal thanks of the general,
and the kind wish that I might discover it to be
convenient to visit him at Mount Vernon.

April was come, and we gladly turned again to
the duties which awaited us both. His Excellency
had gone to watch Sir Guy Carleton penned up in
New York. Congress wrangled, our gay world ate
and danced, and the tardy war fell to such slackness
that it was plain to all a peace must soon come,
although we were yet to see another winter pass
before the obstinate Dutchman on the English
throne gave up a lost game.

In July my father died of a sudden afflux of blood

to the head; and although he was blooded by Dr. Rush several times, never was so far bettered as to speak to me. Only once, as I am told is not rare, he so revived when in the very article of death as to look about and say, thinking my hand in his was my mother's, that she must not grieve for him.

Alas! he had been as one dead to me for many a year. I wore no black for him, because I was and am of the opinion of Friends that this custom is a foolish one. My aunt was ill pleased at my decision, and put herself and all her house in mourning. None the less, for my part, did I regret, not so much the natural, easy death, as the sad fact it seemed to fetch back so plainly, that from my youth up here were two people, neither of them unkindly or ill natured, who were all through life as completely apart as if no tie of a common blood had pledged them to affection.

I saw—I can see now—the gray and drab of the great concourse of Friends who stood about that open grave on Arch street. I can see, too, under the shadow of his broad gray beaver, the simple, sincere face of James Pemberton, my father's lifelong friend. He spoke, as was the custom of Friends, at the grave, there being no other ceremony, an omission of which I confess I do not approve. Much moved, he said:

"Our friend, John Wynne, departed this life on the 23d of July of this year [being 1782]. For many years he hath carried the cross of afflicting sickness, and hath unceasingly borne testimony to the doc-

trine and conduct upheld of Friends. He was a
man of great abilities, and, like our lamented William
Penn, of an excellent gravity of disposition, without
dissimulation, extensive in charity, having neither
malice nor ungratefulness. He was apt without
forwardness, yet weighty, and not given to unseemly
levity. The wise shall cherish the thought of him,
and he shall be remembered with the just." And
this was all. One by one they took my hand, and
with my Aunt Gainor I walked away. I closed the
old home a day or two later, and went with my
aunt to her farm.

I had not seen Darthea for many a day. "Let
her alone," said my aunt. I think Jack was often
with her; but he knew to hold his tongue, and I
asked no questions. At last, a week after the fu-
neral, I recognised her hand in the address of a
note to me. I read it with a throbbing heart.

"Sir: I have heard of your great loss with sorrow,
for even though your father has been this long while
as one lost to you, I do think that the absence of a
face we love is so much taken from the happiness of
life. You know that your aunt hurt me as few could,
but now I am not sorry for what then befell. The
thought of death brings others in its train, and I
have reflected much of late. I shall go to see Mistress Wynne to-day, and will you come and see me
when it shall appear to you convenient? I am for
a little at Stenton, with Madam Logan."

Would I, indeed? My dear old Lucy, a little stiff
in the knees, carried me well, and seemed to share

my good humour as I rode down the long road from
Chestnut Hill.

The great trees about the home James Logan
built were in full leaf, and under their shade a black
groom held two horses as I rode up. Darthea came
out, and was in the saddle before she saw me.

The rich bloom of health was again on her cheek,
and deepened a little as I went toward her.

I said I was glad to see her, and was she going to
my Aunt Gainor's? If so, and if it were agreeable
to her, the groom might stay. I would ride back
with her. Then Mrs. Logan, at the door, said this
would suit very well, as she needed the man to go to
town. After this we rode away under the trees and
up the Germantown road, Miss Peniston pushing
her horse, and we not able on this account to talk.
At last, when I declared Lucy too old to keep up the
pace, the good beast fell to walking.

Soon we went by the graveyard where the brave
Englishman, General Agnew, lay; and here Darthea
was of a mind to be told again of that day of glory
and defeat. At the market-house, where School-house
Lane comes out into the main street of Germantown, she must hear of the wild strife in the fog and
smoke, and at last of how I was hurt; and so we
rode on. She had gotten again her gay spirits, and
was full of mirth, anon serious, or for a moment
sad. Opposite Cliveden I had to talk of the fight,
and say where were Jack and Sullivan and Wayne,
although Jack more concerned her. As we rode up
the slope of Mount Airy I broke a long silence.

"Darthea," said I, "is it yes, or always no?"

"Will you never be contented?" she returned. "Is n't it mean to say these things now? I can't get away. I have half a mind to marry Jack, to be rid of you both."

"Is it *yes* or *no*, Darthea?"

"Yes," she said, looking me in the face. I am a strong man,—I was so then,—but a great rush of blood seemed to go to my head, and then I went pale, as she told me later, and I clutched at Lucy's mane. I felt as if I might fall, so much was I moved by this great news of joy.

"Are you ill?" she cried.

"No, no," I said; "it is love! Thy dear love I cannot bear. Thank God, Darthea!"

"And do you love me so much, Hugh? I—I did not know." She was like a sweet, timid child.

I could only say, "Yes, yes!"

"Oh, Hugh!" she cried. "How can you forgive me? But I am not like other women. My word— you will know—and then you will forgive me." Her eyes were full of tears, her face all aglow.

"There is—there never will be anything to forgive."

"But I was so foolish—and—I was so foolish."

"Let us forget, Darthea. I have thy love. God knows it is enough."

"Thank you, Hugh. Don't speak to me for a little, please." And under the warm August afternoon sky we rode on at a foot-pace, and said no word more until we came to my aunt's door. Then Darthea slyly put on her riding-mask, and we went in.

My aunt had her in her great arms in a moment.
The mask fell, and then my aunt held her off a little,
looked from her to me, and said, "Has he made you
cry, sweetheart? He always was a fool. I am very
glad. You have made an old woman's heart sing
with joy. It is not your fault. Hugh's silly face
was enough. Lord! girl, how pretty you are! Do
you suppose I never was in love? I never was, but
I know the signs." Darthea, released, was pleased
enough to be let go up to my aunt's room. By and
by she came down, saucy and smiling, and later
came Jack, when my aunt, being too happy to hold
her dear old tongue, told him, while poor Darthea
looked at him with a tender gravity I did not understand. He went away very soon, saying he had business in town, and this is what he writ that night:

"And so she will have my Hugh, and he the best
lady alive. I pray the good God to keep them from
all the sorrows of this world. If he love her as I
love her, she can ask no greater love; and he will—
he cannot help it. Now I will write no more. God
bless thee, Darthea!" It was thus a gallant gentleman loved in those stormy days.

And here, with this dear name, his records close,
and there is the date of August 1, 1782, and a line
drawn underneath.

The new relation soon to be established between
us of necessity brought Madam Peniston and my
aunt into frequent council. There were matters of
dress to be considerately dealt with, and I was told
it must be six months before orders could be filled

from France, England being just now out of the
question. Where the mysteries of women's garments are concerned a man hath no better resort
than to submit humbly, as to a doctor or a lawyer.
Here of a certainty knowledge is power, and as to
this matter, a man had best learn to conceal amazement under a show of meekness.

When I ventured to remonstrate Darthea looked
serious, and would I ever have fallen in love with
her unless she had laid snares of gown and ribbon,
and how was my love to be kept if for the future
there were not provided a pretty variety of such
vanities? Even my Aunt Gainor refused to discuss
the question. I must wait; and as this was the single occasion known to me when she had declined a
hand at the game of talk, I began to perceive that
ignorance is weakness, and so at last, calmly con-
fessing defeat, I waited until those consulting chose
to advise me, the patient, of their conclusions.

Meanwhile Mrs. Peniston had ceased to grieve
over the lost lover and the great estate—it never
was really great.

My aunt could not let go of the notion that we
must have a fight for Wyncote. This tendency to
become possessed by an idea, I came to see later,
was a family trait, of value if wisely kept in due
place, but capable, also, of giving rise to mischief.
My aunt, in some of her talks with Darthea's relative, heard of that good dame's past regrets at the
loss of a title and estate and a British lover, and of
how flattered we ought to be.

I presume poor Madam Peniston was well and sharply answered; but it was not in my Aunt Gainor not to boast a little of how we were the elder branch, and of what might chance in the fairy future. When Mrs. Peniston saw the deed, and was told of the search my aunt was making for letters to support our claims, she was too excited not to let out enough to disturb Darthea, and this although my aunt told Mrs. Peniston of my dislike of the whole matter, and how it was never to be mentioned or known to any until more evidence came to light. Thus cautioned, she was just mysterious enough to excite my quick-witted maid, who was as curious as any of her sex.

When of course she questioned me, and some notion of the mischief on hand came thus to my knowledge, I saw at once how it might annoy Darthea. I said that it merely concerned a question in dispute between Arthur Wynne's family and my own, and ought not, I thought, to be discussed just now. The mere name of her former lover was enough to silence her, and so I begged her to put it aside. She was willing enough. I had happier things on my own mind, and no present desire to stir in the matter. In fact, I wished most earnestly to keep it awhile from Darthea. How much she knew I could not tell, but I was well aware that she was, above all things, sensitive as to any reference to Arthur Wynne. That she had once loved him with the honest love of a strong nature I knew, and somewhat hated to remember; but this love was

dead, and if the sorry ghost of it haunted her at
times, I could not wonder. My aunt had once or
twice mentioned him casually, and each time Darthea had flushed, and once had asked her never to
speak of him again. I meant soon—or more likely
later—to discuss the matter quietly with Darthea;
for then, as always, I held to the notion that the
wife should have her share in every grave decision
affecting the honour and interests of her husband.

After this I spoke most anxiously of the matter
to my aunt, and entreated her to quiet Madam Peniston, and to let the thing rest in my hands. This
she declared most reasonable, but I knew her too
well not to feel uneasy, and indeed the result justified my fears.

My aunt, as I have said, had gone wild a bit over
that deed, and when Darthea was not with her was
continually discussing it, and reading over and over
Mr. Wilson's opinion. I got very tired of it all.

One night, late in October, I rode out from town,
and, after a change of dress, went into the front
room with the dear thought in my mind of her
whom I should see.

A welcome fire of blazing hickory logs alone lighted
up the large room, for my aunt liked thus to sit at
or after twilight, and as yet no candles had been set
out. As I stood at the door, the leaping flames,
flaring up, sent flitting athwart the floor queer
shadows of tall-backed chairs and spindle-legged
tables. The great form of my Aunt Gainor filled
the old Penn chair I had brought from home, liking

myself to use it. Just now, as usual, she was sitting
erect, for never did I or any one else see her use for
support the back of a chair. At her feet lay Darthea, with her head in the old lady's lap—a pretty
picture, I thought.

Darthea leaped up to run to me. My aunt said
nothing, not so much as "Good-evening," but went
out, and in a minute or two came back, exclaiming, in an excited way, that she had waited all day,
and now at last she had great news, and we must
hear it.

I was bewildered, until I saw she had in one hand
the deed and in the other a bundle of letters. Then
I knew what a distressful business was to be faced,
and that it was vain to cry "Stop!"

"What is it?" said Darthea.

"It can wait," said I. "I insist, Aunt Gainor."

"Nonsense! The girl must know soon or late,
and why not now?"

"I must hear, Hugh," said Darthea.

"Very well," I returned, as angry with the old
lady as ever I had been in all my life.

"It is a thing to settle," cried Aunt Gainor, in her
strong voice. "We must agree—agree on it—all of
us."

"Go on," said I. And Darthea insisting, I said
nothing more, and was only concerned to be done
with it once for all.

"The war will soon end," said my aunt, "and
something must be done. These letters I have come
upon put a new face on the matter. I have not yet

read all of them. But among them are letters to
your grandfather of great importance."

I was vexed as I have rarely been. "I never
doubted, Aunt Gainor, that in my grandfather's life
some acknowledgments may have passed; but it is
the long lapse of time covered by my father's life
which will fail as to evidence."

"It shall not!" she cried. "You shall be mistress
of Wyncote, Darthea. These letters—"

"I? Wyncote?" said Darthea.

"Let us discuss them alone, aunt," I urged, hoping
to get the matter put aside for a time.

"No; I will wait no longer. I am deeply concerned, and I wish Darthea to hear."

"Why not refer it to Mr. Wilson? Unless these
letters cover far more of a century than seems likely,
they cannot alter the case."

"That is to be determined," said the old lady. "I
shall go to England and settle it there. You shall
be Wynne of Wyncote yet, sir."

"What! what!" cried Darthea. "What does all
this mean? Tell me, Hugh. Why is it kept from
me?" It was plain that soon or late she must
know.

"My aunt thinks Wyncote belongs to us. There
is an old deed, and my aunt will have it we must go
to law over it. It is a doubtful matter, Darthea—
as to the right, I mean. I have no wish to stir it up,
nor to leave my own land if we were to win it."

I saw Darthea flush, and in a moment she was at
my aunt's side.

"Stop!" said I. "Remember, dear, I have not hid it from you. I desired only that some day you and I should consider it alone and tranquilly. But now there is no help for it, and you must hear. The deed—"

"Is this it?" she broke in, taking the yellow parchment off the table where my aunt had laid it.

"Yes, yes," said my aunt; "and you must bring Hugh to his senses about it, my dear. It is a great estate, and rich, and the old house—we have its picture, Darthea. Madam Wynne of Wyncote, I shall come and visit you." The old lady was flushed, and foolishly eager over this vain ambition.

Darthea stood in the brilliant firelight, her eyes set on the deed. "I cannot understand it," she said.

"I will send for candles," cried Mistress Wynne, "and you shall hear it, and the letters too;" and with this she rang a hand-bell, and bade Cæsar fetch lights.

I looked on, distressed and curious.

"And this," said Darthea, "is the deed, and it may give you, Hugh—give us the lands?"

"But *I* do not want it," cried my aunt, greatly excited. "It is to be Hugh's. Yours, my dear child."

"If," said Darthea, speaking slowly, "the elder brother dies, as he surely will before long, it will be —it will be Arthur Wynne who, on his father's death, will inherit this estate?"

"That is it," said my aunt. "But he shall never have it. It is ours. It is Hugh's."

My dear maid turned to me. "And it would be ours," said Darthea, "if—"

"Yes," cried Miss Wynne. "There are no 'ifs.'"

"Do you want it, Hugh—these Welsh lands?" asked Darthea.

I thought she looked anxiously at the deed in her hand as she stood. "Not I, Darthea, and least of all now. Not I."

"No," she went on; "you have taken the man's love from him—I think he did love me, Hugh, in his way—you could not take his estate; now could you, Hugh?"

"No!" said I; "no!"

"Darthea, are you mad?" said Aunt Wynne.

"I will not have it!" cried Darthea. "I say I will not have it, and it concerns me most, madam." I had never before seen her angry. "Do you love me, Hugh Wynne?" she cried. "Do you love me, sir?"

"Darthea!"

"Will you always love me?"

"Dear child!" I exclaimed. "What is it?"

"Give me that deed," said my aunt. "Are you crazy fools, both of you?"

"Fools, Mistress Wynne?" said Darthea, turning from me, the deed still in her hand. "You are cruel and unkind. Could I marry Hugh Wynne if he did this thing? Are there no decencies in life, madam, that are above being sold for money and name? I should never marry him if he did this thing—never; and I mean to marry him, madam." And with this she unrolled the deed, crumpled it up, and threw it on the red blaze of the fire.

There was a flash of flame and a roar in the chimney. It was gone in a moment, and our Welsh lands were so much smoke and cinders.

My aunt made a wild rush to rescue them, but struck her head against the chimney-shelf, and fell back into a chair, crying, " You idiot! you fool! You shall never marry him! "

I picked up the slim little lady in my arms, and kissed her over and over, whilst, as she struggled away, I whispered:

"Thank God! Dear, brave heart! It was well done, and I thank you."

My aunt's rage knew no bounds, and I may not repeat what she said to my Darthea, who stood open-eyed, defiant, and flushed.

I begged the furious old lady to stop. A whirl-wind were as easily checked. At last, when she could say no more, my dear maid said quietly:

"What I have done, Hugh should have done long since. We are to live together, I trust, madam, for many years, and I love you well; but you have said things to me not easy to forget. I beg to insist that you apologise. For lighter things men kill one another. I await, madam, your excuses."

It was a fine sight to see how this fiery little bit of a woman faced my tall, strong aunt, who towered above her, her large face red with wrath.

"Never!" she cried. "I have been—it is I who am insulted and put to shame, in my own house, by a chit of a miss."

"Then good-by," said Darthea, and was by me and out of the house before I could see what to do or know what to say.

"She is gone!" I cried. "Oh, Aunt Gainor, you have broken my heart!"

"What did I say, Hugh?" said my aunt. I do truly think she did not know what she had said; and now she was off and I after her, knocking over Cæsar and our belated candles, and out of doors after Darthea. I saw her join her a few yards away, and did wisely to hold back. I knew well the child-heart my aunt carried within that spacious bosom.

What the pair of them said I do not know. In a few minutes they were back again, both in tears, the whole wretched business at an end. I thought it better to go away and leave them, but my aunt cried out:

"Wait, sir! I am an old ass! If either of you ever mention this thing again, I—I will wring your necks. I make free to say that some day you will both regret it; but it is your affair and not mine. O Lord! if Cat Ferguson ever comes to know it—"

"She never will," said Darthea; "and we will love you and love you, dear, dear mother, and I am sorry I hurt you; but I had to—I had to. If I was wise, I know not; but I had to end it—I had to."

Never before had I heard the sweet woman call my aunt mother. She often did so in after-years. It melted the old spinster, and she fell to kissing her, saying:

"Yes, I am your mother, child, and always will

be." But ever after Mistress Wynne was a trifle afraid of my little lady, and there were no more such scenes.

When my aunt was gone away to bed, though not to sleep, I fear, my dear maid came and sat at my feet on a cushion, and for a time was silent. At last, looking up, she said, "Hugh, was I wrong to burn it?"

Then I was silent a little while, but from the first I was resolved to be ever outright and plain with my lady, who was impulsive, and would need help and counsel and government, that her character might grow, as it did in after-years. I said: "Yes, Darthea. It was not yours, nor altogether mine; it was my father's land, if it belonged to any of us. It is better for me to tell you the simple truth. It would have made no difference had the deed been left undestroyed; it would only have given you the chance to know me better, and to learn that no consideration would have made me take these lands, even had our title been clear. Now you have destroyed my power of choice. I am not angry, not even vexed; but another time trust me, dear."

"I see! I see!" she exclaimed. "What have I done?" And she began to sob. "I was—was wicked not to trust you, and foolish; and now I see Aunt Gainor had reason to be angry. But you are good and brave to tell me. I could not have said what you said; I should have declared you were right. And now I know it was weakness, not strength, that made me do it. I shall pray God to forgive me. Kiss

II.—17

me, Hugh; I love you twice as much as ever I did before."

When I had done her sweet bidding, I said, "Darthea, let us forget all this. Wrong or right, I at least am pleased to have the thing at rest forever; and, wrong or right, I thank you. I was honest, Darthea, when I said so; and now good-night." At this she looked me in the eyes and went slowly out of the room, and, I fear, had no better slumbers than my Aunt Gainor.

XV

ARLY in February of 1783 we were married by the Rev. William White, long after to be our good bishop. Christ Church was full of my old friends, my Aunt Gainor in the front pew in a magnificent costume, and Mrs. Peniston with Jack, very grave of face, beside her. As no De Lanceys were to be had in our rebel town, Mr. James Wilson gave away the precious gift of Darthea Peniston. We went in my aunt's chariot to Merion; and so ends the long tale of my adventures, which here, in the same old country home, I have found it pleasant to set down for those who will, I trust, live in it when I am dead.

In April, 1783, peace was proclaimed. In November of that year I heard from Colonel Hamilton that our beloved general would, on December 4, take leave of his officers, and that he was kind enough to desire that all of his old staff who wished should be present. I was most pleased to go.

In New York, at Fraunce's Tavern, near Whitehall Ferry, I found the room full of the men who had humbled the pride of England and brought our great war to a close. His Excellency entered at noon, and seeing about him these many companions in arms, was for a little so agitated that he could not speak. Then with a solemn and kindly expression of face, such as I had once before seen him wear, he filled a glass with wine, and, seeming to steady himself, said:

"With a heart full of love and gratitude, I take my leave of you, most devoutly wishing that your latter days may be as prosperous and happy as your former ones have been glorious and honourable."

So saying, he drank his wine, and one after another went by him shaking his hand. No word was said, and these worn veterans of the winter camps and the summer battle-fields moved out, and saw their former general pass down, between lines of infantry, to the shore. There he got into a barge. As he was rowed away he stood up and lifted his hat. All of us uncovered, and remained thus till he passed from sight, to be seen no more by many of those who gazed sadly after his retreating form.

There is an old book my grandchildren love to hear me read to them. It is the "Morte d'Arthur," done into English by Sir Thomas Malory. Often when I read therein of how Arthur the king bade farewell to the world and to the last of the great company of his Knights of the Round Table, this scene at Whitehall slip comes back to me, and I seem to see once more those gallant soldiers, and far away the tall figure of surely the knightliest gentleman our days have known.

My years go on in peace. We have enough—far more than enough—for all the wants and even for the luxuries of life. It is late in the night, and Christmas-time, in the great stone house at Merion. The noise of little ones—and they are many—has ceased. I hear steps and laughter in the hall. The elder ones troop in to say good-night. There are Darthea and Gainor, mothers of the noisy brigade now in bed, and here is Hugh, the youngest, and Jack, with the big build of his race. And soon all are gone, and the house quiet.

I looked up where, under my dear Jack Warder's face, which Stuart did for me, hangs Knyphausen's long blade, and across it Jack's sword. Below, my eye lights on the Hessian pistols, and the sword-knot the gallant marquis gave me.

I watch the crumbling fire and seem to see once more the fierce struggle in the market-place, the wild fight on the redoubt, and my cousin's dark face. The years have gone by, and for me and mine there is peace and love, and naught a man in years may not think upon with joy.

Suddenly two hands from behind are over my eyes; ah, well I know their tender touch! Says a dear voice I hope to hear till life is over—and after that, I trust—"What are you thinking of, Hugh Wynne?"

"Of how sweet you have made my life to me, my darling."

"Thank God!"

THE END.

Americans in Fiction

*A series of reprints of 19th century American novels important
to the study of American folklore, culture and literary history*

THOMAS BAILEY ALDRICH
The Stillwater Tragedy

JAMES LANE ALLEN
A Kentucky Cardinal

GERTRUDE ATHERTON
Los Cerritos: A Romance of Modern Times
The Californians
Senator North
Aristocrats
The Splendid Idle Forties

ARLO BATES
The Puritans

OLIVER THOMAS BEARD
Bristling With Thorns

ALICE BROWN
Tiverton Tales
The County Road

FRANCIS H. BURNETT
Through One Administration

WILLIAM A. CARUTHERS
Kentuckian in New York, or the Adventures of Three Southerns
The Cavaliers of Virginia

CHARLES WADDELL CHESNUTT
The Conjure Woman
The Wife of His Youth; and Other Stories of the Colour Line
The House Behind the Cedars

KATE CHOPIN
Bayou Folk

JOHN ESTEN COOKE
The Virginia Comedians
Surry of Eagle's Nest
Mohun: or the Last Days of Lee and His Paladins
My Lady Pokahontas

ROSE TERRY COOKE
Rootbound and Other Sketches

MARGARET DELAND
John Ward, Preacher

THOMAS DIXON
The Leopard's Spots
The Clansman

EDWARD EGGLESTON
Roxy
The Faith Doctor

MARY HALLOCK FOOTE
The Led-Horse Claim

PAUL LEICESTER FORD
The Honorable Peter Stirling

HAROLD FREDERIC
Seth's Brother's Wife

MARY E. WILKINS FREEMAN
A New England Nun; and Other Stories
The Portion of Labor

HENRY B. FULLER
The Cliff Dwellers